GEOLOGY OF THE
STATE OF HAWAII

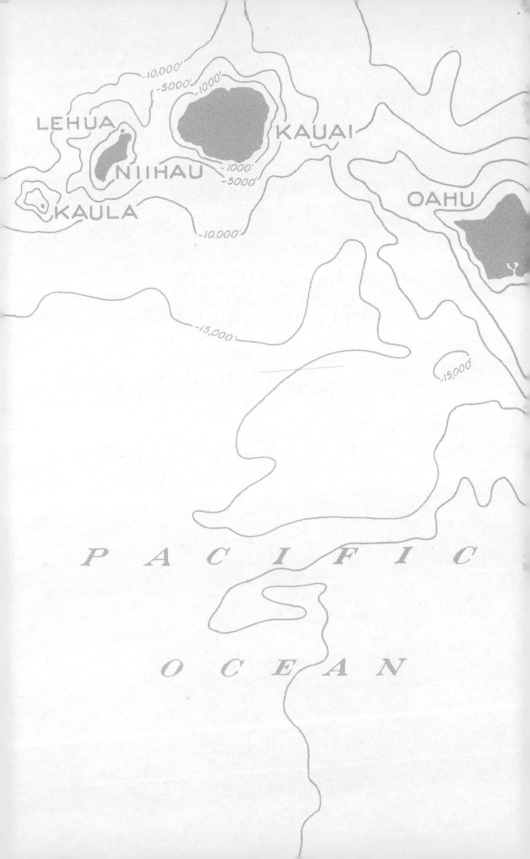

GEOLOGY
OF THE STATE OF
HAWAII

SECOND EDITION

By HAROLD T. STEARNS

PACIFIC BOOKS, *Publishers*
Palo Alto, California

Library of Congress Cataloging in Publication Data

Stearns, Harold T. (Harold Thornton), 1900-
  Geology of the state of Hawaii.

  Bibliography: p.
  Includes index.
  1. Geology—Hawaii. I. Title.
QE349.H3S73 1985   559.69   83-11467
ISBN 0-87015-234-3

Pacific Books, Publishers
P.O. Box 558, Palo Alto, California 94302-0558, U.S.A.

To the oceans for their sense of space,
To the waves for their sense of rhythm,
To the volcanoes for their sense of power,
To the deep canyons for their sense of silence,
To Claudia for her sense of everything.

THE AUTHOR
AND THE BOOK

Harold T. Stearns received his B.S. from Wesleyan University in 1921 and his Ph.D. from George Washington University in 1926. The subject of his dissertation was Kilauea and Mauna Loa volcanoes. He is a Fellow of the Geological Society of America and a member of other learned societies. He received an honorary Doctor of Science from Wesleyan University in 1978.

Dr. Stearns began his study of volcanic rocks in 1921 on the Snake River Plains of Idaho, and while there explored and recommended to the National Park Service the creation of the Craters of the Moon National Monument, an area of youthful volcanic eruptions similar to those on the island of Hawaii. Subsequently he published a guide to the geology of the Monument.[147] He started the first systematic geologic mapping of Kilauea and Mauna Loa volcanoes for the U.S. Geological Survey in 1924. During 1924 and 1925 he made a trip around the world studying the active volcanoes of Japan, the Philippines, Java, and Italy. In 1933, he examined the volcanoes of New Zealand and the volcanic rocks of Fiji and Australia.

In 1930, Governor Wallace R. Farrington asked Stearns to return to Hawaii to study the geology and ground-water resources of Oahu. Because more than 400 scientific articles and books had been written about that subject, Stearns thought little work lay ahead of him. However, after a few weeks in the field he found that the geologic work was superficial, and much of it in a confused state. He spent 16 years as District Geologist, U.S.G.S., mapping the geology of each of the islands. During this time he ascended every major valley, traversed every trail on foot, on muleback, or by car,

7

and scaled the summit of every mountain range in Hawaii. During
these years he wrote or was senior author of 10 volumes on areal
geology published by the Division of Hydrography of Hawaii. He
also did the preliminary field work and mapping for the volume on
Kauai, subsequently published as Bulletin 13. Most of these
geologic maps and government bulletins describing the geology of
each island are now out of print, but they can be consulted in
libraries.

In addition to his Hawaiian studies, he wrote "Geology of the
Samoan Islands" and "Geology of the Wallis Islands," mapped the
geology of Guam, and prepared a classified report to the U.S. Navy
in 1937. During World War II he was Geologist-in-Charge of Pacific
Investigations for the U.S.G.S., working on many of the Pacific
islands and also on Ascension Island in the Atlantic. He was
awarded the Medal for Merit in commendation of his work for the
armed forces under enemy fire in the Pacific. Stearns resigned from
government service in 1946 and is now a consulting geologist on
engineering projects with headquarters in Hawaii and in Idaho.

In 1962 the Hawaii Division of Water and Land Development of
Natural Resources excavated the 26,825-foot tunnel through the
island of Molokai according to the "Stearns plan," to recover water
confined at high levels in the dike complex. He was made Research
Associate of the Hawaii Institute of Geophysics in 1964 and given a
National Science Foundation grant to explore the stratigraphy of
the coastal plain of Oahu by deep bore holes.

Geology of the State of Hawaii is an expansion of *Geology of the
Hawaiian Islands*[8] and includes text abstracted from the geology
and geomorphology studies published in eleven Division of Hydrography volumes listed in the bibliography.

James Y. Nitta prepared most of the illustrations. The late Dr.
G. A. Macdonald was co-author of several of the volumes from
which text and illustrations have been used. Dan A. Davis, District
Geologist, U.S.G.S., Honolulu, kindly lent original drawings that
had been used to illustrate the bulletins. Robert I. Tilling, former
Scientist-in-Charge of the Hawaiian Volcano Observatory, and
many others too numerous to mention, furnished data and photo-
graphs. A useful reference for the reader of this book is the pocket
Dictionary of Geologic Terms published by Doubleday and Co.,
New York.

The Hawaiian Islands are a unique place to study geology because of the active volcanoes in close proximity to deeply eroded volcanic mountains. Oahu, which is visited by thousands of tourists daily, has almost the full spectrum of earth processes compressed into a small area where much of the geology is accessible by auto. One can see dissected as well as recent volcanic craters and fissures from which lava and ash were erupted; coarse-grained intrusive rocks in juxtaposition with fine-grained extrusive lavas; landslides and volcanic flows; spectacular features of marine, stream, and wind erosion; conspicuous evidences of great submergence and emergence; coral reefs; stream and marine terraces; deltas; fans; and tropical rain belts and deserts with their contrasting types of weathering and erosion.

It is hoped that this book will inspire the reader to visit Hawaii and remain longer to see an island in the making by volcanoes and coral reefs, as well as the dramatic evidence of destruction by wind, waves, and water.

GEOLOGIC TIME SCALE[a]

	Approximate duration in millions of years	Millions of years ago (Start of period)

CENOZOIC ERA

Quaternary Period

Holocene Epoch (11,000 ± years) .... 0.0011 ± .... −

Pleistocene Epoch[b] .... 2.0 ± .... 2.0 ±
  Wisconsinan Glacial (sea level falls)
  Sangamon Interglacial (sea level rises)
  Illinoian Glacial (sea level falls)
  Yarmouth Interglacial (sea level rises)
  Kansan Glacial (sea level falls)
  Aftonian Interglacial (sea level rises)
  Nebraskan Glacial (sea level falls)
  Pre-Nebraskan (earth's atmosphere cooling)

Tertiary Period

Pliocene (building of some Hawaiian volcanoes above sea level)	10	12
Miocene (fossils from deep	13	25
Oigocene holes on atolls in	15	40
Eocene the Pacific)	20	60
Paleocene	10	70

MESOZOIC ERA

Cretaceous Period (oldest fossils dredged from seamounts in the Pacific to date)	65	135
Jurassic Period	45	180
Triassic Period	45	225

PALEOZOIC ERA

Permian Period	45	270
Pennsylvanian Period	55	325
Mississippian Period	25	350
Devonian Period	50	400
Silurian Period	40	440
Ordovician Period	60	500
Cambrian Period	100	600

PRE-CAMBRIAN ERA .... 3,900 ± 4,500

[a]The length of the periods was determined by radiogenic measurements. The table is copied chiefly from Treatise on Marine Ecology and Paleoecology, 1957, Geol. Soc. Amer. Mem. 67.

[b]The length of the Pleistocene varies according to the definition used. If limited to the Ice Age, it is about 2,000,000 years long. Stratigraphers have defined it on the basis of the appearance of certain cold water fauna in the Villafranchian type section in Europe. They base their belief that the Pleistocene is about 3,000,000 years long on radiogenic measurements of rocks associated with the type section.

CONTENTS

ILLUSTRATIONS

TABLES

GEOLOGY OF THE
STATE OF HAWAII

1

GEOGRAPHY

AND CLIMATE

The Hawaiian Archipelago is a group of islands, reefs, and shoals, strung out from southeast to northwest for 1,600 miles between 154° 40′ and 171° 75′ W. longitude and 18° 54′ to 28° 15′ N. latitude (Figs. 1-1 and 1-2). Exclusive of Midway, which is an important air base and the site of a cable station, the inhabited islands lie at the southeast end of the archipelago. Hawaii, the largest and southeast-ernmost island, has the only active volcanoes. Honolulu, the principal city and capital, is on Oahu, 2,091 miles southwest of San Francisco, and is a port of call for ships en route from the west coast of North America to the Antipodes and to the Orient. The airport at Honolulu is the most important one in the Pacific.

A detailed map showing submarine contours of the larger islands is given in Figure 1-1. The volcanic peaks that form the islands are shown graphically in relation to each other in the upper inset. Data regarding the major islands are given in the accompanying table.

Although the islands are at the northern margin of the tropics, they have a subtropical climate because currents from the Bering Sea cool the region. The temperature of the surrounding waters is about 10° F. lower than that of other regions of the same latitude. This relative coolness is, in part, the reason for the poor development of coral reefs. The ocean at Waikiki, Oahu, ranges from 70° to 85° F. Air temperatures range from below freezing on high peaks to about 97° F. at sea level on the leeward coasts.

The Hawaiian Islands lie in the belt of northeasterly trade winds that persist throughout the year, but are occasionally interrupted during the winter by southerly or "kona" winds that blow for a few days at a time. Relatively low islands such as Kahoolawe and Lanai

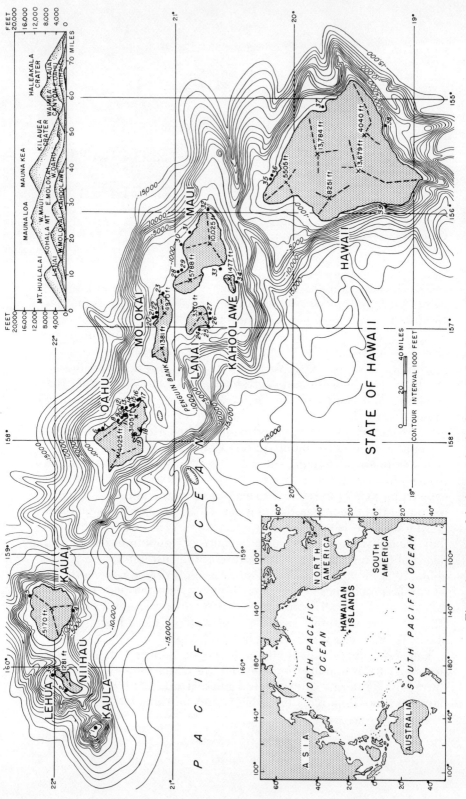

Figure 1-1—Map of the larger islands of Hawaii, their known rift zones, generalized submarine contours in feet, and principal islets. (Explanation of numbers on facing page.)

TABLE 1
AREA, ALTITUDE, MAXIMUM DIMENSIONS, POPULATION,
AND PRINCIPAL CITY OF EACH OF THE LARGER ISLANDS

Island	Area (sq. mi.)	Altitude (feet)	Maximum distance (miles)		Popula- tion[a]	Principal city
			North- south	East- west		
Hawaii	4,030	13,784	87.3	75.3	92,053	Hilo
Maui	728	10,025	25.0	38.4	65,184	Wailuku
Oahu	604	4,025	40.0	26.0	762,874	Honolulu
Kauai	555	5,170	24.5	29.9	39,082	Lihue
Molokai	260	4,970	10.1	37.0	3,574	Kaunakakai
Lanai	141	3,370	13.3	13.0	2,119	Lanai City
Niihau	72	1,281	9.7	9.0	226	None
Kahoolawe	45	1,472	6.4	10.9	0	None
Total	6,435	....	....	....	965.112	....

[a]According to U.S. Census, 1980.

are sheltered from the trade winds by other islands and consequently are very dry. In windy seasons ribbon-shaped dust
clouds from these two islands commonly extend many miles over
the ocean.

Both the trade and southerly winds bring rain to the islands. The
heavy storms usually come from the south. During some storms as
much as 24 inches of rain in four hours has been recorded. Rainfall
exceeding 20 inches in 24 hours has been recorded in several
places. During the 24 hours following the evening of January 24,

◄ – – – –

Explanation of Figure 1-1.

The submarine contours are generalized. Lower inset map shows position of the
Hawaiian Archipelago in the Pacific Ocean, and upper inset shows profiles of the
volcanic peaks of the main islands. The islets are 1. Kaula; 2. Kuakamoku; 3. Lehua;
4. Kalanipuao; 5. Mokuaeae; 6. Mokuauia; 7. Kukuihoolua; 8. Mokolii; 9. Kapapa;
10. Kekepa; 11. Moku o Loe; 12. Moku Manu; 13. Mokolea; 14. Papoia; 15. Mokulua;
16. Manana; 17. Kaohikaipu; 18. Mokuoeo; 19. Ford Island; 20. Mokapu; 21. Okala;
22. Mokohola; 23. Mokuhooniki; 24. Nanahoa; 25. Moku Naio; 26. Poopoo; 27.
Puupehe; 28. Mokeehia; 29. Hulu; 30. Papanui o Kane; 31. Keopuka; 32. Alau; 33.
Molokini; 34. Puu Koae, 35. Mokupuku; 36. Paoakalani; 37. Cocoanut Island; 38.
Mokuokahailani; 39. Keaoi.

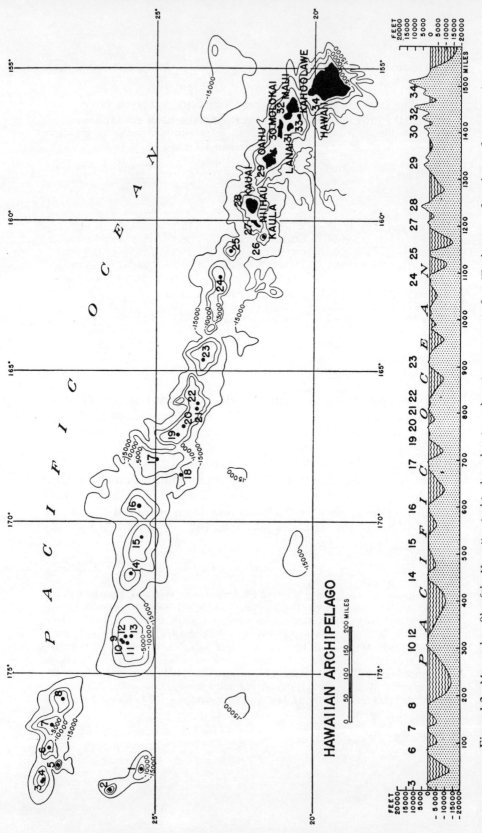

Figure 1-2 — Map and profile of the Hawaiian Archipelago showing submarine contours in feet. (Explanation of number on facing page.)

1956, a rain gage on Kilauea Plantation, Kauai, recorded nearly 40 inches of rainfall, of which 6 inches fell in a single half hour. It shattered all previous records of maximum rainfall in the Hawaiian Islands and may be close to the heaviest known world rainfall.[175]

The northeastern sides of the mountains are usually wettest be-, cause of the prevailing wind. Maximum precipitation occurs between altitudes of 2,000 and 6,000 feet, depending upon the form and height of each island. Above 6,000 feet the precipitation decreases, making high peaks semiarid. As the winds descend the lee slopes, they become warmer, drying winds, causing arid and semiarid climates on the leeward sides of the islands. On the island of Hawaii, however, where the mountains are sufficiently high to pierce the layer of trade winds, eddies result in prevailing southwest winds on the lee side so that the climate in the leeward districts is fairly wet. The annual rainfall ranges from 10 inches or less on the lee coasts to about 450 inches in the wettest belts. In one year, 624 inches of rain was recorded on the summit of Kauai at an altitude of 5,170 feet.

It is difficult to grasp the immensity of the oceans of the earth until one flies over them and sees the Hawaiian Islands as tiny green specks floating in a vast blue sea. The oceans cover 71 per cent of the earth's surface, and sea water averages 2⅓ miles in depth over 139 million square miles. If all the salt in the sea were withdrawn and piled upon the continents, it would cover the land with white crystals to a depth of 500 feet.[26]

◄ — — — —

Explanation of Figure 1-2.

1. Unnamed shoal; 2. Bensaleux Reef; 3. Kure or Ocean Island; 4. Green Island; 5. Nero Bank; 6. Midway Islands; 7. Gambia Shoal; 8. Pearl and Hermes Reef; 9. Lisianski Island; 10. Fisher Reef; 11. Minor Reef; 12. Neva Shoal; 13. Springbank Reef; 14. Laysan Island; 15. Maro (Dowsett) Reef; 16. Raita Bank; 17. Gardner Pinnacles; 18. Two Brothers Reef; 19. St. Rogatien Bank; 20. Brooks Banks; 21. La Pérouse Pinnacle; 22. French Frigate Shoal; 23. Necker Island; 24. Nihoa; 25. Unnamed shoal; 26. Kaula; 27. Niihau; 28. Kauai; 29. Oahu; 30. Molokai; 31. Lanai; 32. Maui; 33. Kahoolawe; 34. Hawaii.

2

GEOMORPHOLOGY

STREAM EROSION

The major islands are basaltic volcanic domes or shields in various stages of dissection. Oahu and Niihau have the only extensive coastal plains. The great permeability of the basalt and coral rock has an important bearing on the geomorphology of the islands. For some time after the cessation of volcanic activity, streams are unable to develop water courses because the lava surface is highly porous. For example, even though the rainfall is high, stream channels are not developed on most of Kilauea Volcano. Because temperatures are uniformly high and, except on high peaks, do not drop below freezing, chemical weathering dominates over mechanical disintegration. Gradually, thick soils form and reduce the porosity of the slopes, and stream courses develop. Although flashy, the streams are powerful agents of destruction because of the steep slopes and fractured condition of the rocks.

The amount of stream erosion varies enormously on the different slopes of the same dome. The northeastern slopes of the larger islands may be incised by deep canyons because of the high rainfall, whereas the leeward sides may have relatively small gulches. Anomalous physiographic relationships are common. On some of the domes, high fault scarps have protected one slope from lava flows while another slope was being covered. Differences in the age of the rocks on the two sides of a mountain give rise generally to vastly discordant stages of erosion; for example, on the Waianae Range, Oahu, the leeward slope is older, hence much more eroded than the windward side. Further, the rate of erosion on a volcano may be slackened by the growth of another volcano to the wind-

Figure 2-1.—Halawa Valley, Molokai, a typical amphitheater-headed valley. (Photo by U.S. Army.)

ward, as happened when the Koolau dome cut off the trade winds from the Waianae dome (Plates 3–6).

Origin of amphitheater-headed valleys. The unusually high rainfall, zoned by altitude, together with the steep radial drainage developed on alternating layers of weak and strong vertically jointed rocks dipping seaward, have produced on these islands a distinctive type of valley best described as amphitheater-headed (Figs. 2-1 and 2-2, D). Most of the larger islands, except those veneered with more recent lava, are incised by valleys of this type. Radiogenic measurements indicate that the weathering and deep erosion of an island took from one to two million years. Several factors are concerned in the development of amphitheater-headed valleys:

1. Original slope of the surface—Streams that flowed originally on slopes of about 3° or less have not developed amphitheater-headed canyons; those that flowed on steeper slopes have developed amphitheaters (for example, Manoa Stream on Oahu). The original

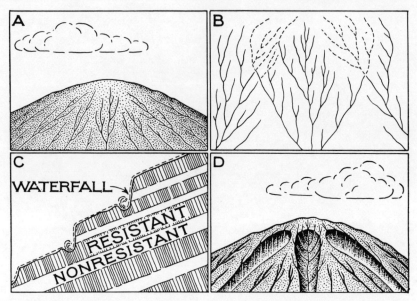

Figure 2-2.—Diagram illustrating the formation of amphitheater-headed val-leys. A. Youthful dome with radial drainage. B. Details of stream piracy that lead to a master stream, the precursor of an amphitheater-headed valley. C. Waterfalls caused by alternating resistant and nonresistant beds of basalt. D. Dome with amphitheater-headed valleys formed by the master streams.

slope seems to be the most fundamental influence in the formation of these valleys.

2. Alternate resistant and nonresistant beds, usually dipping downstream (Fig. 2-2, C)—The nonresistant clinker beds are undercut beneath the resistant layers of dense basalt and form waterfalls as they are cut back. Such falls increase in height as they follow the dip upstream and tend to coalesce into one high fall. Most of the streams have a "fall point," above which the stream actively incises its canyon in the bedrock and below which the stream cuts laterally. Haiku Stream, Oahu, has a 3.8 per cent gra-dient below the fall point and an 88 per cent gradient above the point (dropping 1,500 feet in a horizontal distance of 1,700 feet).

3. Rainfall and stream capture—The streams flowing more or less radially from the center of the dome are spaced relatively far apart in the region of low altitudes and low rainfall (Fig. 2-2, A). With increasing altitude and rainfall, streams increase in number for a unit area, and stream capture becomes dominant (Fig. 2-2, B). Thus,

the catchment basin of the stream enlarges into an amphitheater near its source. The process is vastly more effective here than on an ordinary linear mountain range because of the radial pattern, or headward convergence, of the drainage on the upper part of the dome. The ground water confined in the rocks of the dike complex is tapped first by the dominant streams, and this perennial additional water accelerates their ability to capture new streams. Sapping by the springs also widens the amphitheater.

4. Plunge-pool action—Captured tributaries entering a master stream form coalescing plunge pools around the amphitheater wall. The narrow ridges between the plunge pools are undercut and fail under their own weight, generally breaking off during heavy storms along some layer of ash or cinder weakened by saturation and weathering. Landsliding is an active process in Hawaii, but the scars are overlooked because they become covered so quickly with vegetation. After the "kona" storm in November 1930, 14 new landslides were counted in the upper Nuuanu Valley, Oahu. Streams of low gradient do not develop high waterfalls and consequently cannot form plunge pools large enough to undermine the divides at the fall point.

5. Cliff-forming rocks—Rocks must be competent to stand in vertical or nearly vertical walls. Basalt readily stands in high cliffs. Vertical jointing common in basalts is a contributing factor to sheer walls. If rocks are weak, the sheer amphitheater walls cannot develop at the head of a valley.

6. Inclination of the bedding—The attitude of the beds is probably important, but in Hawaii, where strata rarely dip steeply, the part played by this factor cannot be determined readily. Steeply dipping beds, however, might not form sheer walls.

Effect of cones on stream erosion. A secondary cone on the slopes of a large volcanic dome commonly deflects runoff. In time, especially in rainy areas, such deflected streams erode deep canyons out of proportion to their neighbors. An unusually wide pie-shaped dome remnant between the mouths of streams thus formed generally indicates the history even after all vestiges of the secondary cone have been eroded. The four chief stages in the development of the stream pattern are shown diagrammatically in Figure 2-3. The sea cliff is lower between the two master streams in this figure because the cone erupted after a sea cliff had been cut in the dome. If the cone had erupted before the streams had started cut-

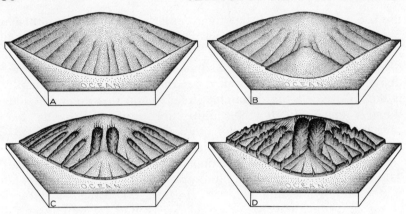

Figure 2-3—Diagram showing effect of a late cone on stream erosion. A. Dome with radial streams. B. Secondary cone displacing drainage. C. Two major valleys resulting from concentration of drainage into two streams. D. Very wide pie-shaped remnant of dome indicating former cone.

ting the dome or before the sea cliff had formed, the history would be the same, except that the sea cliff would have a more uniform height along the entire coast.

WORK OF THE WIND

In the wake of overgrazing and deforestation, the wind has eroded large quantities of soil from some of the islands. On Kahoolawe and Lanai, large areas have been stripped to bedrock and dunes of red soil occur. Wind erosion affects localities where more than 100 inches of rain falls annually, if the surface becomes bare as a result of landslides or other causes. Dust blown from the ash-covered Kau Desert on Kilauea constitutes an appreciable part of the ash deposits in the Kau District, Hawaii. Dunes composed of calcareous beach sand and reaching heights of 100 feet have drifted far inland on Oahu, Maui, Molokai, Kauai, Lanai, and Niihau. Most of these dunes are of late Pleistocene age and migrated inland when sea level was lower than it is at present. Some are now thoroughly lithified, and the rock is called eolianite (Fig. 2-4).

Most of the loose rocks that lie on the summit of Kahoolawe Island lie with their small ends pointing upward and to the leeward and their broad, heavy ends partly sunk below the surface to the windward. At first the rocks lie buried as residual remnants of a decomposed lava bed. Gradually the matrix is blown away, leaving

Figure 2-4—Typical thin-bedded lithified dunes near Waimanalo, Oahu. (Photo by H. T. Stearns.)

the rocks supported by pedestals of softer material. They are exposed to a sand blast, and when the wind removes the pedestals, the rocks topple with their heavy ends down. The rocks set up eddies that scour at the windward side, sinking each rock deeper at its heavy end. Meanwhile, sand is deposited under the sheltered, leeward side as the rock tilts. Probably the rock rotates slightly during this process if the heavy end has not fallen exactly to the windward at first. Parallel grooves up to six inches deep have been scoured in the hardpan by the wind in some places.

MARINE FEATURES

Marine cliffs. Marine erosion is most effective on the northeast or trade-wind coasts, where sea cliffs of nearly 3,000 feet have been cut. Because many of the severest storms come from the south and southwest, however, the coasts facing these directions—where not veneered by recent lava flows and not sheltered by other islands—

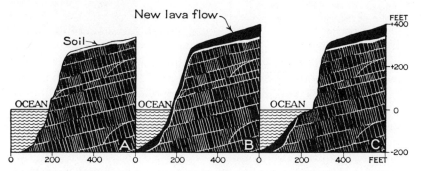

Figure 2-5—Three stages showing the geologic history of a sea cliff veneered with lava. A. Before veneering. B. Immediately after emplacement of lava flow. C. After veneer has been removed by subsequent wave erosion.

also have high sea cliffs, some up to 1,000 feet or more in height. Some sea cliffs have been retarded in their development by later lava flows that have been eroded away (Fig. 2-5). The sea cliffs generally plunge into deep water or are skirted by low, emergent fringing reefs. These conditions indicate that the cliffs were cut when the sea stood lower than it does at present, probably in part during glacial epochs. Most of the high cliffs and great valleys have been cut simultaneously. Waves are far more effective in cutting high cliffs in the same length of time on steep slopes because the material from steep slopes can be transported into deep water more easily (Fig. 2-6). Also, steep cliffs tend to ravel and slide faster, once cutting action has started.

Fretwork weathering. Many basaltic boulders along the coast are covered by fretwork. This type of weathering must be caused by alternate wetting and drying in the spray and splash zone, for it does not occur on rocks beyond this zone. Bartrum reached the same conclusion regarding similarly honeycombed rocks along the

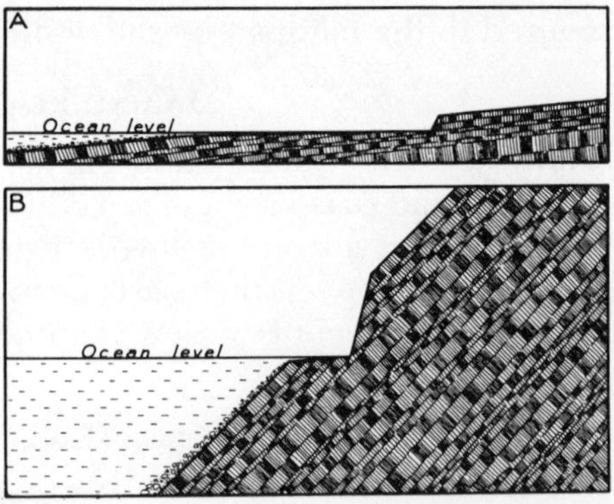

Figure 2-6—Diagrams illustrating how a higher cliff will be formed by wave attack on a steep slope than will be formed on a gentle slope. A. Gentle slope. B. Steep slope. The dip of the lavas in B has been exaggerated.

New Zealand coast.[17] How much of the action is mechanical and how much is chemical are not known, but it is probable that both processes operate, and the relative effectiveness of one in comparison with the other may depend upon such factors as the composition and texture of the rock. The depressions commonly contain salt. The bottoms of most of the pits slope gently downward and outward. The walls are generally rough and covered with slightly loose crystal grains, as though some of the rock had been dissolved, leaving the rest to fall apart by mechanical weathering. Alteration penetrates about one quarter of an inch. The surface of rocks that

Figure 2-7—The Needles, typical stacks on the coast of Lanai. (Photo by H. T. Stearns.)

have been riddled by sea boring organisms may resemble fretwork weathering, but such rocks are found within tidal range.

Shore platforms. Many stretches of the shore are platforms reaching 50 feet in width and extending up to 5 feet above sea level. Some are relict benches of the 5-foot stand of the sea and others are the work of the present sea.[194, 201] Notches in limestone at mean tide level are due chiefly to biological activity and solution by sea water. They occur at Laie Point, Oahu, and emerged notches indicate former high sea levels (Fig. 2-12).

Stacks. Headlands projecting into the sea are reduced in places to isolated pinnacles, which develop interesting forms (Fig. 2-7).

Blowholes or spouting horns. Blowholes are caused by waves rushing into a cavern whose roof is between wave levels, compressing the air within, and forcing air or water out through a small hole or crack in the roof. Many exist besides the well-publicized "Blowhole" near Koko Head, Oahu, and the one near Koloa, Kauai (Fig. 2-8). Water rising in domes as waves recede is a common occurrence off the leeward coast of West Maui. These blowholes are generally lava tubes that release water through the roof without a jet of air. Many are reported to be fresh water springs, but samples

Figure 2-8—The Spouting Horn at Koloa, Kauai. (Photo by D.A. Davis.)

collected by divers in several domes have all been determined to be ocean water.

TSUNAMIS OR SEISMIC SEA WAVES

Tsunamis have taken a heavy toll in the last three decades in Hawaii. The destructive waves of April 1, 1946, which resulted from an earthquake in the Aleutian Islands, killed 175 persons in Hawaii, mostly at Hilo, and caused damage amounting to $25,000,000. Much damage was also done on Oahu, Kauai, and Maui. The writer's former home at Spreckelsville, Maui, was destroyed. At Haena, on the north coast of Kauai, the waves reached a height of 45 feet above sea level, wrecking homes and taking several lives. The tsunami reached 55 feet on the island of Hawaii. The waves traveled 2,240 statute miles in 4.57 hours, or an average speed of 490 miles an hour. A tsunami usually comes in a series of waves. The first waves were at 15-minute intervals, indicating a wave length from crest to crest of 122 miles. At most places the third and fourth waves did the greatest damage.[188]

Another tsunami from the Aleutian Islands did great damage in Hilo and elsewhere in the islands on March 9, 1957. The writer witnessed it at Haleiwa, Oahu, and noted that as the waves receded, they ceased to counterpoise the ground water stored inland. As a result, at each crevice or cavity in the limestone along the shore, voluminous fountains of fresh ground water rose several inches to a foot above the ground and formed rivulets as it ran down the temporarily abandoned underwater beach slope.

The tsunami of May 23, 1960 originated off the coast of Chile. It traveled 6,600 miles from its source to Hilo in 14 hours 56 minutes, at an average speed of 442 miles per hour. The third wave rose 35 feet at Hilo. It killed 61 people and caused damage amounting to $23,000,000.[50] This was the sixth tsunami to cause severe damage in the Hawaiian Islands (1837, 1868, 1877, 1946, 1957, and 1960). Ten-ton blocks high above the south coast of Hawaii probably indicate a terrific wave there in the past, perhaps in 1868.

An earthquake with an intensity of 7.2 on the Richter scale, the second most severe in Hawaii's history, with its epicenter near Kalapana, Hawaii, occurred at 4:48 A.M., November 29, 1975. It caused a short eruption in Halemaumau and generated a tsunami 18 feet high, which damaged a restaurant and several homes at Punaluu in the Kau District. Total damage from the temblor and wave was estimated at $3,000,000. The beach at the Halape Campground, on the south shore of Kilauea, subsided several feet where 36 campers were asleep. Two men were drowned there and 19 injured. Horizontal changes along the shore amounted to 18.5 feet. The whole south side of Kilauea moved seaward to cause a gain in land area of 28 acres, but coastal subsidence of 13 acres reduced the net gain to only 15 acres.[79] Only the April 2, 1868 earthquake, estimated at 7.7, was stronger.

The Hawaiian Islands have been struck by 96 tsunamis in the last 162 years. Tsunamis have caused at least 385 deaths and $60,000,000 damage, and destroyed more than 1,500 homes. The 1837 tsunami was the first destructive seismic sea wave to be recorded. It killed 62 persons on Maui and Hawaii and destroyed 200 homes.[163] The highest wave to hit Oahu was the 37-foot wave that struck Makapuu in 1946.

A tsunami warning system is now in effect to warn coastal dwellers when a wave is approaching. However, little protection is available from waves originating in South America or in the intervening ocean area, because no islands lie in that region on which a

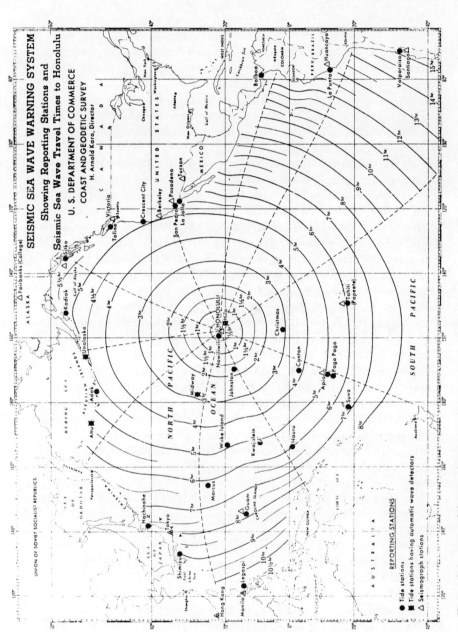

Figure 2-9—Map of the Pacific Ocean showing tsunami travel times.

gage can be placed to measure the height of the oncoming wave. Strangely enough, the Good Friday earthquake in Alaska in 1964 did not cause a destructive wave in the islands.

SUBMERGENCES AND EMERGENCES OF THE ISLANDS

The great submergence. Oahu has become a classic place for the study of ancient shorelines. The highest fossiliferous marine limestone known in the central Pacific was discovered by the writer on Lanai at an altitude of 1,070 feet.[196]

The tremendous piles of lavas forming the Hawaiian Ridge have overloaded the crust and caused it to sag, creating a trough or deep alongside the ridge, with a bulge farther out known as the Hawaiian Arch (Fig. 2-10). This type of downbowing is called isostatic adjustment. The total submergence caused by this adjustment may amount to 12,000 feet or more. Much of this slow process may have occurred during the building of the volcanic domes. Adjustment to overloading would be downward and is usually gradual.

The central Pacific formerly was dotted with about 10,000 volcanoes.[133] About 2,000 of these heavy volcanic piles on the thin earth's crust have been beveled by the sea and subsequently have subsided 5,000 feet or more because of isostatic and other types of adjustment. Hess, who discovered their presence by soundings, named these flat-topped seamounts "guyots," after a French geographer.[75] The seamounts, the Mid-Pacific Mountains, and other parts of the Pacific ocean floor have subsided by thousands of feet.[69]

The writer anticipated the discovery of the guyots and the great subsidence by plastic basining when he ". . . visualized the Pacific Basin at the close of the Pliocene characterized by isolated volcanic cones and many narrow elongate islands built by volcanoes along fissures, some of which were separated from adjacent islands by fairly narrow straits. The plants and animals (not man, who came much later) crossed on the island stepping stones and spread unimpeded over extensive dome-shaped mountains. They were dispersed chiefly by wind and water. . . ."[207]

Dredge samples and borings indicate that the guyots so far examined carry Cretaceous and Eocene fossils on them and show subaerial erosion or weathering prior to submergence.[133] Thus, subsidence started earlier than the Pliocene, but hundreds of the guyots have not yet been studied. Menard states that all studies confirm large local and regional subsidence of the central and

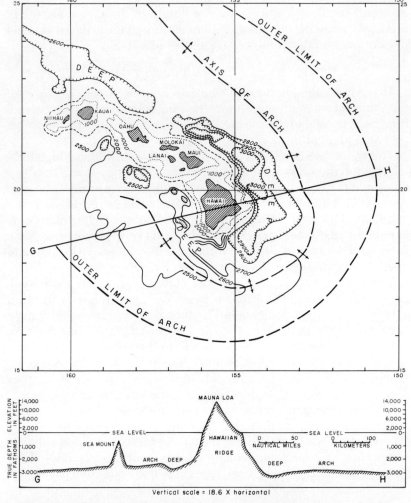

Figure 2-10—Generalized structure in the vicinity of the southern end of the Hawaiian Ridge, and profile across the Hawaiian Arch, Deep, and Ridge. The Deep was officially renamed Trough in 1965. (Modified after Hamilton, 1957.)

western Pacific sea floor.[132] Strange concluded from density studies that the Hawaiian Islands have been submerged 6,600 to 10,000 feet.[254]

The most striking feature on the ocean floor (Fig. 2-11) is the broad platform between 500 and 600 fathoms (3,000 to 3,600 feet) surrounding all the islands except a portion of Hawaii, where the platform is missing off the shores of Kilauea, Mauna Loa, and the west side of Hualalai. It is present between Niihau and Kauai, but is less prominent around Kauai than elsewhere. It extends 40 miles off the western tip of Oahu, which is here selected as the type locality. It is named Waho shelf, from the last two syllables of Kaieiewaho Channel, which crosses the area. No hypothesis seems adequate to explain the surrounding platform except a long still stand during which marine and stream erosion cut wide benches along the shores of the islands and coral reefs grew. The platform cannot be the result of lavas banking against submarine mountains, because steep high slopes exist off the edge of the platform in many places.

The platform is shallower between closely spaced islands because of the addition of sediments and later lava flows, but the theory of continuous subsidence by isostatic adjustment is controverted by the platform's existence, which requires a still stand. The absence of a wide platform around Kauai, which has been subject to erosion longer than the other islands, is probably due to nearly complete burial by sediment and late lavas. Determining the origin of the platform is one of the challenging problems not yet solved.

The shelf is 0.9 to 2.5 miles wide along the north coast of Molokai, and appears to carry one or two ancient coral reefs. Seismic reflection profiles south of Molokai and west of Lanai show coral reefs with sedimentary deposits 500 feet thick ponded behind the reefs.[122,123]

A detailed study of the shelf was made at its type locality between Oahu and Kauai.[146,147] Dredging indicated that the shelf is composed of lava, volcaniclastic sedimentary rocks, some carbonates, and little pelagic material. By hydration rind dating of the palagonite, Morgenstein determined that the lava flows range in age from 534,000 to 993,000 years and that the volcaniclastic sedimentary rocks are as old as 805,000 years.[146] He also found the Kahipa-Mamala, the Lualualei, and the Waho shelves off Kauai. The lowermost unnamed terrace is 6,600 to 7,800 feet below the surface of the ocean. Most of the Waho shelf off the western tip of Oahu, except for one hill, is relatively flat, with a relief between 60 and 300 feet. The average sediment cover on the Kauai shelves is 3,800 feet thick, as determined by a sparker.

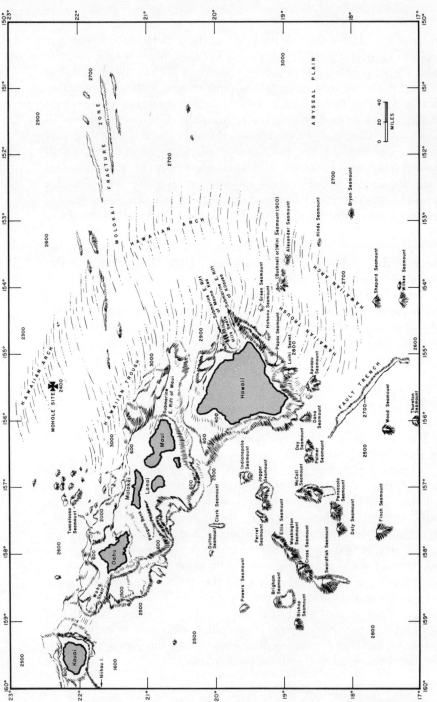

Figure 2-11—Relief map of the ocean floor surrounding the major Hawaiian Islands, based on U.S. Navy Hydrographic Chart 1604N. Shown are the Mohole site, known seamounts (submarine volcanoes), Molokai Fracture zone, a long fault trench south of Hawaii, and the 600-fathom Waho shelf. The Waho shelf is the most extensive submarine shelf around the islands and indicates long stability of the land. Most of the seamounts were named by the writer to honor deceased scientists who have contributed to knowledge of Hawaiian geology.[10] Depths are in fathoms: 1 fathom = 6 feet.

Numerous elongated seamounts off the coast of the island of Hawaii, especially to the west, are conspicuous features on the undersea map (Fig. 2-11). Nearly half the seamounts have tops either at or near 3,000 feet, which indicated that these high undersea mountains probably were above sea level at some time and were truncated by erosion when the 500–600 fathom platform was developed around the major islands. Vesicular weathered basalt, which is indicative of subaerial eruptives, has been dredged from a depth of 5,200 feet from Bushnell (Wini) Seamount and from two seamounts between it and Hawaii (Fig. 2-11).[144] They appear to be large landslide blocks. Moore believes that Mauna Kea subsided about 3,000 feet in the Pleistocene in relation to present sea level.[139]

The downward movement would be countered by local upward movements, or tumescence, caused by lava being injected as sills, stocks, laccoliths, or other intrusive bodies. Actual measurements of tumescence are made daily by the observatory on Kilauea Volcano. Caldera movements are gradual, and collapse generally follows as soon as an eruption occurs, so that little or no net rise in the mountain results. Macdonald states that the Hawaiian volcanoes are largely the result of upthrust at individual volcanic centers.[108] The low dip of the lava beds in most of the volcanoes does not bear out this statement. Exceptions are Kauai, East and West Maui, Mauna Kea, and Hualalai, which have steeper dips in the tholeiitic basalts than the other volcanoes. A possible explanation for the steep dips in these particular volcanoes is that the lavas may veneer steep submarine cones containing a large quantity of ash. The large undersea landslides probably are sliding on ash beds or submarine lava delta deposits.

Also important in the movements of the islands has been the intrusion of countless dikes a few inches to a few feet wide along the rift zones. The horizontal spread of each mountain by this process of injection may amount to as much as a mile in the Koolau Range, and probably ranges from one-fourth mile to one mile for the larger domes formed during the period since the piles were built above sea level. The total spread at their base may be much greater.

The land movements described above were in three directions: up, down, and sideways. A large part of the sinking of Oahu after the canyons were cut can be attributed to isostatic adjustment. The canyons have been traced down to more than 6,000 feet below sea level.[70]

Land movements were complicated by important processes that caused eustatic changes. During the Tertiary and probably well into the Pleistocene, when the Coast Range of California was being thrust high above the sea and the submerged Mid-Atlantic Ridge and East Pacific Rise were being pushed up nearly to sea level along with similar changes elsewhere on the globe, the world's seas must have been forced into smaller areas, and thus caused to rise on the land an appreciable amount. At the same time, other parts of the ocean floor were sinking, especially the so-called "deeps."[207] No one knows to what extent these two opposing forces balanced each other, but the ocean level on the Hawaiian Islands certainly was fluctuating. Recent earth movements, such as those that caused the great Tokyo earthquake of 1923 and the Alaskan earthquake of 1964, affected the levels of the world's oceans minutely. Restless seas bathe the islands.

Many of the high older shorelines on the islands, and probably some of the low submerged ones, may have been caused chiefly by the change in the configuration of the ocean basins concomitant with the vast changes in the earth's relief in the period of volcanism and mountain building that characterized the Tertiary.[206] Shorelines made by these forces are called tectonic eustatic shorelines.

Polar ice caps and changing shorelines. As the tectonic eustatic movements continued into the Pleistocene, the effects of glacioeustatism—that is, fluctuations caused by the withdrawal of vast quantities of water to form polar ice caps during the four major ice advances—were superimposed. Lowering of the oceans during each of these advances is estimated to be not less than 300 feet and, more likely, as much as about 450 feet,[30,47] but the 300–350-foot submarine shelf is most dominant around the older islands. A shelf 450 feet below sea level exists off Kauai.[80]

When the ice caps receded during the interglacial epochs, the water was returned to the sea. Some geologists believe that the sea has not risen appreciably above the present shoreline since the ice started receding from its maximum position about 11,000 years ago.[18,187] Evidence exists in the Hawaiian Islands that it stood 5 feet above sea level about 3,500 years ago.

Figure 2-12—Cliff cut into ancient lithified dunes and notched by the sea at 22 and 27 feet above sea level near Kailua, Oahu. The base of the cliff indicates the 12-foot shoreline. (Photo by H.T. Stearns.)

A very complete history of eustatic fluctuations of sea level in the Hawaiian Islands has been worked out.[210,216,222] A list of the ancient shorelines in the Hawaiian Islands is given in Table 2. Many of the submerged shorelines have been found by scuba divers and with a submersible (Fig. 2-13). The submerged shelves have been sufficiently dredged to prove that they are chiefly drowned coral reefs and marine sediments.[31] As shown in Figure 2-14, the ocean was constantly fluctuating during the Pleistocene. Oahu was sinking during the early Pleistocene, as shown by drilled holes at Ewa,[223] but has been very stable since the middle Pleistocene. During the Yarmouth interglacial epoch, about 500,000 years ago, the sea rose 95 to 100 feet above present sea level. More reefs grew during this warm epoch than at any time since, and the extensive emerged reefs in Lualualei Valley and on the Ewa plain were laid down at this time.

During the Illinoian glacial epoch, the sea fell to about 350 feet below present sea level, and great quantities of sand blew inland to form high dunes, now lithified by percolating rain water. Some, like those of Coral Hill near Waimanalo, are being quarried for aggregate and being ground up for sand. This low stand is known as the Waipio, after the type locality on Waipio Peninsula in Pearl Harbor (Figure 2-15).

As the Illinoian ice sheet melted, water returned to the sea and at the peak of the Sangamon interglacial, about 120,000 years ago, the ocean rose to 22 and 27 feet, the Waimanalo stand, and cut notches in the hardened dunes (Fig. 2-12). Then it dropped down below

TABLE 2
ANCIENT SHORELINES AND SHELVES
IN THE HAWAIIAN ISLANDS†[222]

Approximate Altitude		Shelf or Terrace	Age Before	Type Locality
(Feet)	(Meters)	(Name)	Present	(Island)
0	0	Present	Present	—
5	1.5	Kapapa	4,000 ±	Oahu
− 15	− 4.5	Koko	Late Holocene	Oahu
− 350±	− 106±	Mamala	12,000 ±	Oahu
− 60	− 18	Makai Range	Late Wisconsinan	Oahu
− 120*	− 36.5	Makapuu	Late Wisconsinan	Oahu
− 135*	− 41	Nawiliwili	Late Wisconsinan	Kauai
− 155	− 47	Lahaina Roads	Wisconsinan	Maui
− 80*	− 24	Kaneohe	Wisconsinan	Oahu
− 190*	− 58	Kahe	Wisconsinan	Oahu
− 205*	− 62	Ewa II	Wisconsinan	Oahu
− 220*	− 67	Barbers Point	Wisconsinan	Oahu
2±	0.6	Leahi	115,000 ±	Oahu
Low	Low	Kawela	Early Wisconsinan	Oahu
25**	7.5	Waimanalo	Sangamon, 125,000 ±	Oahu
12	3.6	Kailua	Sangamon	Oahu
− 30	− 9	Olomanu	Sangamon	Oahu
Low	Low	Coral Hill	Illinoian	Oahu
High	High	Unnamed	Illinoian	Oahu
− 350(?)	− 106±	Waipio	Illinoian	Oahu
− 240±	− 75±	Makua	Illinoian (?)	Oahu
45	12	Waialae	Early Illinoian (?)	Oahu
70	21.5	Laie	Early Illinoian	Oahu
95–100	29–30	Kaena	Yarmouth, 650,000 ±	Oahu
− 350(?)	− 106(?)	Kahipa	Kansan	Oahu
− 205*	− 62	Ewa I	Kansan	Oahu
25*	7.5	PCA	Kansan	Oahu
55*	17	Kahuku Point	Kansan	Oahu
250±*	75±	Olowalu	Aftonian (?)	Maui
325±	100±	—	—	Lanai
375±	114±	—	—	Lanai
560	170	Manele	Pleistocene	Lanai
625	190	Kaluakapo	Pleistocene	Lanai
1,200±	365±	Mahana	Pleistocene	Lanai
− 1,200 to − 1,800	− 365 to − 550	Lualualei	Late Pliocene (?)	Oahu
− 3,000 to − 3,600	− 915 to − 1,100	Waho	Tertiary	Oahu

†The Penguin Bank at −185 ft. is present but has a complex history; hence it is not a single halt.
*Position in sequence uncertain.
**Two shorelines 22 and 27 feet above mean sea level.

present sea level an unknown amount, and returned to about 2 feet above present sea level, to the Leahi shoreline. It then dropped to the Mamala low stand, about 350 feet below present sea level,

Figure 2-13—Notch of the minus 80-foot shoreline with overhanging visor in dead coral reef in Kaneohe Bay, Oahu. (Photo by U. S. Navy.)

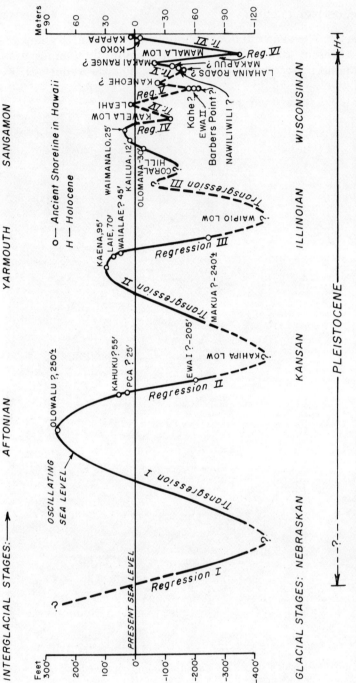

Figure 2-14—Graph showing glacioeustatic fluctuations of sea level and Hawaiian Pleistocene shorelines. Question marks after shoreline names indicate that the order in time sequence is uncertain. (Modified after Lum and Stearns, 1970.)

during the Wisconsinan or last glacial epoch. This ice age ended about 11,000 years ago. The sea rose rapidly, at the average rate of about 3 feet per century, to about 3,500 years ago, when it halted 5 feet above sea level (the Kapapa stand) long enough to cut benches and to leave reefs, now above sea level, at Midway and Kure islands before withdrawing to present sea level.[68, 201]

It is apparent that the sea level never returned to its former earlier height following a retrogression during a glacial epoch, which means that: (1) sea level fell from worldwide tectonic causes concurrent with the glacial epochs; (2) more ice was stored on the poles during each succeeding interglacial epoch; or (3) the Hawaiian Islands were rising. The decline of sea level during the Pleistocene was worldwide and is thought to have been due to the increase in the capacity of the ocean basins.[256] Dury believes that the fall of sea level amounts to more than 1,000 feet since late Pliocene time.[49]

Significant data on subsidence and sea level fluctuations were obtained from two holes drilled in the Pearl Harbor area under an NSF grant in 1965.[223] Hole 1, which is 6 feet above mean sea level and 1,107 feet deep, penetrated 15 coral reefs separated by marine muds, lignite, marl, beach rock, basaltic sand, gravel, and fossil soils. Preliminary studies of Hole 1 indicate that the Koolau basalt was weathered deeply and eroded before subsidence of Oahu by a minimum of 1,071 feet; that the sea halted at $-634'$, $-464'$, $-202'$ (Ewa I shoreline), at the Penguin Bank shelf level ($-176'$), at $-46'$, and at other levels. A soil at $-360'$ correlates with the Kahipa shelf level. A striking change in the paleo-environment occurs at -570 feet. Studies of the fossils,[176] geomagnetics,[71] and age of the basalts[64] have been made from the cores.

Hole 2, located two miles inland from Hole 1 at an altitude of 20 feet, was drilled to a depth of 544 feet into deeply weathered Koolau basalt. It encountered only three reefs. The core is mostly deltaic sediments derived from a weathered volcanic terrane.

During 1965, two holes were drilled on Midway Islands.[99] Cores proved that a deeply weathered and eroded basaltic volcano had sunk beneath the waves before middle Miocene time, or about 20 million years earlier than the great submergence of Oahu. Thus, the islands northwest of Kauai are much older than the main Hawaiian Islands.

To date, a sequence of 35 terrace and shelf levels, above and below sea level in the islands, has been found, and many more must exist below sea level. Their order and heights are given in the preceding table, and the type localities are shown in Figure 2-15.

It is difficult for most people to believe that Honolulu and all the world's coastal cities would be drowned under more than 200 feet of water if all the ice on the poles were to melt today. The total world ice volume is estimated by Donn as about 7,500,000 cubic miles.[47] The maximum ice extent apparently occurred during the Third or Illinoian glacial stage, when the ice volumes reached about 20,000,000 cubic miles. These are quantities that stagger the imagination; the water stored as ice affected the world's ocean levels and had a profound effect on the Hawaiian Islands. During cool glacial epochs, rainfall increased on the islands, and the rain-belts moved lower. Thus the forests that existed on Kahoolawe Island until they were destroyed by goats in historic time, and on the other islands in areas that are now barren, were relict forests of wetter times. When the sea was lower, the rivers cut their canyons deeper. The valleys, now drowned at Pearl Harbor, were formed

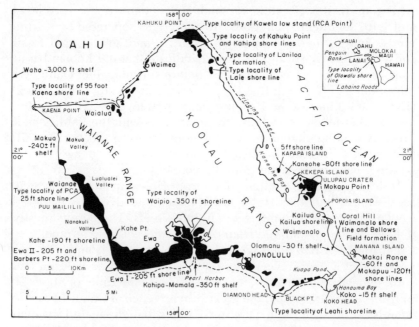

Figure 2-15—Map of Oahu showing areas of emerged reefs (solid black), fringing reef (dashed line) and type localities of emerged and submerged shorelines and shelves.

Figure 2-16—Emerged reef limestone of the Kaena 95-foot sea in Lualualei Valley, Oahu. (Photo by H. Ries.)

when the sea was lower. Foundations for bridges across streams near the coast and for pilings to support tall buildings along the shore must penetrate the soft mud laid down as the ocean rose. Deep soil lost rapidly from sugar cane fields is gone forever. In fifty years some of the plantations now farming thin soil areas may have no soil left. Perhaps the areas will be covered by housing and golf courses by that time, but soil in Hawaii is an irreplaceable gift of millennia.

Origin of Coral Reefs

Hawaiian coral reefs have diverse origin and composition. Hawaii lies at the northern edge of the coral seas, so corals grow slowly and are not abundant. Corals are too weak to build reefs without coralline algae or nullipores, which secrete lime and bind the fragile corals into a solid mass to resist the pounding of the waves. Because most Hawaiian reefs are composed primarily of algal skeletons, they are lithothamnion or nullipore reefs. Most of the "reefs" along the shore consist of beach rock or beds of cemented sand and gravel. They show bedding dipping gently seaward, and the rock is used for building stone. Beach rock has a complex origin, but some of it was formed by ground water escaping along the beach.[1,56] Pinnacles of "staghorn" coral can be seen from a glass-bottom boat in Kaneohe Bay and in other lagoons where they are protected from strong waves.

The greatest development of reef occurred during the warm interglacial periods in the past, especially when the sea stood about 100 feet higher than it does at present. It was then that the broad emerged reefs of Lualualei Valley developed, which are now so valuable as lime in the production of cement (Fig. 2-16).

Reef-building corals thrive only at moderate depths, usually less than 200 feet below sea level in warm, fairly clear ocean water. They are killed quickly by fresh water or by a day or two of exposure to the sun. Contrary to statements in old textbooks, coral atolls are not formed generally by growth upward from crater and caldera rims (Fig. 2-17). All coral reefs rest on shelves built with their own talus or on antecedent platforms of any origin. Because coral reefs grow upward only 6 to 20 feet in 1,000 years under favorable conditions, even a fairly slow rate of submergence may drown a growing reef. All reefs are killed by permanent emergence at sea level. Coral reefs grow most rapidly at their outer edges in the breaker zone, where the food and oxygen supply is greatest. The steepness of slopes has had a deleterious effect on the formation of coral reefs, especially during the fluctuating seas of the Pleistocene. Fringing reefs are able to grow as rapidly as submerged reefs on gently shelving shores, but may fail to do so on a steep shore. Where they keep up with submergence, they may become barrier reefs. This is a likely explanation of the origin of the barrier reef at Kaneohe Bay, Oahu. The absence of a reef is in some places due to its burial by a Pleistocene lava flow (Fig. 2-18). The late lava flows on Oahu have buried many reefs, as shown by well logs.[4] The history of the cen-

Figure 2-17—Wake Island, a typical atoll. (Photo by B. P. Bishop Museum.)

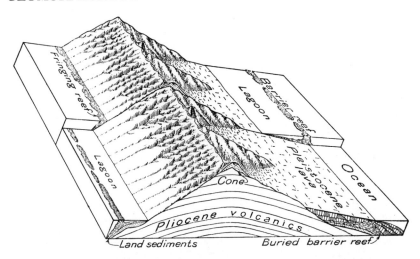

Figure 2-18—Diagram showing effect of slope on formation of coral reefs. Front block shows conditions prior to a rise in sea level. Rear block shows conditions after a rapid rise in sea level, with a barrier reef developed on the gentle slope and a fringing reef on the steep slope.

Figure 2-19—Map of the Pacific. The Sial or Andesite line is the approximate eastern edge of the platform of Australasia. The islands west of the line are Sialic (continental) islands, and those to the east are Simatic (oceanic) islands. *Sial* is a word coined from silica and alumina, and *simatic* from silica and magnesia.

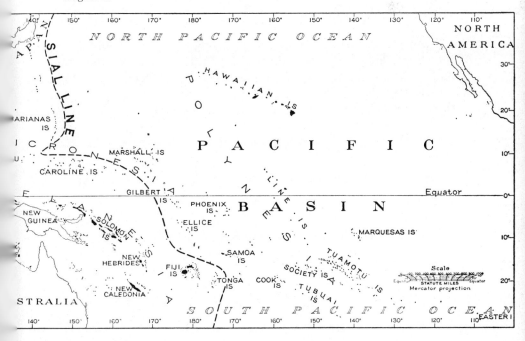

tral Pacific has been one of great subsidence, whereas the islands bordering the basin contain folded rocks of continental type and have in general been uplifted (Fig. 2-19).

There are several hypotheses as to the origin of reefs. Their merits vary according to the geologic epoch in which the reef grew, as well as with the location of the reef's foundation on the earth's crust relative to regions of uplift or subsidence.[208] All living reefs, regardless of the origin of the underlying reefs they cap, are due to return of glacial melt water to the seas since about 11,000 years ago. The sea rose eustatically 5.85 inches at Honolulu between 1910 and 1945, a rate of about one foot per century.[149] This indicates a slowing down of return melt water.

The various theories and their originators and exponents may be listed according to the type of foundation as follows:

A. Intermittently subsiding
   foundations: Darwin, Dana, Davis
B. Rising foundations: Semper, Guppy
C. Still-standing foundations: Rein, Murray, Wood-Jones
   (1) Truncated or partly
       truncated by ero-
       sion: Wharton, Tyerman, Bennet, Guppy, Agassiz
   (2) Truncated or partly
       truncated but with
       sea fluctuating: Daly (glacial), Stearns (preglacial)[a]

[a]The writer does not exclude other theories but believes that many reefs started in the Pliocene when sea levels were fluctuating because of tectonic eustasy.

Figure 2-20 illustrates the growth of an atoll on an island following its gradual subsidence during the Pliocene and the development of a platform by erosion. Figure 2-21 shows the superposition and destruction of reefs, since the 100-foot Kaena stand, caused by fluctuations resulting from the change in the volume of the ocean concurrent with the waxing and waning of the polar ice caps. No emerged reef exists younger than that which grew during the Waimanalo 25-foot stand.

CHEMICAL WEATHERING AND ORIGIN
OF "ONION SKIN" BOULDERS

Most persons arriving in Hawaii from areas of mechanical weathering or glaciated regions are surprised at the deep red soil so conspicuous in the sugar cane and pineapple fields. In Hawaii's warm, moist climate, rocks slowly decompose by chemical weathering, and on the gentle slopes the rocks disintegrate completely and are converted to red soils. The red color is due to oxidation of black iron oxide (magnetite), common in all the lavas, to red iron oxide. It takes very little red oxide to color soil.

In the deep road cuts along Kamehameha Highway near Schofield Barracks, one can see 10 feet of red soil in which all traces of the original lava are gone, lying on 50 or 60 feet of decomposed basalt in which the original pattern and vesicles of pahoehoe or aa lava can be discerned. The iron-rich, formerly glassy crusts of the pahoehoe now appear as red streaks. An excellent exposure is in the 85-foot bluff under the former Pineapple Research Institute at Waipio Acres along the highway near Wahiawa. Capping this bluff is 20 feet of decomposed waterworn gravel and cobbles, topped by red soil and overlying a fossil red soil on the underlying decomposed Koolau lavas. The cobbles are so soft that they can be cut with a knife as easily as cheese. Many of the pineapple fields in this area are underlain by similar decomposed gravel. Irregular bands of bog iron ore (limonite) one-quarter to one-half inch thick are common in road cuts in this area.

The decomposed basalt grades downward into "onion skin" boulders, or spheroidally weathered basalt with a perfectly round, dense, hard core of undecomposed black rock. Many of these round masses projecting from road cuts have been misinterpreted as waterworn cobbles and boulders, and some observers ask whether the sea at some time in the past has rounded them (Fig. 2-22). Decomposition in the deep well opposite the entrance to Wheeler Air Force Base near Wahiawa extends to a depth of 150 feet. If radiometric measurements are correct, this decomposition required one to two million years.

In the past, when the islands stood higher, and during the ice ages, when the rainfall was greater than it is today, chemical weathering proceeded at a faster rate than it does now at low elevations such as the Schofield Plateau, Oahu. The red soil that covers the cane fields behind Lahaina, Maui, and the pineapple fields of Lanai, and caps Kahoolawe and Niihau islands, could not have formed under the semiarid climates that exist today. They are fossil soils. Most of the red soils on the island of Hawaii have a different origin. They are relatively young, decomposed or partly decomposed fine ash (chiefly Pahala ash) and are measured in thousands

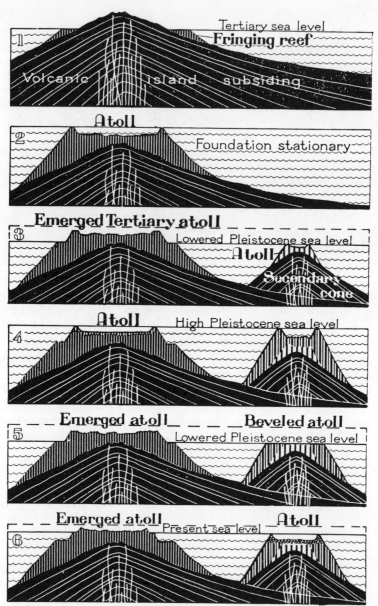

Figure 2-20—Six stages in the development of atolls east of the Sial line in the Pacific. Vertically exaggerated, fluctuations of sea level reduced to two, and structure of cones simplified. *Stage 1.* Eroded volcanic island subsiding in Pliocene time with fringing reef. The earth is ice-free. *Stage 2.* Island ceases to subside. An atoll has developed at the end of the Pliocene. *Stage 3.* Effect of glacial lowering of sea level. The atoll emerges and becomes eroded. The rim is beveled during a pause in the fall of the sea. A secondary cone erupts and develops an atoll. *Stage 4.* Effect of interglacial rise of sea level. A thin veneer of reef grows on the eroded atoll and the right atoll continues its growth. *Stage 5.* Effect of next glacial lowering of sea level. Erosion removes the newly formed reef on the left atoll and planes off the right atoll. *Stage 6.* Present sea level with two atolls having different histories, one Tertiary and the other Pleistocene.

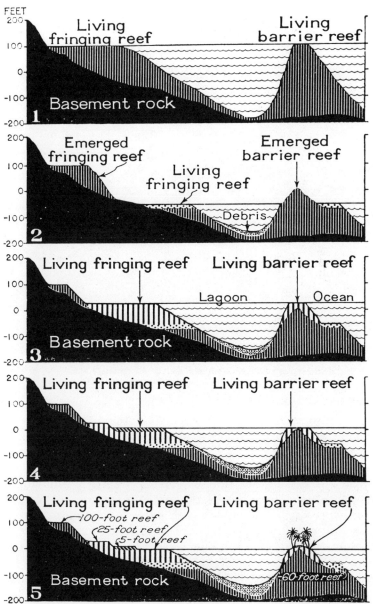

Figure 2-21—Five stages showing effects of the last five shifts of sea level on growth of barrier and fringing reefs. *Stage 1.* Fringing and barrier reef during the +100-foot interglacial stand of the sea. *Stage 2.* Reefs during the minus 60-foot glacial low stand of the sea resting on wave-eroded and weathered reefs of the +100-foot stand. *Stage 3.* Reefs during the +25-foot stand of the sea. In some places older reef has been destroyed; in other places it has been built up by coral growth. *Stage 4.* Effect of the +5-foot stand of the sea. Part of the fringing reef of the +25-foot stand has been destroyed and the remainder veneered with a living reef. A living reef too thin to show veneers the older barrier reef. The sea fell apparently about 350 feet below present sea level in the interval between the Leahi 2±-foot halt and present sea level. No 5-foot reef exists today. *Stage 5.* Present sea level. Only the beach conglomerates of the 5±-foot stand exist today. The living reefs are thin veneers on the older reefs.

Figure 2-22—Spheroidal weathered basalt near Kapaa, Kauai. The original joint cracks in the lava can be discerned. (Photo by H. T. Stearns.)

of years instead of a million years. Also, they are readily distinguishable from the soils on the older islands because they lie on fresh rock.

In spite of the ubiquitous iron oxide in the soil, little is available for plant life because the iron oxide is locked in the soil with manganese oxide in a form that plant roots cannot absorb. The pineapple growers spray their fields with an iron solution to make the plants fruit properly.

When stripped of their vegetation, the red soils develop a hardpan layer about a foot below the surface. It slowly bakes in the sun to form laterite, a hard, red, bricklike material, the name of which is derived from the Latin word for brick. Elmer Hill, a soil scientist for the U.S. Department of Agriculture in Hawaii, reported that he saw a layer of laterite 4 inches thick harden within a year. Lateritic crusts are common on all the older islands. They are rich in iron and aluminum, low in silica, and chemically acidic.[131] Fortunately, the soils in Hawaii develop a pellet structure commonly about 1/64 of an inch in diameter. This structure greatly increases absorption of rainfall, thereby reducing erosion. Some of the soils have the capacity to absorb up to one inch per hour of rainfall.

LANDSLIDES, MUDFLOWS, AND SOIL AVALANCHES

Disastrous landslides and mudflows are less frequent than might be expected in the Hawaiian Islands, where so many steep-walled canyons and cliffs exist. Relative stability is due chiefly to the lack of slippery ash beds and clays interbedded with the spinose basalts. Falling segments of cliffs cause landslides. If saturated enough to liquefy, such slides are mudflows. Minor slides involving the soil cover and vegetation on the slope are called soil avalanches.[242,249]

Hawaii Island. The only historic landslide in the islands to cause loss of life occurred at Wood Valley Camp, 5 miles north of Pahala in the Kau District, on April 2, 1868, following an earthquake. It was caused by the sliding of a lava flow on a wet ash bed from an altitude of 3,500 feet to an altitude of 1,620 feet, through a horizontal distance of 2½ miles. The water and mud acted as a lubricant, and the whole mass moved rapidly down the valley, burying a village with 31 persons and more than 500 head of livestock. Landslides fell at the same time above Waiohinu and from the sea cliff one mile northwest of Waimanu Canyon in the Kohala District.

Large landslides occurred in Honokane Nui Valley during the earthquakes of 1929. These earthquakes also shattered and upset blocks of crust in the black pahoehoe near Honaunau in Kona. A large landslide fell from the sea cliff just east of the mouth of Honopue Valley during heavy rains in January, 1941, and built a fan similar to that of the Laupahoehoe landslide in 1868, two miles to the southeast. About half the slide has been removed by the waves since 1941. The cliff along this stretch of the coast is subject to slides because of thin saturated ash beds. In 1942 a landslide fell into the West Branch of Honokane Nui Stream at an altitude of 1,500 feet. A pond 100 yards long, still in existence in 1944, was formed. Other landslides have occurred in the past. One blocked the East Branch of Honokane Nui Canyon near its head and formed a temporary dam behind which 30 feet of horizontally bedded silts and clays were deposited.

A huge undersea landslide extends from Kealakekua Bay to South Point and from the shoreline 50 miles out to sea. It was discovered in 1978 by the U.S. Geological Survey ship. The fault at Kealakekua Bay appears to be the head of a landslide block.

Maui Island. For at least a century, and maybe for many centuries, weathering had been going on undisturbed in the canyons in the rainbelts of Maui, when at 10:03 P.M., January 22, 1938, the Hawaiian Islands were shaken by a destructive earthquake with its epicenter at sea 25 miles north of Pauwalu Point and 65 miles below the surface, as reported by the U.S. Coast and Geodetic Survey. Damage, which was limited to Maui, totaled about $200,000. The author, who was living in a wooden frame house on the sand beach at Spreckelsville, estimated the intensity there as 6.7 on the Richter scale. No tidal wave accompanied the shock. No destructive earthquake had been recorded previously on Maui.

A great difference was noted in the damage and intensity of the shock in several parts of Spreckelsville. Damage in the center of the village, which was built on bedrock consisting of old Kula lavas, was negligible. Less than half a mile away, residences built on loose beach sand were damaged considerably.

The geomorphic significance of the earthquake was the great change wrought in the terrane. Vast quantities of debris had crumbled, weathered, or crept into position where, saturated from winter rains, it was ready to slide. More soil and rocks moved during the few seconds of the quake than would move by normal erosion in several centuries. Ridges in the ditch country of East Maui were decapitated, and great slides choked valleys and buried roads and ditches. Much of the road from Kailua to Nahiku was buried, and it took several months to clear away the landslides. The green-forested steep-walled canyons of West Maui were marred with hundreds of landslide scars, the largest of which were still bare three years later. The streams with steep canyon walls were muddy for months after the earthquake, and much of the heavy debris was still being washed downstream during floods in 1940.

Rocks loosened and cliffs cracked by the 1938 earthquake fell for several years afterwards during intense winds and storms. Manawainui Canyon near Kaupo was hazardous to climb in 1941 because of falling rocks and trees. The floor was cluttered with debris. Talus slopes in Haleakala were still sliding and readjusting in 1941. The important role of minor catastrophes in erosion was made evident by the Maui earthquake.

Figure 2-23—Mudflow breccia at the mouth of Kaupo Valley, Maui. (Photo by H. T. Stearns.)

The Kaupo mudflow, which is the largest single prehistoric mudflow deposit found in the islands, crops out over 1½ square miles at the mouth of Kaupo Valley. It is consolidated into a hard breccia (Fig. 2-23), which projects through the later lavas and Pleistocene gravels and forms cliffs 300 feet high along the coast. It is 335 feet thick in one hill, but it must be much thicker, as it extends below sea level. It is overlain by gravels that were apparently graded to the 100-foot stand of the sea; hence the mudflow occurred in the middle Pleistocene. It carries blocks up to 50 feet across.[7]

Test holes drilled in 1975 for a water development project between Iao Valley and Waihee on West Maui encountered a thick mudflow breccia interstratified with older alluvium.[221]

Molokai Island. While the author was camping in the deep Wailau and Pelekuna valleys on Molokai in 1935, he was awakened nearly every night by local tremors caused by landslides nearby. Wild goats had made their first appearance in these valleys only a few years earlier. They had disturbed the soil on the cliffs and eaten much of the vegetation. The great number of landslides in 1935 appears to be directly related to the destructive work of the goats in this belt of steep canyon walls and high rainfall.

Oahu Island. A great boulder train stretches for a mile from the foot of the cliff on the northeast side of Nanakuli Valley. It consists of rounded boulders of extremely massive lava, some reaching 30 feet in diameter, lying on the surface of the valley fill. Near the top of the cliff is a large mass of the same rock. Apparently a great landslide from this wall carried blocks of the rock into the valley a long time ago. Subsequent erosion removed the smaller material of the slide but failed to remove the large blocks, and weathering has rounded and pitted the surface of the large blocks so that they are no longer angular and no longer look like part of the landslide.

Oahu has true volcanic mudflows (cold lahars) caused by an eruption depositing ash and ejecta over a large area of steep terrane. The debris is then swept down the valleys by heavy rains. The explosions from Kaau Crater resulted in a deposit that differs in many respects from the deposits in tuff cones around the other paroxysmal vents. Most of the other explosions of this type on Oahu occurred before the domes had been dissected by erosion. Consequently, their ejecta remained as a more or less complete mantle over the surrounding areas. The Kaau explosion occurred when the Koolau Range was essentially the same as it is at present, with steep canyons and a well-developed drainage. Thus, the ash fell on steep valley walls, and storms accompanying the explosions or occurring soon after swept the unconsolidated ash and ejecta into the stream beds. The streams became so loaded with debris that they reached the consistency of thick mud and were able to carry along large angular blocks. The mudflow is exposed along Palolo Valley and is 60 feet thick in places. It resembles the mudflow deposit that rushed down Hat Creek from Lassen Peak in California during the eruption of 1914.

Another volcanic mudflow is exposed near Fort Shafter. It may be correlative with the eruption of Aliamanu Crater. In a bluff 1,200 feet east of the mouth of Moanalua Stream, a thin mudflow resting unconformably on pumiceous alluvium is exposed. The lower four feet of the mudflow consists of boulders as much as four feet in diameter in a black tuffaceous matrix. Above the boulders is about six feet of indurated laminated lithic tuff, which, at a point nearby along the road, is full of small fragments of fossil wood. The jumbled and broken character of the wood fragments indicates that the mudflow swept considerable vegetation along with it. When it came to rest it was evidently sufficiently plastic to allow the heavy boulders to settle to the bottom. This same mudflow, without the laminated facies, also is well exposed as a cap rock both above and below the point where Kamehameha Highway crosses the same terrace, west of Kahauiki Stream. Above the concrete septic tanks at Fort Shafter, just south of the lower road crossing over Kahauiki Stream, the tuffaceous matrix of the boulders is very rich in well-preserved fossil leaves and wood.

The amphitheater-headed valleys on Oahu, especially those near Honolulu and Kaneohe, once carried powerful streams when the canyons were being actively cut. Now that rapid cutting has ceased, small landslides and soil avalanches are commonplace. After each big storm dozens of fresh scars appear on the cliffs. The scars are covered rapidly by vegetation and can be distinguished only by comparing the size of the growth on them with the size of growth in nearby areas. Upper Manoa Valley is particularly subject to slides because of the many thin ash beds interbedded with the basalt.

Kauai Island.   The steep-walled canyons and sea cliffs of Kauai are the sites of many landslides and rock falls. Interbedded with the Pleistocene valley-filling volcanics is the Palikea formation of breccias 100 to 700 feet thick, composed in places of chaotic landslide and mudflow deposits. They are chiefly next to Waialeale summit, where formerly deep canyons headed. These voluminous landslides were probably triggered by earthquakes accompanying the eruptions of the Koloa vents,[13] and thus resemble the landslides of 1868 on the island of Hawaii and the voluminous slides caused by the 1938 earthquake on Maui.

EARTHQUAKES

Two strong earthquakes are known to have occurred on the Island of Hawaii during the nineteenth century before intensities were measured on the Richter scale. On February 19, 1834, a strong earthquake destroyed stone walls in Hilo, and on April 2, 1868, a second one in the Kau District, estimated to have been 7.7, caused a tsunami and numerous slides, destroyed hundreds of homes, and killed 79 people.

During the twentieth century a number of major earthquakes have been recorded. On January 22, 1938, an earthquake registering 6.7, with its epicenter north of the Island of Maui in the ocean, caused more than $200,000 damage on Maui. On August 21, 1951, an earthquake registering 6.75 occurred in the Kona District on the Island of Hawaii, destroying 20 buildings. On November 29, 1975, an earthquake registering 7.2 occurred in the Puna District, Island of Hawaii, causing a local tsunami and killing two people. On November 16, 1983, an earthquake registering 6.7 occurred on the southwest slope of Mauna Loa. No deaths were reported, but about $2,500,000 damage was done in Hilo and in the National Park area.

A list of earthquakes in Hawaii is given in "A study of past earthquakes, isoseismic zones of intensity and recommended zones for structural design for Hawaii" by Augustine Furumoto, N. Norby Neilsen, and William R. Phillips, Engineering Bulletin PACE 72033, University of Hawaii, 1972.

GEOMORPHIC SURFACES

A series of terraces, or geomorphic surfaces, exists on all the older islands and on Kohala Mountain, Hawaii. They occur like a flight of steps, with the oldest one at the top. Most appear to be the result of stream erosion and deposition when the sea stood higher in relation to the land. The lower ones are definitely related to the higher stands of the sea in the Pleistocene, but the older ones ranging from 300 to 1,200 feet above sea level may be related to land movements. They are later than the deep soils on bedrock, as is evidenced at Waipio Acres in central Oahu, where fanglomerate in one of these terraces overlies red soil and deeply weathered basalt, and is overlain by a soil. The gravel in all the higher terraces is thoroughly decomposed and each terrace carries a distinct soil mapped by the U.S. Soil Conservation Service. Eleven surfaces have been mapped on Oahu. The writer is indebted for the foregoing data to R. V. Ruhe of the U.S. Soil Survey Investigations, who lent a copy of his unpublished manuscript on the subject and discussed the evidence in the field.

3

VOLCANIC TERMS,

FORMS,

AND PRODUCTS

Lava

The molten rock poured out of Hawaiian volcanoes is a complex solution of silicates and oxides containing gases and usually solid crystals of various minerals that have separated from the solution. It is *magma* when it lies beneath the crust and *lava* when it pours out on the surface. *Volcanics* is a general term for all the products laid down by a volcano.

Calderas and Grabens

The terms *caldera* (Spanish for cauldron) and *crater* are often used interchangeably. A caldera is a large crater with a diameter many times its depth. For example, Halemaumau is a crater within the caldera of Kilauea Volcano (Fig. 3-1 and Fig. 6-21). A caldera is a large, more or less circular or amphitheatral basin, chiefly or entirely formed by engulfment and collapse, usually on the summit of a volcano over the volcanic hearth.[250] The sinking results from the stoping and melting of the core of the volcano by the underlying magma at depth. *Grabens*, sunken fault blocks, leading away from calderas have a similar cause, but die out along rift zones. A small fraction of the missing material is floated upward as small solid fragments and carried away in the lava flows. Another fraction may be blown out as ash or ejecta, as at Kilauea Volcano, but the main cause of calderas is collapse of the floor into the depths below, where the material is remelted and extruded again as lava indistinguishable from any other lava. A caldera floor is usually composed

69

Randy Humiston

Figure 3-1—Air view of Halemaumau Crater, Kilauea Volcano, Hawaii. The cliff of the caldera is to the right and Mauna Loa Volcano is in the background. (Photo by U.S. Army.)

of horizontal or nearly horizontal bedded lava flows commonly more massive than those on the slopes of the volcano. They are *pooled* lavas; hence they are less vesicular and usually exhibit good *columnar jointing* (Fig. 3-2). Also, the vesicles may contain secondary minerals, deposited during the slow cooling, or from gases subsequently rising through them. The pooled lavas are in the "stew pot" for a longer period of time than the lava flows that pour down the slopes, cool rapidly, and lose their gases immediately. Such pooled lavas can be seen behind Lanikai, Oahu.

Some of the calderas in the older volcanoes were partly or completely filled before extinction. However, the circular caldera faults and the remnant depression direct the surface and ground water toward one or two streams, giving them dominant drainage and thereby leading to the erosion of larger canyons than would be eroded otherwise. Hence, the conditions favorable to drainage and the weak rocks along the circular faults are important factors in forming larger canyons. Graben structures on Kauai predated the cutting of Waimea Canyon, and faults on Kohala Mountain caused

Figure 3-2—Huge column, 6 feet on each side, formed by shrinkage of the lava in Makuopuhi Crater, Kilauea Volcano, Hawaii. (Photo by U.S.G.S.)

Waipio and Waimanu valleys on Hawaii to be larger than their neighbors.

Tourist literature commonly states that Haleakala Crater on Maui is the largest in the world. The summit depression is 7½ miles long and 2½ miles wide. It is very large and handsome, but it is neither a crater nor a caldera. Even if it were a caldera, it would not rank among the top 60 in the world for size. Haleakala was caused by huge amphitheater-headed valleys cutting into the mountain summit. Drainage was probably increased by faults on the summit that directed the drainage chiefly into two valleys. If, as is probable, a caldera existed at one time, it was completely buried by subsequent cones and flows. After a long period of erosion, eruptions began again, and voluminous lava flows and bulky cinder cones partially filled up the heads of Keanae and Kaupo valleys, and almost completely covered the divide between them (Plates 11 and 12).

In 1939, the writer found evidence of the largest caldera in the Hawaiian Islands. It formerly existed on Kauai Volcano. It was 13 miles across in its widest part and 11 miles wide. The graben or fault trough that leads away from it is now occupied by Waimea Canyon. The dense ponded lavas that accumulated on the caldera floor were so much more resistant than those in its rim that streams left the hard rocks in the form of a giant mesa or plateau, now covered by Alakai Swamp (Fig. 10-14).

The "Lihue Depression" on the east side of Kauai is of unknown origin. It is about 11 miles long and 6 miles wide (Fig. 10-3). Cox and others believe that it is a partially filled-up caldera.[13] The writer has proposed an erosional origin for it. Perhaps it is the product of both processes. A density survey by Krivoy indicates a high gravity reading in the depression probably indicating a dense intrusive mass below.[94] The mass could be an intrusive related to the post-erosional lavas, a thick section of valley-filling basalts, or a "shadow" offset similar to the highs on the island of Hawaii that are south of the summits.

The second largest caldera apparently indented the summit of the Koolau Volcano on Oahu. It was about 6 miles long and 4 miles wide, with a graben running northwestward and possibly southeastward (Plate 4). The rocks, or talus, that fell into one of its firepits now form the hill behind Pohai Nani, the retirement home near Kaneohe, and are well exposed with cross-cutting dikes in the banks of the Kailua outdoor theater. The lavas in the floor of the caldera sagged from withdrawal of support and formed the Kailua syncline behind Lanikai (Fig. 3-3). Numerous feeder dikes are exposed in the road cut near Kaneohe Junction (Fig. 3-23).

The caldera that formerly indented the summit of the Waianae Range, Oahu, was about 3 miles wide and 5 miles long. It had a fault trench or graben running to the west and possibly another toward the southeast (Plate 3). Puu Kailio, the hill below Kolekole Pass, traversed by the road connecting Schofield Barracks and the

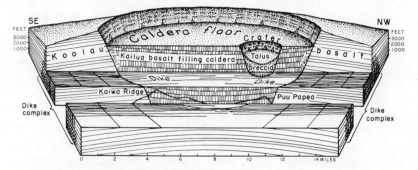

Figure 3-3—Diagram showing the probable relation of the syncline of Kailua basalt to the dike complex and ancient Koolau caldera near Lanikai.

Figure 3-4—Mokuaweoweo caldera and adjacent pit craters on the summit of Mauna Loa. View from the southwest. The large caldera is about 9,000 feet from left to right. (After Wentworth and Macdonald, 1953.)

United States Naval Lualualei Ammunition Depot, consists of talus that fell into the ancient firepit and a syncline of sagged ponded lavas. Numerous cross-jointed dikes cut through the talus breccia. Mount Kaala, the highest point on Oahu, may be horizontal lavas ponded in a firepit or an alcove of the caldera that has resisted erosion to form a plateau.

The largest caldera on Hawaii Island, on the summit of Mauna Loa Volcano, is called Mokuaweoweo (Fig. 3-4). It is 19,500 feet long and 9,200 feet wide, or roughly 3.7 miles long, 1.74 miles wide, and 600 feet deep. It seems to be of recent origin. Kilauea caldera, Hawaii, ranks next in size. It is 2.93 miles long and 1.95 miles wide. Since the 1921 lava flow on its floor it has been rimless on one side, but Uwekahuna Bluff on the northwest rim at the museum is 450 feet higher than the floor (Fig. 6-21).

Hualalai and Mauna Kea on Hawaii have no calderas. Kohala Mountain had a caldera about 3 miles long and 2 miles wide, but it is largely filled with later volcanics so that only a graben 3 miles long and half a mile wide crosses its summit. These faults directed the major drainage to the northeast and the huge Waipio and

Figure 3-5—Air view of Waipio Valley, Hawaii, showing its flat alluvial floor and cinder cones of the Hawi volcanic series in distance. The taro patches and houses were destroyed by the tidal waves of 1946. (Photo by U.S. Army.)

TABLE 3
CALDERAS IN THE HAWAIIAN ISLANDS

Island	Mountain or Name	Length (miles)	Width (miles)
Kauai	Mount Waialeale	13	11
Kauai	Lihue depression[a]	11	6
East Maui	Haleakala[b]	7½	2½
Oahu	Koolau	6	4
Oahu	Waianae	5	3
Lanai	Palawai Basin	4	3
Molokai	East Molokai	4½	2
Hawaii	Mauna Loa	3.7	1.74
Kahoolawe	No name	3	2½
Hawaii	Kilauea	2.93	1.95
Kauai	Haupu caldera	2½	1
Maui	Iao Valley	2	1½

[a] Proof of a caldera in this depression is not certain.
[b] Believed to be chiefly due to erosion perhaps guided by summit faults. If so, it is not a caldera.

Waimanu canyons resulted (Fig. 3-5). The summit of the ancient West Molokai Volcano is slashed by faults caused by collapse of its summit. Here we have an example of a caldera in the making, but subsidence had not proceeded far enough before extinction to form a caldera.

Caldera complex. A caldera complex is the diverse rock assemblage underlying a caldera and comprises dikes, sills, stocks, vent breccias, crater fills of lava, crack fills of lava or talus, beds of tuff, cinder, and agglomerate, fault gouge, fault breccias, talus fans along fault escarpments, and other products laid down in a caldera. (See Figs. 6-7, 6-8, and 6-21.)

Rift zone grabens. Grabens, which are downfaulted trenches bordered by infacing fault scarps, are a common feature of rift zones of Hawaiian volcanoes. They are usually deepest near the summit vent and become shallow on the downslope. They are formed by the settling of the rock along a rift zone into the elongated void below. Although the total depth of subsidence of a rift zone graben is commonly large, the graben may at all times be shallow because of repeated filling by lava erupted from fissures within it. When the volcano is active, the faults bounding the graben are frequent loci for earthquakes.

Grabens exist on the southwest and southeast rift zones of Kilauea and on Lanai. Before erosion, they existed on both the ancient Koolau and Waianae volcanoes of Oahu. The ancient Makaweli graben on Kauai is partly filled with lavas, and Kipahulu Valley on Maui may have tapped an ancient graben structure on Haleakala. Grabens also exist on the summit of Kohala Mountain and on the ancient West Molokai Volcano. At least one known graben exists at Makanao in the Kau District, Hawaii, that is not associated with a rift zone, but was caused by an inland fault block sinking faster than the seaward block.[224]

CRATERS

A *crater* is a volcanic depression that is much smaller than a caldera. Those on Hawaii range from a few feet to three-quarters of a mile across. They fall into three types: negative forms produced by collapse; positive forms that were orifices of either lava fountains or explosions and did not collapse; and orifices of lava fountains later enlarged by collapse.

Those that were orifices of cinder, lava, and spatter cones will be called *craters*. Those produced by collapse only will be called *pit craters* (Fig. 3-6). Little or no lava flowed from them. Those formed by violent explosions will be called *explosion craters*. Such craters are greatly enlarged by collapse.

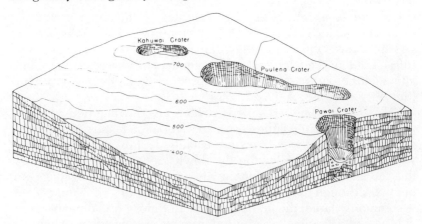

Figure 3-6—Block diagram showing pit craters along the east rift zone of Kilauea Volcano. Contour interval, 50 feet. (After Wentworth and Macdonald, 1953.)

Many craters have been enlarged by loose cinders sliding from the rim into the vents after lava fountaining ceased. Some have been enlarged by collapse when the magma column subsided or drained away through tubes in the slopes of the cone. Most craters of spatter cones retain their original form because the walls are sufficiently agglutinated to withstand failure when lava fountaining ceases.

DOMES

The mountains of Hawaii fall into two types: (1) broad *shield-shaped domes* consisting chiefly of thin-bedded lava flows dipping away from their respective summit vents and rift zones, and (2) steep domes studded with cinder cones. Mauna Loa, Kilauea, and

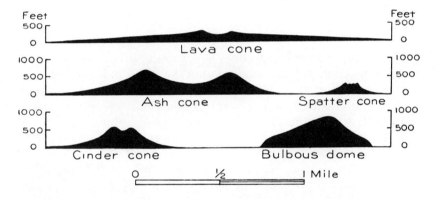

Figure 3-7—Profiles of secondary cones. Ash cones, after consolidation, are called tuff cones.

Kohala are the flat type of dome; Mauna Kea and Hualalai are the steep type (Fig. 6-2).

Most steep domes are underlain by typical flat shield-shaped domes of tholeiitic lavas and owe their steepness to a cap of differentiated lavas or pyroclastics, or both (Fig. 6-5). Kohala Mountain is capped by cones and flows of differentiated lava, but the cap is too thin to alter the form of the mountain appreciably. *Rift zones* are the loci of repeated fissure eruptions. They radiate from the summit of a volcano (Fig. 1-1) and in eroded volcanoes are distinguished by *dike complexes* (Fig. 3-23).

Figure 3-8—Typical bedded glassy ash or tuff on Round Top Drive, Oahu, laid down by the Tantalus-Sugar Loaf-Round Top fire fountains. (Photo by H. T. Stearns.)

SECONDARY CONES

Six types of secondary cones are superimposed on the main domes; in order of decreasing number they are cinder cones, spatter cones, bulbous domes, lava cones, pumice, and ash or tuff cones. The profile of each type is given in Figure 3-7. Adventive or accidental ash or tuff cones formed by the explosion of lava when it runs into the sea are *littoral cones*.[240] They are rootless cones.

Cinder cones. The cinder cones range from 50 to 700 feet in height and may reach three-quarters of a mile in diameter. The largest cones are not tholeiitic basalt, but are the product of eruptions of either less or more siliceous types of magma.

Cinder cones are built by lava fountains or the frothing of the erupting magma (Fig. 3-5). They consist of bedded magmatic ejecta only. The agglutinated clots are *spatter;* the scoriaceous fragments are *cinders;* the small fragments, lighter in weight than cinders and extremely cellular in texture, are *pumice;* and those ellipsoidal, discoidal, or spheroidal forms produced by the action of mechanical forces during their flight through the air are *bombs.* Some of the ejecta contain crystals of olivine, augite, and feldspar; others are composed of glass commonly blackened with magnetite dust.

During eruptions, *Pele's hair, Pele's tears,* and thin glassy ribbons are made by lava fountains, but they are so fragile that they soon weather away. Strong winds during eruptions, especially those on high ridges, cause cones to grow asymmetrically and spread pumiceous material fanwise for several miles leeward. Before consolidation, much of this fragile debris commonly breaks into fine dust, and as such is called *ash* or *ashy soil*, depending upon the degree of weathering. In some places it alters to *palagonite*, a waxy yellow silicagel mineraloid; in others it oxidizes brilliant red. These layers upon consolidation form the commonest type of *vitric* or *glassy tuffs*, or *vitric-crystal tuffs* if they carry crystals[168] (Fig. 3-8). The terms *ash* and *tuff*, if not qualified by descriptive adjectives, refer herein to such lava fountain deposits. Cinder cones are not great ash makers, but deposits as thick as 55 feet have accumulated where conditions were favorable. All degrees of consolidation are present, commonly in the same deposit. Hence, the terms ash and tuff are not very specific, but firmly compacted deposits are referred to herein as *tuff* and *palagonitic tuffs*.[73]

A few cinder cones contain fragments of older rock. Such fragments fall into vent cracks when eruptions start and are carried up by the magma, or they may be brought up in the magma from considerable depth. The fragments are commonly coated with vesicular glass and are called *cored bombs*.[21] Cinder cones are not the product of catastrophic blasts that tear wall rock from the volcanic throat,

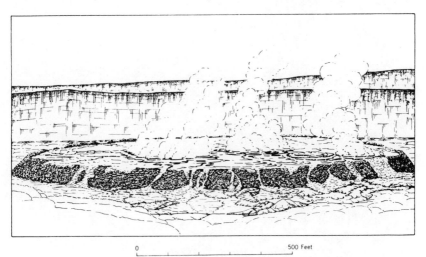

0   500 Feet

Figure 3-9—Lava ring at Halemaumau, Kilauea, in March 1894. The lava lake stood about 40 feet above its surroundings and was about 1,200 feet in greatest diameter. (After Wentworth and Macdonald, 1953.)

80 GEOLOGY OF THE STATE OF HAWAII

but are the result of relatively mild gas effervescence in magma rising through an open conduit.

Spatter cones and lava rings.   When a lava column froths feebly or the magma is very fluid, spatter 5 to 50 feet deep accumulates around isolated vents as mounds, or along fissure vents as ramparts. Such mounds and ramparts are called *spatter cones* (Plate 1). These agglutinated masses resulting from the splash of lava fountains typify eruptions of early tholeiitic basalts, but are less common among later differentiated lavas. Spatter cones on the top or slopes of a cinder cone are the result of dying gasps of the lava fountains. Most bombs are made during this stage.

Figure 3-10—Madame Pele, a driblet spire on the southwest slope of Kilauea Volcano, Hawaii. (Photo by W. O. Clark.)

Walls of agglutinated spatter form *spatter ramparts* a few to 20 feet high and from 1 to 10 feet thick along eruptive fissures along which fire fountains have played. Similar ramparts, circular in form, surround the lava lake in Halemaumau at intervals and are called *lava rings* (Fig. 3-9).

Where spatter is ejected feebly around a small hole, the lava clots accumulate in *driblet spires* a few feet across and up to 16 feet high (Fig. 3-10). Some form over cracks in lava tubes where the escaping gases carry spatter. This variety is known as a *hornito* or *spiracle*.

Bulbous domes. Viscous lava of more siliceous composition than basalt, such as trachyte, commonly erupts in the form of bulbous domes (Fig. 3-11). They range from 100 to 600 feet in height and from 1,000 to 3,000 feet in diameter. These mammalon-shaped bodies are bordered by breccia produced by fragmentation of the mass during protrusion. Stubby lava flows spread from them and a few are preceded by high fire fountains that build a rim around them separated by a moat. They are common on West Molokai, West Maui, and Kohala Mountain.

Lava cones. Secondary *lava cones* are miniature shield-shaped lava domes. The lava is emitted in highly fluid condition with little or no gas effervescence. The cones are built of layers of lava a few inches to a few feet thick, commonly highly scoriaceous or spattery in texture near the vent. The flows spread far and wide and build dome-shaped cones with gentle slopes when they are erupted on nearly level land (Fig. 3-7). They are asymmetrical when built on fairly steep grades, because most of the lava flows downslope. They are composed mostly of tholeiitic basalt.

Ash cones. The term *ash cones* is restricted herein to cones built by violent or cataclysmic explosions. Consolidated ash cones are *tuff cones*. Such cones are formed by the explosions of lava erupting under water or water-saturated rocks. They lie near the coast. Ash beds laid down during such explosions are called *vitric-lithic ash*, the word *lithic* referring to the stony fragments present. If consolidated, the deposits are called *vitric-lithic tuff*. The littoral cones typically contain a much larger proportion of ash and are better bedded than true cinder cones.

BRECCIAS AND TUFFS

Explosion deposits. Explosions deposit *essential* or *magmatic ejecta*—fragments expelled in a fluid state and derived from the magma causing the explosion; *accessory ejecta*—fragments torn

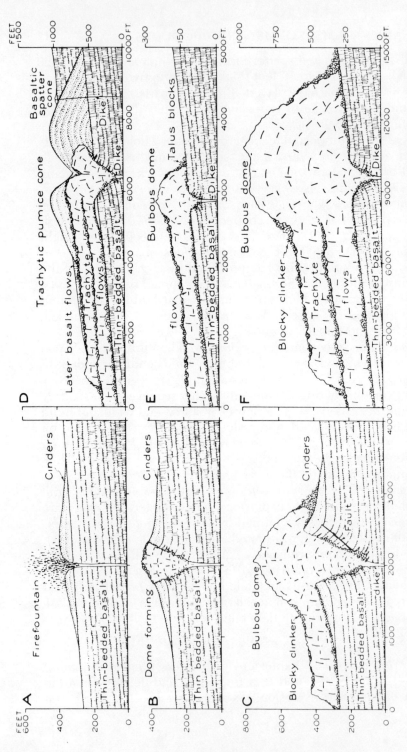

Figure 3-11—Diagrammatic sections of typical bulbous domes of trachyte and mugearite in the Hawaiian Islands. A. Fire fountain building trachytic cinder and pumice cone. B. Formation of a bulbous dome. C. Complete bulbous dome of trachyte with short flow. Basalt beds are pushed upward and faulted. D. Trachytic pumice cone contemporaneous with flows and burying the bulbous dome at the source. It is surrounded by later basalt flows, one of which erupted through the trachytic cone. Puu Waawaa on Hualalai Volcano, Hawaii, was formed in this way. E. Small bulbous dome of mugearite with thin long flow and no cinders. F. Large dome of trachyte with two thick stubby flows and little or no pumice.

Figure 3-12—Cauliflower explosion cloud at Halemaumau Crater, Kilauea Volcano. It is 11,500 feet high and rising at the rate of 13 feet a second. (Photo by H. T. Stearns, May 22, 1924.)

from older related volcanic rocks in the walls of the conduit; and *accidental ejecta*—fragments of sedimentary or other rocks of the subvolcanic basement, genetically unrelated to the exploding magma.[91] The whole gamut of fragmental rocks blown out by explosions and deposited from the air is called *pyroclastic rocks*. The large masses are *blocks* or *bombs*, the small pea- to walnut-sized fragments are *lapilli*, pellets formed by rain drops falling through ash are *accretionary lapilli*, and the fine material is *ash* (Fig. 3-8).

Several types of explosions have occurred on Hawaii. *Magmatic explosions* are characterized by the presence of plastic incandescent essential ejecta and violently expanding magmatic gases. This type is subdivided into *catastrophic* or *paroxysmal magmatic explosions*—those of sufficient intensity to shatter the wall rock and hurl out accessory and essential ejecta, and, if available, accidental ejecta (the explosion of Kilauea in 1790); and *lava* or *fire fountains*—those of much milder intensity that seldom hurl ejecta more than 1,000 feet in the air and rarely expel accessory ejecta. Lava fountains are the commonest type on Hawaii (Plate 1). The so-called *curtain of fire*, typical of Mauna Loa eruptions, consists of coalesced lava fountains along a fissure.

Hydro-explosions is a general term for explosions caused by the generation of steam from any body of water.[240] Several varieties have occurred on Hawaii. *Phreatic explosions* are primarily the result of conversion of ground water to steam (phreatic refers to ground water). Such steam explosions have a low temperature and do not expel essential ejecta. The explosion of Kilauea in 1924 was phreatic (Fig. 3-12). *Phreatomagmatic explosions* occur when ascending magma contacts ground water.[1] Essential as well as accessory ejecta are violently expelled. These differ from magmatic explosions, in which the bulk of the gases is derived from the magma. *Submarine explosions* occur when magma rises into the sea, and *littoral explosions* occur where lava flows from the land contact sea water at the coast[224] (Plate 2). Miniature explosions occur when lava covers saturated ground or wet logs, or runs into pools in stream beds. Some of these small explosions occur 300 feet from the margin of a lava flow.

It takes more than 50 million cubic yards of lava entering the sea to form a littoral cone and only aa flows explode to form such cones. Usually less than 5 per cent of the lava entering the ocean is blown back on the land, and not all aa flows make cones. Multitudes of fish are killed. The 1840 lava flow in Puna, Hawaii, heated the ocean for 20 miles along the coast.[141]

The coarse compacted deposits of angular blocks lying in a matrix of ash and laid down by cataclysmic explosions are called *explosion breccia*. They are abundant around Kilauea caldera. The fine-grained deposits of such explosions are *lithic ash*, which when consolidated are termed *lithic tuff*. Some beds carry sufficient crystals and glass to be *vitric-crystal tuffs*, but the presence of many accessory ejecta readily differentiates the coarse deposits from the vitric-crystal tuffs laid down by lava fountains. All pyroclastic rocks are called *tephra*.

Vent breccia. The chaotic assemblage of angular and subangular fragments in a rock-powder matrix that falls into a vent or pit crater as a result of collapse, explosion, or landslide is called *vent breccia* (Fig. 7-5). It may be loosely or firmly consolidated. Some vent breccias contain debris washed into the vent by water; hence,

Figure 3-13—Fault trace with about 4 feet of gouge and breccia along it cutting thin-bedded basalts on Lanai. (Photo by H. T. Stearns.)

rounded pebbles may be present. In others, cinder and pumice are found, either deposited from nearby lava fountains or subsequently washed into the vents. Vent breccias formed close to the surface usually have poorly developed bedding, dipping toward the center of the vent. Those formed far below ground are not bedded. They usually contain many dense fragments of intrusive rock and are cut by dikes. Vent breccia deposits are roughly cylindrical in outline and generally have nearly vertical contacts. In contrast, beds of explosion breccia laid down outside the vent have nearly horizontal contacts or conform to the underlying lava beds.

Fault breccia. The rupture of the crust where collapse occurs is a *fault*, commonly bordered by *gouge*, or rock pulverized by friction, and wide zones of fault breccia or crushed rock (Fig. 3-13). Scratches along the faults are *slickensides* and indicate the angle of movement. Along the coast, *seaward slip* faults may be found where large slices of the volcanic edifice fail and slide seaward.

Figure 3-14—Typical pahoehoe lava flow from Mauna Loa Volcano with entrail forms and scaly surface. (Photo by H. T. Stearns.)

Fans of rubble at the foot of cliffs or scarps are called *talus,* in contrast to the breccia along the fault plane.

EXTRUSIVE ROCKS

Pahoehoe. Lava that congeals with a relatively smooth, billowy, entrail-like surface, in places ropy, is called *pahoehoe* (pah-hóay-hóay) (Fig. 3-14 and Plate 2). When extrusion occurs on a fairly flat surface, *tumuli* or *pressure domes* develop. They may be formed by collapse as well as by pressure. Commonly, when the crust cracks open, lava wells up as *squeeze ups.* Tumuli and tessellated crusts impart what appears to be an "elephant hide" texture to the flow when seen from an airplane. A pahoehoe flow is spread from the vent through a system of ramifying tubes that range from a few inches to more than 25 feet in diameter. If the lava in these conduits drains out at the close of the eruption, as is usual on steep slopes, a cavern called a *lava tube* results (Fig. 3-15). Lava dripping from the roof of such tubes forms *lava stalactites,* and where it accumulates on the floor, *lava stalagmites* are formed (Fig. 3-16). The lava forms *lava cascades* if it pours over cliffs, and *lava deltas* if it flows into the sea. Pahoehoe flows are commonly composed of several *flow units,* one above the other.[152] Each unit or layer represents a different period of spreading, either hours, days, or months apart, during a single eruption. Glass skins a fraction of an inch thick characterize the surface of the units. Upon weathering, they turn red or yellow and show as wavy streaks in cross-section. Scoriaceous lava, containing closely spaced round vesicles caused by gas bubbles, forms the upper or crusted part of the units. This rock is known in Hawaii as *pukapuka* (póoka póoka), meaning full of holes. The crust of

Figure 3-15—Thurston lava tube on Kilauea Volcano, Hawaii. (Photo by T. Kelsey.)

some flows, especially near vents high on Mauna Loa, is so vesicular that fragments are indistinguishable from highly cellular ejected pumice. It is sometimes called *thread-lace scoria*[41] to differentiate it from *reticulite*, the highly scoriaceous pumice of lava fountains. Where subsequent movement upturns pahoehoe crusts it is called *slab pahoehoe*. In other places it has crusts named from their appearances, such as *shelly, sharkskin, entrail, corded, ropy, festooned, filamented, pumiceous,* or *blistered.*

If the flow unit is thick, the lower part is usually dense, with a zone of vesicles close to the bottom and in places lying on slaggy, doughy-looking masses a few inches across. In many units the un-

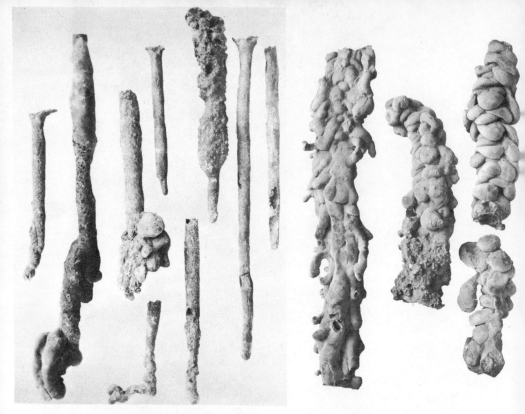

Figure 3-16—Lava stalactites (left) and stalagmites (right) from tubes in lava flows on Kilauea Volcano, Hawaii.

Figure 3-17—Ellipsoidal forms in a typical cross-section of pahoehoe on Kahoolawe Island. (Photo by H. T. Stearns.)

Figure 3-18—Dunite inclusions or xenoliths in a boulder of Koloa lava in Hanalei Valley, Kauai. Watch indicates scale. (Photo by D. A. Davis.)

drained tubes have concentrically arranged vesicles, giving an ellipsoidal form to the rock in section (Fig. 3-17). These forms have been mistaken by some writers for *pillow lavas,* which are ellipsoidal masses formed only in the presence of steam, snow, or water.[45] No true pillow lava has been found on the island of Hawaii. Small undrained tubes with their concentric structures are sometimes mistaken for fossil logs. *Xenoliths* (zeé-no-liths), or fragments of older rock, are found enclosed in lava flows. They may come from deep within the earth and may be fragments of the walls of the magma reservoir or conduit (Fig. 3-18).

Pahoehoe that inundates the trunks of trees may form *tree molds.* The lava is chilled around the tree trunk, often preserving the checks in the charred tree, but rarely details of the bark. The tree burns away, leaving a cylindrical well-like depression, or, if the trunk was recumbent, a trough or tube. If the lava is sufficiently fluid, the lower portions may drain away, lowering the flow surface and leaving projecting above it rough columns of lava that were chilled and solidified by contact with the tree trunks. The upper end of the column furnishes a rough indication of the original level of the flow surface. These projecting columns are known as *lava trees*[145] (Fig. 3-19).

Aa. Lava flows composed of dense basalt with stretched and deflated irregular vesicles lying between and in places including beds of spiny clinkers are called *aa* (ah'ah). The front moves as a wall of livid clinker (Plate 2). If the flows are massive, they have well-developed *columnar jointing.* Tubes are rarely formed. Lava river channels, 5 to 30 feet wide, extend almost to the terminal margins of aa flows. On steep slopes the river channels are bordered by agglutinated splash and veneers of glassy vesicular rock. These spattery *levees* along aa channels are easily confused with spatter ramparts. The aa channel in the 1942 lava flow from Mauna Loa coincides with the fissure vent for half a mile or more. The

Figure 3-19—Lava trees on the lava flow of 1961 on Kilauea Volcano, Hawaii, show charred trees still standing in the casts. (Photo by J. G. Moore.)

surfaces of aa flows are indescribably rough and form black dull bands when seen from the air, in contrast to the shiny pahoehoe. Some flows carry on their surface large numbers of balls from a few inches to 12 feet in diameter. Some balls are masses of clinker subsequently wrapped with lava; others are large masses of the levees or walls of the aa channel undermined and floated downstream by the lava flow. The latter have highly vesicular layered materials inside. All have been called *bombes de roulement*, but they are not true bombs, and the name *accretionary lava balls* is preferable.[104] In some places, blocks of lava slide against each other while still hot, producing *grooved* or *plastic striated* lava. They are also called *shark-teeth slickensides*. A rare form of aa occurs on Kilauea and Mauna Loa; called *arborescent aa* because of its arborescent pattern, its origin is unknown.

Pahoehoe is emitted with much included gas. If the gas is dissipated rapidly by flowing, cooling, or violent lava fountaining so that crystallization starts, the lava changes to aa. The two types are easily separated except at the point of transition. The conversion of pahoehoe to aa is not yet thoroughly understood. A review of the

Plate 1. _ _ _ _ _ _ _ _ ⟶

Aa lava flow of Kilauea Volcano, 1955, moving across a paved road and pushing trees over. *Photo by Jerry Eaton, U.S.G.S.*

Typical ropy pahoehoe in the 1955 lava flow on the east rift zone of Kilauea Volcano. *Courtesy Lewis Cooksey.*

Lava flow from Kilauea Volcano falling over a cliff about 30 feet high into the sea on March 28, 1955. *Photo by Jerry Eaton, U.S.G.S.*

A typical fissure eruption with its spatter rampart and curtain of fire on the east rift of Kilauea in 1955. A river of pahoehoe is flowing away from the firefountains. *Courtesy Lewis Cooksey.*

During the early phase of the 1959 eruption, numerous lava rivers flowed into Kilauea Iki Crater. The firefountain is about 200 feet high and is producing cinder, spatter and pumice. *Courtesy Hawaiian Service.*

literature covering this subject is given elsewhere.[224] It is definitely established, however, that aa cannot revert to pahoehoe. It may appear to do so where pahoehoe emerges from a tube beneath aa, or when a new phase of the eruption sends pahoehoe streaming over previously erupted aa.

Most lava flows in Hawaii can be classified either as pahoehoe or aa, but in the trachyte flows, angular blocks instead of spiny clinker dominate the fragmental part. Such flows are better called *block lavas*.[60]

Kipukas. Island-like areas of older land ranging in size from a few square feet to several square miles surrounded by later lava flows are called *kipukas* (key-poó-kas). Kipukas result from either topographic irregularities or the viscosity of the lava. The surface of a kipuka may be lower or higher than the surface of the lava surrounding it. Commonly, it lies below the level of the lava, although prior to the eruption it may have been a knoll.

Crater fills. Lava in pit craters and in the craters of cinder cones generally congeals as a dense lenticular mass with pronounced columnar jointing (Fig. 3-2). These masses are called *crater fills* (Fig. 7-5). Some fills are coarse-grained and, except when well exposed, are difficult to distinguish from an intrusive body. The tops of crater fills have the usual crustal features of lava flows—valuable criteria for recognizing their origin if they have not been destroyed by erosion. Such features do not form in intrusives. The fact that crater fills become narrower downward is not always diagnostic. If dikelets or offshoots from the body intrude the adjacent walls, it may be assumed, with rare exceptions, that the body is not a crater fill. Cinders, talus, and weathered rock usually border a crater fill and where present are the best diagnostic criteria.

Pillow lavas. Pillow lavas are an unusual form of lava in spheroidal masses; many are flattened slightly on their undersides. Commonly they resemble a stack of bed pillows, which gave them their name. They are best exposed on Kauai[198] and occur only where pahoehoe has flowed into water or over wet ground.[209] Thus, these lavas indicate a water environment where no water may now exist. The most accessible locality is on the west side of the Waimea River, Kauai, 1.3 miles above its mouth at the Menehune Ditch. The pillows range from less than one foot to about 10 feet in diameter, and the visible exposure is 50 feet thick (Fig. 3-20). Many of the interstices are filled with grayish marl, the whole mass having been

←-------- **Plate 2.**

Figure 3-20—Pillow lava along the Menehune Ditch on Kauai, showing a log mold just above the hammer. (Photo by H. T. Stearns.)

formed by a lava flow of the Koloa volcanic series entering water or wet ground.

The 1859 lava flow of Mauna Loa, where it entered the sea, produced pillows or spheroidal masses that sank with a hiss of steam. A small exposure of pillow lava on Oahu can be seen near the shore of Kaneohe Bay where the Haiku basalt crops out.[1] Except for those on Kauai and Oahu, no other pillow lavas above sea level are known in the islands. All occur in late lava flows.

A similar display of pillow lava crops out at the base of Wailua Falls, Kauai (Fig. 10-8), where it was caused by lava spreading over the swampy flood plain of the ancestral Wailua River.[13] Other pillow lavas crop out in Olokele Canyon, Kauai, where they have been formed by lavas entering water ponded by blocked drainage.

Logs of trees are present in the pillow lavas. A mold is shown in Figure 3-20. The largest tree mold occurs on the north bank of the South Fork of the Wailua River.[13] The mold is 30 feet above the river; it is 35 feet long and 5 feet in diameter at its larger end. Several branches diverge from the small end. All the logs in Hawaii have rotted away, leaving only a cavity, probably because of the lack of circulating water carrying silica.

Figure 3-21—Basalt dike crossing throat breccia in the ancient firepit of the Waianae Volcano near Kolekole Pass, Oahu. (Photo by H. T. Stearns.)

Excellent photographs of pillow structures in fresh lavas have been obtained at a depth of 14,400 feet off the southeast coast of Hawaii, proving for the first time that pillow lavas can be formed at great depths in the ocean.[144] They have been photographed forming on the coast of Kilauea.[142] They also formed in 1801 on Hualalai.[140]

FUMAROLES

Fumaroles are small vents from which steam and other volcanic gases escape. *Primary fumaroles* are found on cracks or major faults in the calderas or rift zones, where they remain active for many years. Those at Kilauea have been active since they were first re-

Figure 3-22—Diagram of a dike on the eastern shore of Pelekunu Bay, Molokai, showing arched bands of vesicles. (After Stearns and Macdonald, 1947.)

Figure 3-23—Dike complex in road cut near Kaneohe Junction, Oahu, showing closely spaced dikes disintegrating upward into soil. Much of the intervening rock is older dike rock. (Drawn by Stanley Stearns from a photograph.)

corded in 1823. Those that deposit sulfur, such as the Sulfur Bank at
Kilauea, are *solfataras*. Short-lived fumaroles are gas vents, chiefly
on lava flows; they die when the lava cools. Around some of these
vents, sulfur is deposited.

INTRUSIVE ROCKS

Dikes and sills.   In general, flows are fed by magma that rises
through fairly straight, vertical, narrow cracks. The solidified
magma in such a crack is called a *dike* (Fig. 3-21). Dikes formed
close to the surface of extrusion are usually vesicular, with the
vesicles arranged in parallel vertical zones commonly separated by
vertical *joint planes*. One dike was found with arched bands of
vesicles in the center (Fig. 3-22). Vesicles and vertical jointing dis-
appear with depth, and the rock becomes dense and cross jointed.
Most dikes have borders of black glass a fraction of an inch thick,

Figure 3-24—Platy jointing at the contact of an intrusive body in Palolo Valley, Oahu. (Photo by H. T. Stearns.)

called *tachylyte*. In places glassy *dikelets*, offshoots from the dikes, fill cavities and joint planes in the country rock. A few dikes fill pre-existing tubes, and sometimes they contain aa, breccia, conglomerate, pumice, etc. (Figs. 9-5, 9-6, 9-7, and 9-13).

Groups of parallel, closely spaced dikes are referred to as *dike swarms*. Underlying the rift zones are dike swarms 1 to 3 miles wide comprising hundreds of dikes; they are called *dike complexes* (Fig. 3-23).

Relatively few intrusions follow the bedding planes. Those that do, however, form vertical-jointed, nearly horizontal *sills*. Sills are relatively scarce in comparison with dikes, but they are fairly abundant around the main vents. Sills more than 300 feet long are scarce in Hawaii.

Moore found dikes at Makaopuhi Crater, Kilauea, that had been formed by lava lakes leaking downward through pre-existing joints in the older crater fill.[137] These are *rootless dikes*.

Stocks, bosses, and plugs.   A relatively small subjacent intrusive body is called a *stock.*[34] If roughly cylindrical in form, it is called a *boss.* If it can be established that this body fills a volcanic throat, it is called a *neck, plug,* or *pipe.* Bosses, plugs, and pipes are found in or close to the main vents, but few flows were fed through circular holes. Bosses, plugs, and pipes are dense rocks. The larger bodies are coarse-grained in the center *(gabbros)* and fine-grained near the margin, and they may show well-developed platy jointing near their contacts (Fig. 3-24).

4

GEOLOGY

The Hawaiian Islands are a chain of shield-shaped basaltic domes formerly thought to have been built over a fissure 1,600 miles long in the ocean floor. The vents are spaced about 25 miles apart. The Hawaiian Chain may be related to the great submarine Murray and Molokai fracture zones, which extend westward from the coast of North America, but they trend southwestward whereas the Hawaiian Chain trends northwestward.[132] The Molokai Fracture zone (Fig. 2-11) is apparently buried by lavas on the Hawaiian Ridge, because magnetic surveys have located it 200 miles to the southwest of Molokai.[235]

An aeromagnetic survey completed in 1965 indicated that the magma from active Hawaiian volcanoes, as well as the cooled dense intrusives existing in the rift zones of the older eroded volcanoes, do not lie along the southeast-northwest ridge of the Hawaiian Archipelago (Fig. 1-2), but along rifts parallel to the Molokai Fracture zone (Fig. 13-1).[121] The only exceptions shown in this survey are Oahu and Molokai, where the rift zones have southeast-northwest trends on the land but the rifts bend undersea toward the Molokai Fracture zone. Malahoff thinks that the volcanoes above the water are later than their foundations.

The deep ocean basins are under tension, in comparison with the continents, which are in most places under compression. In 1963, Wilson set forth the hot spot theory for the origin of the Hawaiian Islands.[251] Numerous articles have been written since that time to explain the linear arrangement of the Emperor and Hawaiian chains as being the result of the Pacific plate sliding northwestward and northward over a hot spot in the earth's crust located under

Kilauea and Mauna Loa volcanoes.[27,28,38,39,74,81,125,185,186] The rate of movement of the plate has been variously given as 0.8 to 5 inches per year, on the basis of the fact that the islands progressively increase in K-Ar age northwestward from Kilauea (Fig. 4-1). The hypothesis is based on the fact that the oldest seamount at the northern end of the Emperor Chain was submerged about 70 million years ago, and Midway Island, near the western end of the Hawaiian Chain, is about 27 million years old, while Kilauea, at the eastern end of the Hawaiian Chain, is still erupting.

The hot spot hypothesis has much merit, but some unusual conditions need to be explained. First, the theory would require not one but two different "hot spots," or chimneys, about 25 miles apart, because the Hawaiian Islands consist of paired volcanoes along two distinct parallel rifts. Or, if both chimneys tap the same hot spot, then the partition between them must be explained.

Second, the plate would have had to slide northwestward in a decidedly jerky motion—about 25 miles fairly quickly with a stop of 500,000 or more years—long enough for distinct volcanoes to reach heights up to 13,784 feet above the ocean level, or 33,000 feet above the ocean floor. If the plate moved progressively northwestward at a rate of 0.8 to 5 inches per year, only two elongated volcanic ridges would have been built over the two hot spots for the entire length of the Emperor Seamounts and the Hawaiian Islands.

Third, if the "hot spots" remained stationary and the crust moved, how is the late volcanism accounted for on Kauai, the northernmost inhabited Hawaiian island, at the same time as Kilauea and Mauna Loa have been in eruption? All of the eight main Hawaiian Islands had late Pleistocene eruptions except Lanai, which has been extinct longer than any of the other islands.[8]

Fourth, the late Pleistocene and Holocene basalts on Kauai and Oahu contain xenoliths of rocks from deep in the mantle. Dalrymple and others state, ". . . geochemical and geophysical evidence indicates that nephelinitic lava is generated at greater depths than tholeiitic lava and that both come from the mantle."[39] If these volcanoes slid northwestward away from the "hot spots," how does it happen that the latest eruptions on these islands tapped a deeper source than Kilauea and Mauna Loa, which are producing tholeiitic basalts?

Fifth, terrigenous and pelagic sediment in cores from the deep sea floor adjacent to Kauai and to Hawaii indicate that the Hawaiian

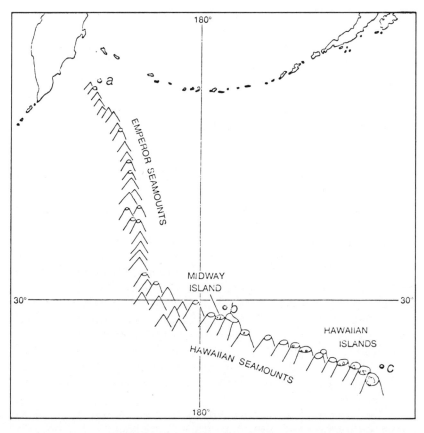

Figure 4-1—Line of seamounts, the Emperor Chain (*left*) and the Hawaiian Chain (*right*), traces the past movement of the Pacific plate over a "hot spot" rooted in the mantle near Hawaii. As the plate moved northwestward over the hot spot, volcanoes appeared; the seamounts are their submerged remnants. A seamount (*a*) at the northern end of the Emperor Chain is the oldest known: 70 million years. This contrasts with an age of 27 million years for Midway Island (*b*) and one of less than a million years for the volcano Kilauea on Hawaii (*c*). (By Heezen and MacGregor.[74] Copyright by *Scientific American, Inc.* All rights reserved.)

Islands were in existence in the Eocene, long after the plate was supposed to have migrated to the Emperor Chain.[184]

Sixth, numerous large submarine volcanoes, called seamounts, are scattered over a large area adjacent to the Hawaiian Islands.

They are not in line with the main volcanoes of the Hawaiian Chain, as shown in Figure 2-11. Loihi, a recently active submarine volcano 21 miles southeast of Pahala, Hawaii, is 15 miles long and 8 miles wide. It rises about 12,000 feet above the ocean floor and lies 3,000 feet below the surface of the ocean. On its summit is a caldera containing two craters. The National Oceanic Survey and Atmospheric Administration photographed the volcano in 1980 and found hydrothermal fields and much fresh pillow lava present. Loihi seamount is explained by James G. Moore, et al.,[145a] as being over an extension of the hot spot to the southeast. They found alkalic basalt also, as well as tholeiites in the dredged samples.

The current theory is that the hot spot is many miles in diameter, extending from Kilauea to Kauai, and each volcano has a separate magma chamber which drifts with the plate.

Soundings indicate that the Hawaiian Ridge is bordered by a moat or Deep about 18,000 feet below sea level, which is enclosed by the broad Hawaiian Arch, rising about 2,000 feet around the Deep (Fig. 2-10). The Arch hooks around the island of Hawaii and dies out on the northwest side of the ridge.[44] The Deep and Arch are thought to have been caused by the downbowing of the crust as a result of plastic or elastic response to the weight of the islands. The Arch, Deep, and Ridge are 500 miles (800 km) across and are called the Hawaiian Swell. Detailed soundings have revealed numerous seamounts adjacent to the islands, some of which are probably volcanic cones (Fig. 2-11). Those adjacent to Oahu align with the northeast-southwest rifts of the secondary Quaternary cones on Oahu and with the third and secondary northeast-southwest rift zone of the Koolau Volcano. Hamilton thinks that the mounts were probably built by eruptions after the major erosion of Oahu and belong to the Honolulu volcanic series.[70] One may have a caldera on it.[257]

A trench 1,200 feet deep and about 120 miles long lies about 45 miles south of the south tip of Hawaii (Fig. 2-11). Apparently it is a great graben, if the bathymetry is correct. The graben appears to be the only major submarine fault system that clearly parallels the Hawaiian Ridge in Figure 2-11. Possibly the steep, nearly straight cliff extending below 500 fathoms between Penguin Bank and the western tip of Oahu is another great fault scarp also with this trend.

Exposed parts of the Hawaiian volcanoes contain by volume less than one-half of one per cent of explosive debris, which indicates the dominance of lava outpourings. The flows range from a few inches to 900 feet thick, but most are from 10 to 30 feet thick. Phreatic and phreatomagmatic explosions have occurred occasionally.

The main bulk of the domes consists of lava beds dipping 3° to 10° away from their source and rarely separated even by thin soil beds, which indicates rapid accumulation of flows such as that taking place now on Mauna Loa Volcano, Hawaii. Thin soils between flows in some volcanoes show that the time interval between eruptions lengthened toward the close of the dome-building epoch. Many of the soil beds are decomposed vitric tuff, which, during the early phase of eruption, is generally deposited in small quantities by lava fountains near the vents.

Fissure eruptions characterize Hawaiian volcanoes. The usual eruption is preceded by a local earthquake as the ground opens to allow the exit of the magma. The fissures are a few inches to a few feet wide, and during the rapid dome-building epoch are limited to definite rift zones (Fig. 1-1).The widest single dike known in Hawaii is 40 feet across, but the average width is about 2 feet. Eruptions often begin with a lava fountain that is caused by frothing at the top of the lava column when pressure on the enclosed gases is released. If effervescence is slight, a line of spatter cones 5 to 50 feet high is built; if voluminous, a line of cinder cones 50 to 300 feet high results. Rivers of pahoehoe pour from the fissure, but as it flows down the mountainside, the lava usually changes to aa. Some of the lava flows entering the sea disrupt violently and build fragmental cones. Recorded eruptions have lasted from a few hours to 18 months, and the flows have ranged in length from a few feet to 35 miles. The lava flows reach velocities in their main channels of 10 to 25 miles per hour, depending upon the steepness of slope. The discharge of juvenile water from deep in the earth's crust increases in direct proportion to the amount of effervescence. Profiles of typical secondary cones superimposed on the great lava domes are shown in Figure 3-7.

Seismic records indicate that the magma starts rising from the mantle about 35 miles below the surface and forms a reservoir within the crust at a depth of several miles. From there it finds its way to the surface through narrow dikes. Under the volcanoes the crust is downwarped into the mantle because of the superimposed load (Fig. 4-2). The crust is about 10 miles thick under the islands but is deeper locally. Hawaiian eruptions are self-extinguishing because eruption of lava to the surface is far more rapid than its

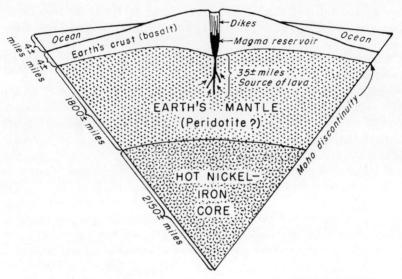

Figure 4-2—Hypothetical section showing relation of a Hawaiian volcano to the interior of the earth.

replenishment from the source far below. Large volumes of magma are stored for many years in the rift zone cores. These cores can transmit pressure from the inflating reservoir to rocks confining magma in the rift zone many miles from the reservoir.[50]

STAGES IN THE DEVELOPMENT OF A VOLCANIC ISLAND

Hawaiian volcanoes pass through the following more or less similar stages in development (Fig. 4-3).[200]

Stage 1. Building of a volcano from the ocean floor to sea level. During the submarine phase, the volcano lays down chiefly pillow lavas and produces large quantities of ash and pumice at depths of less than 5,000 feet[132] as a result of the contact of the magma with sea water. When a cone first rises above sea level, it is composed largely of weakly consolidated ash, which is eroded rapidly by the sea. Lava flows soon veneer the cone, and the erosive effectiveness of wave action is decreased greatly, but seaward slip faults on the periphery of the cone may occur from failure of the underlying rocks to carry the load.

Stage 2. Once the cone is above sea level, thin sheets of highly fluid tholeiitic basalts are poured out rapidly, usually from one minor and two major rifts as well as from a small crater at their

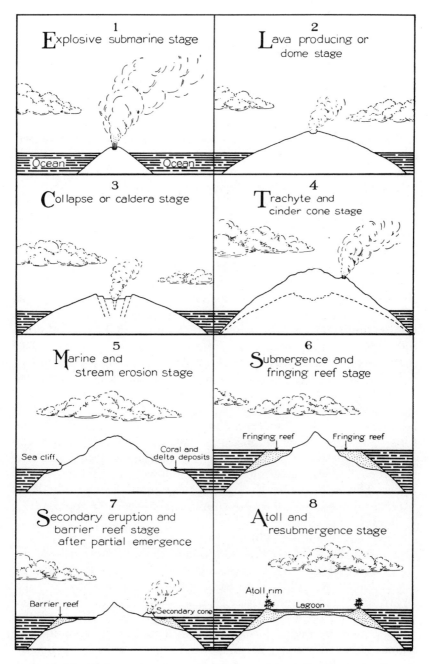

Figure 4-3—Eight stages in the geologic history of a typical volcanic island in the central Pacific.

intersection. Eventually a shield-shaped dome is built. In the dominantly olivine-bearing basalts, small feldspar phenocrysts are common and pyroxene phenocrysts are scarce. Cinder cones seldom form during this stage. Usually a vent is either a fissure bordered by low spatter heaps or an opening concealed by a flat mound of pahoehoe. A few thin beds of lithic and vitric tuff may be deposited. Because the surface is highly porous and the time interval between eruptions is short, stream erosion is nonexistent. All Hawaiian volcanoes have passed though this youthful second stage.

Stage 3.   The volcano gradually collapses over the vent areas to form a caldera on the summit (Fig. 3-4) and shallow grabens along the major rifts. The composition of the lavas does not change appreciably, nor does the time interval between eruptions lengthen. Lavas ponded in closed fault basins are very massive, however, and in physical appearance differ greatly from the pre-caldera lavas. When eroded, they form sheer cliffs that usually show columnar structure. The rate of lava extrusion may continue to be large, as shown by Mauna Loa Volcano, which liberated approximately 4 billion cubic yards of lava between 1850 and 1950. Lithic and vitric tuff beds may be developed more frequently in the third stage than in the second phase. The highest wall of the caldera usually bounds a segment between the two rift zones, which intersect at an obtuse angle. Generally, the seaward slope of this high wall ceases to be flooded with lavas; as a result, canyons are eroded into it, while lava continues to veneer the other slopes. Sea cliffs are another characteristic feature of the high-walled slope. Two distinct physiographic stages may exist, therefore, on the same volcano.

Mauna Loa, Kilauea, and Lanai are now in the third volcanic phase. The other domes have passed through this stage. The West Molokai dome adjacent to the summit collapsed, but apparently a caldera did not form.

Stage 4.   When the volume of the lavas poured out exceeds the amount of the collapse, the caldera and grabens are partly or entirely obliterated. Time intervals between eruptions grow progressively longer, and the composition of the lavas may change slowly or abruptly to more feldspathic types. Trachyte, and closely related rocks are laid down in thick sheets, chiefly as aa flows. In this phase, the more highly ferromagnesian lavas usually contain large phenocrysts of one or all of the following minerals: pyroxene, olivine, and feldspar. Peridotitic and gabbroic cognate inclusions are common. High lava fountains that build large cinder cones characterize most eruptions, and bulbous domes may be formed (Fig. 3-11). Vitric tuff beds increase in number and thickness. The profile of the dome steepens and becomes studded with cones. Some of the vents lie outside of the rift zones. Erosion has resulted in local unconformities between some of the flows. Hualalai, Mauna Kea, and Kohala domes are in this phase.

Volcanoes passing through stage 4 take either of two courses. One is the course followed by West Maui, Kohala, and East Molokai, in which the tholeiitic basalts are succeeded by (1) a thin, incomplete veneer of olivine porphyritic basalts, usually carrying augite phenocrysts, (2) a relatively short pause, and (3) eruptions of alkalic basalts and trachytes, which form an incomplete veneer and add only a few hundred feet of lava to the summit of the volcano. The second is the course followed by Haleakala and Mauna Kea, in which no inactive period occurs, trachytes and mugearites are rare or absent, and alkali basalts dominate but are interbedded with both olivine basalts and picrite basalts carrying large augite phenocrysts. These lavas may add several thousand feet to the height of the volcano.

Stage 5. Marine and stream erosion partly destroy the volcanic dome. The effectiveness of these agents depends upon the height of the dome which determines the rainfall, and upon the exposure—whether or not the island lies to the lee of another. Islands that have been in this stage for a long period develop fringing reefs, high sea cliffs, and deep valleys.

Stage 6. Deep submergence partly drowns the islands, and extensive fringing reefs develop. Barrier reefs may develop, or the growth of coral may be interrupted by secondary volcanic eruptions during the next stage.

Stage 7. A rejuvenation of volcanism occurs and secondary eruptions occur. These lavas, extruded during Pleistocene and Holocene times, commonly contain either nepheline or melilite, or both. The basalts may contain or lack pyroxene, feldspar, and olivine phenocrysts. Peridotitic and gabbroic cognate inclusions are usual. Vitric or crystal-lithic-vitric tuffs may be widespread. The latter result chiefly from phreatomagmatic explosions. These lavas are unconformable upon extruded rocks of all three preceding phases, indicating the intervention of a long erosion period. The domes of Haleakala, West Maui, East Molokai, Kahoolawe, Koolau, Waianae,

Kauai, and Niihau are in the seventh phase. Many of the later vents show no close relationship to the ancient rift systems of the volcanoes on which they are formed. Some lie on north-south rifts, especially on Niihau, Kauai, and Oahu. Some volcanoes never go through this stage.

TABLE 4

STRATIGRAPHIC ROCK UNITS IN THE HAWAIIAN ISLANDS

Age	Niihau	Kauai	Oahu
			Waianae Range
Historic			Coral fill
Holocene	Younger alluvium, playa deposits, and unconsolidated calcareous beach and dune sand	Younger alluvium, unconsolidated calcareous beach and dune deposits and marly lagoon deposits.	Younger alluvium and unconsolidated calcareous beach and dune deposits
—————————Local unconformity—————————			
Pleistocene	Lithified calcareous dunes, emerged marine limestone, dunes of volcanic sand, older alluvium, and Kiekie volcanic series	Lithified calcareous dunes, older alluvium and rocks of the Koloa volcanic series, including the Palikea formation.	Lithified calcareous dunes, emerged marine limestone, older alluvium, and Kolekole volcanics
~~Great erosional unconformity~~~~~~~~			
Pliocene	Paniau volcanic series	Waimea Canyon volcanic series; main caldera-filling (upper or Olokele formation), graben-filling (upper or Makaweli formation), secondary caldera-filling (Haupu formation) and extra-caldera (lower or Napili formation).	Waianae volcanic series; upper, lower, and middle members

Age	Kahoolawe	Maui		Kohala Mountain
		West Maui	*East Maui*	
Historic	Red loess	Younger alluvium and unconsolidated calcareous beach and dune deposits	Volcanics of 1790(?)	Younger alluvium, unconsolidated calcareous beach deposits, and black sand dunes
Holocene	Younger alluvium, unconsolidated calcareous beach deposits and late volcanics		Younger alluvium, unconsolidated beach and dune deposits, and younger rocks in the Hana volcanic series	
—————————Local unconformity—————————				
Pleistocene	Older alluvium	Emerged marine limestone, older alluvium, and Lahaina volcanic series	Kaupo mudflow, older alluvium, and older rocks in the Hana volcanic series including the Kipahulu member	Older alluvium, Pahala ash, and Hawi volcanic series
~~Great erosional unconformity~~~~~~~~				
Pleistocene	Kanapou volcanic series; caldera and extra-caldera members	Honolua volcanic series Wailuku volcanic series	Kula volcanic series Honomanu volcanic series	Pololu volcanic series

Stage 8.   If submergence continued or the island was planed off by marine and stream erosion during the fluctuating seas of the Pleistocene, an atoll may be found on the eroded and submerged volcanic mass. The atolls in the leeward part of the archipelago were formed in this manner (Fig. 2-17), but they carry thick lime-

TABLE 4

STRATIGRAPHIC ROCK UNITS IN THE HAWAIIAN ISLANDS

Age	Oahu	Molokai		Lanai
	Koolau Range	West Molokai	East Molokai	
Historic	Coral fill			
Holocene	Younger alluvium, unconsolidated beach and dune deposits, and younger rocks in the Honolulu volcanic series	Younger alluvium and unconsolidated calcareous beach and dune deposits	Younger alluvium and unconsolidated calcareous beach deposits	Younger alluvium and unconsolidated calcareous beach and dune deposits
Pleistocene	Lithified calcareous dunes, emerged marine limestone, older alluvium, and older rocks in the Honolulu volcanic series	Lithified calcareous dunes and older alluvium	Emerged marine limestone, older alluvium, Kalaupapa basalt, and Mokuhooniki tuff	Lithified calcareous dunes, emerged marine limestone, and older alluvium
Pliocene and Early Pleistocene	Koolau and Kailua volcanic series	W. Molokai volcanic series	E. Molokai volcanic series; upper, lower, and caldera complex members	Lanai volcanic series

Age	Hawaii			
	Mauna Loa Volcano	Mauna Kea	Hualalai Volcano	Kilauea Volcano
Historic	Historic member of the Kau volcanic series and mudflow of 1868	Younger alluvium, unconsolidated calcareous beach deposits, volcanic sand dunes, vitric ash deposits, and upper member of the Laupahoehoe volcanic series	Historic member of the Hualalai volcanic series, (Volcanics of 1800–01)	Historic member of the Puna volcanic series
Holocene	Black sand dunes, and the prehistoric member of the Kau volcanic series		Unconsolidated calcareous beach deposits, and younger rocks of the prehistoric member of the Hualalai volcanic series	Black sand dunes, and prehistoric member of the Puna volcanic series
Pleistocene	Pahala ash and Kahuku volcanic series	Glacial deposits, older alluvium, lower member of the Laupahoehoe volcanic series, Pahala ash, and younger rocks in the Hamakua volcanic series	Pahala ash and older rocks of the Hualalai volcanic series including the Waawaa volcanics	Pahala ash and Hilina volcanic series
Pleistocene	Ninole volcanic series	Older unexposed rocks in the Hamakua volcanic series	Probably deep unexposed rocks in the Hualalai volcanic series	

stones formed in deep water.

A correlation of the stratigraphic rock units in the Hawaiian Islands is given in the accompanying table.

GEOLOGIC HISTORY AND AGE OF THE ISLANDS

Much of the geologic history of the Hawaiian Islands remains to be deciphered. The long and complicated development of the submarine basement may never be unraveled. At present, only the times of extinction of each volcano can be determined, and these estimations depend upon two methods. One method is based on finding lavas of younger volcanoes ponded against their neighbors so that the beds dip less where they came to rest against the adjacent dome. Erosion has exposed a few unconformities or overlaps of lavas from one cone on those from another. By using available information of this type, a tentative order of extinction has been projected. The succession from oldest to youngest is: (1) Waianae Range; (2) Koolau Range; (3) West Molokai; (4) East Molokai; (5) West Maui and Lanai; (6) Kahoolawe; (7) Haleakala. Further study may suggest changes in this order. Kauai is too far from Oahu and Hawaii is too far from Maui for overlaps to occur. Kohala Mountain became extinct before Mauna Kea. Hualalai, Mauna Loa, and Kilauea have erupted in historic time. The eastern part of the Niihau Volcano is below sea level; hence dips cannot be used for determining the relative ages of Niihau and Kauai. The primary Kauai dome appears to be as old as, if not older than, the Waianae Range. The age relationships of the islets and atolls stretching northwest from Kauai are unknown. These islets may be (1) large, high volcanoes planed off by fluvial and marine erosion and then submerged, (2) small, low volcanoes, or (3) submarine volcanoes that approached near enough to sea level to support coral reefs. Kaula and Lehua are late cones that can be correlated with secondary cones on the other islands.[160] Midway is an example of (1).

A second method of determining age is by radiogenic measurements. McDougall published the first measurements of the potassium-argon ratio (K-Ar method) of 36 samples from seven of the Hawaiian volcanoes.[125] These ages are minimal rather than excessive because of the possibility of argon leakage. They indicate Pliocene age for the oldest rocks tested and deep erosion of the older islands during the Pleistocene. McDougall believes that it took from 1 to 2 million years to build a volcano from sea level to

TABLE 5

AGES IN MILLIONS OF YEARS OF HAWAIIAN VOLCANOES

Island	Island Volcano	Range of K-Ar Ages (millions of years)
Midway atoll	————	27.0[a]
La Pérouse Pinnacle	(French Frigate Shoals)	11.7[a]
Necker Island	————	10.0[a]
Nihoa Island	————	7.0[a]
Kauai Island	————	5.6–3.8[b]
Niihau Island	Paniau	3.0[c]
West Oahu	Waianae Range	3.4–2.7[b]
East Oahu	Koolau Range	2.5–2.2[b]
West Molokai	————	1.8[b]
East Molokai	————	1.5–1.3[b]
Lanai Island	————	1.25[d]
West Maui	Wailuku Mountains	1.3–1.15[b]
East Maui	Haleakala	0.8[b]
Hawaii	Kohala Mountain	0.68[e]
	Pololu volcanic series	0.4[f]
	Hawi volcanic series	0.25–0.06[f]
Hawaii	Puu Waawaa	0.4[h]
Hawaii	Ninole volcanic series, Mauna Loa	<0.5[g]
Hawaii	Laupahoehoe, Mauna Kea	0.6[h]

[a] Dalrymple et al.[38]
[b] McDougall[125]
[c] Jackson et al.[84]
[d] Bonhommet et al.[20]
[e] Dalrymple[37]
[f] McDougall and Swanson[129]
[g] Two tests made by Evernden et al.[57]
[h] Funkhouser et al.[64]

its present height. The ages are roughly verified by magnetic studies.[45,227]

The ages of the post-erosional eruptions on each island have a considerable range. On Kauai they range in age from possibly 10,000 years to 1.43 million years. Those on the Koolau Range, Oahu, have a wide range, probably from about 32,000 years to nearly one million years. The reef limestone fragments in the Koko Head tuff cones are older than 32,000 years. Kalaupapa Volcano, on Molokai, the island that is known for its leper settlement, is the only post-erosional lava on that island. It probably predates the 25-foot stand of the sea; hence it is more than 120,000 years old. The

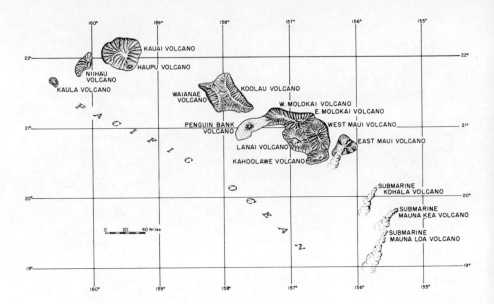

Figure 4-4—The Hawaiian Archipelago in the early Pleistocene, on the basis of radiogenic dates. The shoreline used for this figure is the minus 1,200-foot Lualualei stand of the sea.

Lahaina eruptives on West Maui are probably 100,000 years old, or older, but Haleakala has erupted every few hundred years, the most recent time about 1790. Kahoolawe has late flows that issued from cracks in the face of a sea cliff on the east side. These flows appear to be less than 5,000 years old. Lanai has had no post-erosional eruptions. Hawaii, Kilauea, Mauna Loa, and Hualalai all have erupted in historic time. Lavas from Mauna Kea overlie glacial debris near the top of the mountain; hence the most recent eruptions are probably less than 5,000 years old. The youngest lava flow on Kohala Mountain may be as much as 500,000 years old, but K-Ar ages are much younger.[129, 215]

It is probably conservative to say that the Hawaiian Islands started from the ocean floor about 25,000,000 years ago in the Miocene period. Kauai, Niihau, and Oahu were built above sea level in Pliocene time. The rest of the islands are Pleistocene in age. The end of the Pliocene is still the subject of disagreement, but in this book it is assumed for convenience to be about 2,000,000 years ago.

Dana states that the volcanoes became extinct from northwest to southeast.[40] If secondary activity is disregarded, his statement is nearly true. During the soil-forming epoch, which followed extinction, drainage systems were developed and sea cliffs were cut. The

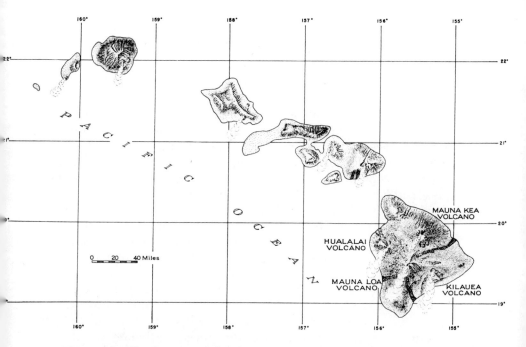

Figure 4-5—The Hawaiian Archipelago during the minus 350-foot stand of the sea in the middle Pleistocene.

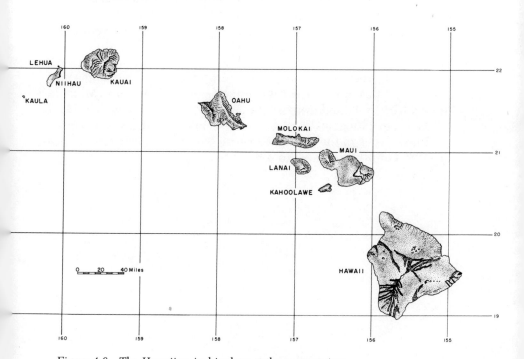

Figure 4-6—The Hawaiian Archipelago at the present time.

erosion period lasted from one to two million years on the older islands, during which time deep canyons and high cliffs were cut and soils 5 to 100 feet thick were formed.

A period of great submergence, amounting to about 9,000 feet, followed the long erosion period of the older islands. Concurrently, a new epoch of volcanism began and secondary outbreaks continued into Holocene time. The eruptions occurred on all the major islands except Lanai. The great submergence may have been complex and at times interrupted by emergences, but subsidence dominated for a long period. Then there was a complex series of emergences and submergences alternating so rapidly that little reef was laid down and very little cliffing accomplished. As a present result, the older islands are emerged about 1,200 feet from the all-time low.

A single dredge haul from the submerged terrace at a depth of 1,700 feet, 6 miles southwest of Honolulu, contained shallow water fossil corals of Miocene age, but this age is now in doubt. [134,216] There is a conflict between the radiogenic and paleontological datings. The submerged terrace at 3,600 feet around Oahu is so broad that the possibility of a base under the island of a former guyot or flat-topped seamount is worth considering. The geologic history of the Pacific is one of great submergence.[207] Numerous submarine canyons off the windward coast of Oahu have their mouths 6,000 to 9,000 feet below the sea.[70] These canyons could not have been cut in hard lava rock by turbidity currents; hence, they indicate a subsidence of this amount that must have taken a long time. Miocene fossils were obtained from a submarine core in the Hawaiian Deep off Gardner Pinnacles[189] and from test holes on Midway Islands.

A few stages in the geologic history of the Hawaiian Archipelago are shown in Figures 4-4 to 4-6.

5

ISLAND OF OAHU

GEOMORPHOLOGY

Major geomorphic provinces. Oahu, which has an area of 604 square miles, has four major geomorphic provinces: (1) Koolau Range; (2) Waianae Range; (3) Schofield Plateau; and (4) Coastal plain.

The Koolau Range forms the eastern part of the island and is the one lying behind Honolulu (Fig. 5-1). Puu Konahuanui, the highest point, is 3,105 feet high. The range is 37 miles long and is deeply eroded by streams. In places it has high sea cliffs along its shore. It consists entirely of thin, narrow, basaltic lava flows piled one upon the other like shingles, with minor amounts of volcanic ash and numerous dikes. Conspicuous secondary geomorphic forms are the Nuuanu Pali and the younger secondary tuff cones. All evidence points to the main volcano having been built during a single episode.

The Waianae Range, forming the western part of the island, is 22 miles long. Mount Kaala, the highest point on Oahu, is 4,025 feet high and is now accessible by a steep paved road, which was finished in 1964 but is not open to the public. Huge valleys have been carved by erosion into the Waianae Range; most of them discharge to the southwest. The range is composed almost entirely of basaltic rock. The Waianae Volcano became extinct before the Koolau, as shown by the Koolau lavas overlapping the eroded, soil-covered Waianae lavas. Owing to submergence and long erosion, the mountain is nearly buried in its own waste.

The Schofield Plateau was formed by the lavas from the Koolau Range banking against the older Waianae Range. Considerable al-

115

luvium from the Waianae Range is piled against and interfingers
with the Koolau lavas on the west side of the plateau and along the
rim of Kaukonahua Valley. At Waipio Acres, ancient gravels crop
out on top of the soil capping the Koolau basalts. Much of the area of
Koolau basalt between Pearl Harbor and Waipio, shown in Figure
5-12, is covered with a thin veneer of alluvium. If mapped as alluvium, it would obscure the geologic relation of the Koolau lavas
to the Waianae alluvium.

The Coastal plain lies mostly on the ponded lavas of the Koolau
Volcano north and south of the Schofield Plateau. The plain is composed chiefly of marine sediments deposited on the lavas when the

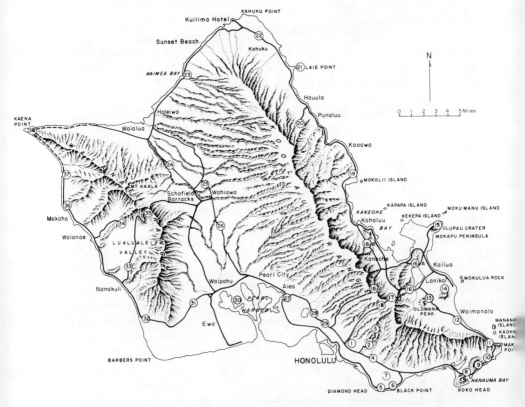

Figure 5-1—Relief map of Oahu. Numbers refer to descriptions of points of
geologic interest in *Road Guide to Points of Geologic Interest in the Hawaiian
Islands.*

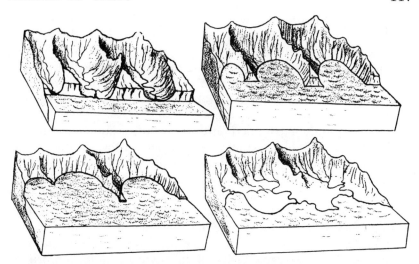

Figure 5-2—Stages in the development of the Pali on Oahu after the caldera
had been deeply eroded. Upper left, *Stage 1*, showing amphitheater-headed
valleys and remnants of original volcano slope. Upper right, *Stage 2*, showing
valleys partly drowned owing to submergence of the island. Lower left, *Stage
3*, showing final stage of submergence amounting to about 1,200 feet. Lower
right, *Stage 4*, showing formation of pali by ocean receding from the drowned
valleys and leaving their deltas exposed.

sea stood higher in mid-Pleistocene time. The Ewa coral plain,
lying west of Pearl Harbor, is the most extensive part. The Waipio
and Pearl City peninsulas project into Pearl Harbor. The Honolulu
plain extends eastward from Pearl Harbor and is occupied by the
city and Waikiki. The northern sector is called the Waialua-Haleiwa
plain and the northeastern sector, the Kahuku plain.

Origin of the Pali. The Pali, or great cliff, on the windward side
of Oahu, with its fluted, nearly vertical wall 22 miles long and 2,000
feet high, is one of the great scenic features of the world (Plate 7).
Its origin is complex, but its present form is due chiefly to stream
erosion and subsequent alluviation of the valley floors while the
sea battered back the headlands. Great amphitheater-headed valleys cut their way to the top of the Koolau Range and in places
beyond, so that some of the leeward valleys, such as Kalihi, were
beheaded. Four stages in the development of the Pali are given in
Figure 5-2. Huge amphitheater-headed valleys are found on all the
windward slopes of the older Hawaiian volcanoes. Also, the valleys
tapped a caldera in the Kaneohe-Kailua area (Fig. 3-3), but if the

caldera was a broad, shallow depression full of dense ponded lavas, the existence of the hard rocks may have slowed down the streams. However, faults and dikes associated with a caldera direct the ground water toward valleys tapping it; hence such valleys have a larger and steadier flow than other streams, which produces larger and deeper canyons than would otherwise be produced on the volcanic dome.

A shallow graben extended northwestward, as shown by faults in the Waiahole tunnels, and may have extended toward the eastern tip of the island from the caldera, but the pattern of the existing interstream divides does not indicate influence by grabens. The geologic map of Oahu[2] shows regularly spaced interstream divides nearly buried by alluvium. The great subsidence of Oahu and the constantly shifting sea levels of the Pleistocene did much to bury the divides and to provide fresh wave attack on them, especially the eastern end of the scarp. Seaward slip faulting along the original eastern coast may have occurred, as postulated by Palmer[158] and Moore,[136] but the writer does not believe that the whole eastern half of the Koolau Range foundered along a fault marked by the Pali, as proposed by early geologists. Seaward slip faulting would have increased stream gradients, but a great volume of rock would have been removed by stream and marine erosion. Wentworth and Winchell came to the same conclusion after a long study of the Koolau Range and state, "[We] must give major credit to streams."[247]

The fluting of the Pali is caused primarily by waterfalls that have worn gigantic pot holes or plunge pools to the foot of the Pali. The pot hole near Sacred Falls in Kaluanui Valley is about 30 feet in diameter and extends up the valley wall about 300 feet. It is the most accessible example. During a heavy rain, when every groove is the site of a thundering waterfall, the Pali is a great spectacle.

Origin of Pearl Harbor. Anyone who flies over Pearl Harbor, or visits the U.S.S. *Arizona* Memorial, must wonder how such a unique harbor was shaped by geologic forces. Essentially, it is a drowned river system with its several branches, much as San Francisco Bay is a drowned ancient valley where the Sacramento and San Joaquin rivers joined and flowed to the sea. The geologic history of Pearl Harbor is long and complex. More details resulted from the investigation started in 1965 by means of deep core borings.[64, 71, 176, 223]

The Pearl Harbor re-entrant was caused primarily by the banking of the Koolau lavas against the older Waianae Range. Waikakalaua

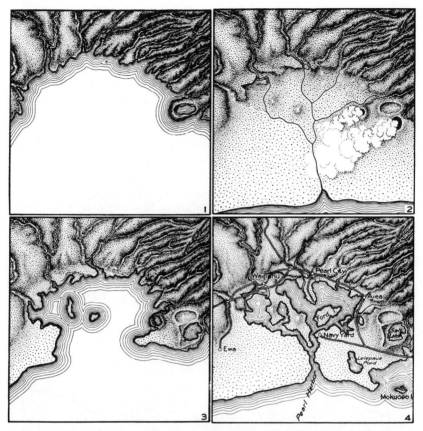

Figure 5-3—Diagram showing the geologic history of Pearl Harbor lochs. *1.* When the sea stood 95 feet higher. *2.* When the sea stood about 60 feet lower. *3.* When the sea stood 25 feet higher. *4.* Present sea level.

(called Waikele near its mouth) and Waiawa streams flowing off the Koolau Range were deflected southward, following the course of the lavas. Two other large streams also entered the bay. They have a very large drainage and come from a high rainfall belt. They cut deep canyons in the hard basalt and flowed much farther out to sea than Pearl Harbor before the great submergence of Oahu. Wells near Pearl Harbor penetrate 1,072 feet of alternating beds of limestone, tuff, alluvium, and marine clays that buried the original Koolau land surface. During the 100-foot Kaena stand of the sea the Pearl Harbor re-entrant was a broad unsheltered bay (stage 1, Fig. 5-3). So much silt was brought into the harbor that the corals there were suffocated. Thus a continuous reef was not built, but chiefly a

fill of gravel and mud was emplaced. Borings in these muds en-
counter scattered corals in the position of growth.[180] A terrace 100
feet above sea level marks the Kaena stand. Slowly the sea retreated
as the ice caps on the poles grew during the next glaciation, and the
sea fell about 350 feet or more lower than the present shoreline
(stage 2, Fig. 5-3). During this epoch the rivers and their tributaries
re-established themselves and cut steep-sided deep valleys across
the flat. Salt Lake crater erupted and deposited several feet of
well-bedded ash over the area. Numerous tree molds in the tuff
indicate that the region was covered with vegetation. Tree molds
occur in the tuff below sea level (Fig. 5-4).

Slowly the sea rose again as that glacial epoch ended, and the
valleys were flooded to a height 25 feet above present sea level
(stage 3, Fig. 5-3). Oyster beds flourished on the drowned interstream divides, and thin coral reefs grew in stretches of clear
water. The oyster beds, reefs, and beach deposits are well exposed
on Waipio Peninsula below Waipahu.

Again the sea receded with the waxing of the polar ice caps, and a
new cycle of stream erosion started. The old valleys were partly

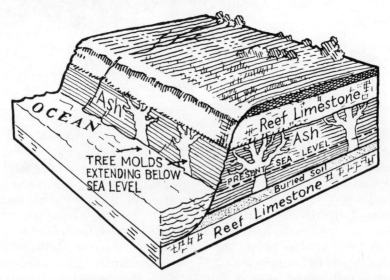

Figure 5-4—Diagram showing ash-covered forest below sea level in the Pearl
Harbor area, Oahu. The buried soil layer is not present everywhere. The term
"soil" is not used in a pedalogical sense, but refers to any deposit on which
vegetation grew.

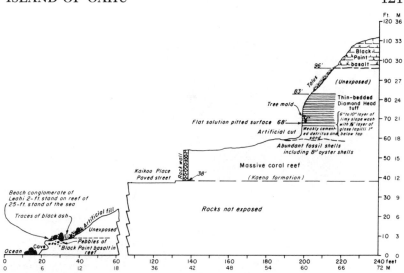

Figure 5-5—Diamond Head tuff, containing tree molds, overlying an ancient emerged reef at Kaikoo Place, Black Point, Oahu.

re-excavated, and some of the reefs and associated deposits on the ancient divides were washed into the sea. Then, about 11,000 years ago, when the Ice Age ended, water was again returned to the sea. It flooded back into the ancient valleys to form East, Middle, and West Lochs. Ford Island and Waipio Peninsula are the old divides extended by reefs and sediments (Fig. 5-3, stage 4).

Fossil oyster beds at Pearl Harbor. A few fossil oysters reaching a foot in diameter occur in the emerged reef at Black Point, Oahu, but extensive oyster beds grew during the 25-foot stand of the sea on what is now Waipio Peninsula, which juts into Pearl Harbor from Waipahu. An excellent oyster deposit was formerly exposed at the city dump at Waipahu, where two oyster beds of different ages occur. These oysters have been dated by the C^{14} method as older than 39,000 years.[179] Oysters still live in Pearl Harbor, but they cannot be harvested because the water is polluted.

Origin of Diamond Head. Diamond Head is a prominent feature on Oahu with an interesting history. The name comes from the crystals of calcite found on it. It differs in shape from most other Hawaiian cones. It belongs to the secondary eruptions (Honolulu volcanic series) that occurred after the Koolau Range had been inactive for more than a million years and had become deeply eroded.

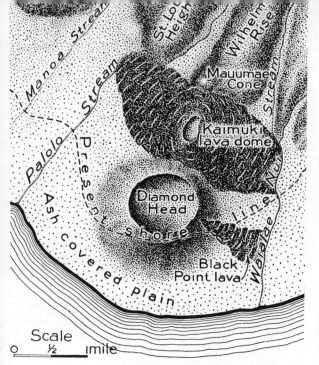

Figure 5-6—The Kaimuki area after the Mauumae, Kaimuki, Diamond Head, and Black Point eruptions, and approximate position of the shoreline at that time.

Close examination of Diamond Head reveals deep gullies that have cut most of the original outer slope away, leaving just the crater and its rim. Some gullies have eroded beyond the original rim.

About 500,000 years ago, a crack opened through an emerged reef limestone plateau covered with trees and shrubs about 100 feet above sea level, as shown by tree molds in the tuff overlying the reef at Kaikoo Place on the shore at Black Point (Fig. 5-5). The crack allowed sea water and ground water to pour downward to the hot lava that was ascending the crack. The water caused the lava to explode and great quantities of the limestone were blown out. The lava, comminuted and at the same time inflated by its own gases, produced black pellets, most of them the size of peas and buckshot (lapilli), together with much fine ash. The debris rose in a great cauliflower-shaped ash and steam cloud several miles above the surface where Diamond Head stands today. Each explosion laid down a layer of ashy mud that was a foot or more thick near the vent. The ash fell over a wide area as well as at the cone, and extended the coast line (Fig. 5-6). Doubtless, thunderstorms and lightning played in the rising ash cloud, caused by the rapid updraft of hot air into the colder atmosphere above.

Each explosion was followed by an inrush of more water, and as the funnel-shaped crater grew larger, the explosions occurred more

LANIHULI PEAK   NUUANU PALI

MAKUKU CONE

PACIFIC HEIGHTS

NUUANU LAVA FLOW

Figure 5-7—The lava from Makuku cone devastated Nuuanu Valley.

frequently, until the rising hot lava supply was exhausted. Such explosions are hydromagmatic, to differentiate them from true magmatic explosions. Similar cones built elsewhere in the world are usually short lived—a matter of days or weeks, but rarely of years. Usually the soft ash is eroded during the building of the cone by rain falling from the condensed steam; hence much of the erosion of Diamond Head may have occurred very early in its history. Consolidation of the ash to tuff occurred mostly by the alteration of the glassy ash to the yellowish mineral palagonite. Also, volcanic ashes cement quickly from the puzzolani or chemical reaction of the material itself. Italians have known for years of this process for making cement from volcanic ash on Vesuvius, and similar ashes are added to large concrete jobs now to save buying additional cement. The pulverized lime from the underlying reef also aided in the cementing process.

The Diamond Head eruption was soon followed by a thin black lava flow on its southeast side which formed what is now called Black Point, and by voluminous lava flows from a vent on the northeast side to form the Kaimuki lava dome, on which the Kaimuki section of Honolulu is now built. These lavas differ in composition from the Diamond tuff (Fig. 5-6). Much later, another eruption occurred that laid down a mantle about a foot thick of black glassy ash in the Diamond Head area. It is pisolitic at Black Point; it is interbedded with beach sand in the Kahala District; and

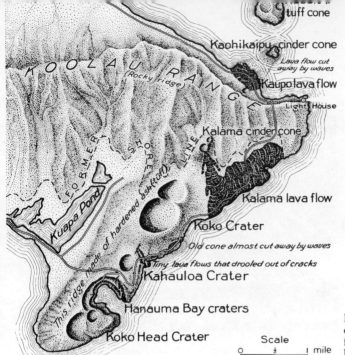

tuff cone

Kaohikaipu cinder cone

Lava flow cut away by waves

Kaupo lava flow

Light House

Kalama cinder cone

Kalama lava flow

Koko Crater

Old cone almost cut away by waves

tiny lava flows that drooled out of cracks

Kahauloa Crater

Hanauma Bay craters

Koko Head Crater

Scale

0   ½   1 mile

KOOLAU RANGE

(Rocky ridge)

FORMER SHORE LINE

Kuapa Pond

This ridge is made of hardened ash (tuff)

Figure 5-8—Eastern end of Oahu after the Koko fissure eruptions. Dash line indicates shoreline prior to eruptions.

it forms dunes in gullies along Diamond Head Drive. Its fine texture indicates a distant vent.[5.239] The bedded "coral" sand along the upper side of Diamond Head Drive between the Lighthouse and Kapiolani Park was blown by the wind up the slope from the wide, exposed, sand-covered abandoned sea floor during the low stand of the sea, in a glacial epoch when water was removed from the world's oceans and stored as ice on the poles.

Origin of Punchbowl Crater and similar craters and cones. Punchbowl Crater had an explosion history similar to that of Diamond Head, owing to the sudden contact of abundant water with the rising hot lava or magma beneath this spot. One of the anomalies about Punchbowl Crater is that the National Cemetery is in loose young black ash that fell into the crater during the eruption of Tantalus and Round Top. The tuff of Punchbowl cone is not black, but is brown and hard. It is well exposed along the road to the cemetery.

Makalapa and Salt Lake craters, Hanauma Bay Crater, Koko Head cones, Manana (Rabbit Island), Makapu Head (at Kaneohe Naval Air Station), and Moku Manu (Bird Island) also were formed by hydromagmatic explosions similar to those that produced Diamond Head and Punchbowl.

Cause of the flat floor of Nuuanu Valley. The flat floor of Nuuanu Valley was caused by several lava flows that issued in Late Pleistocene time from Makuku and Luakaha cones, and possibly from the Pali cinder cone near its head. One of the lava flows was penetrated by wells at the Dole Cannery, indicating that the lava flowed seaward of the present shore (Fig. 5-7). Two of the lava flows are well exposed along the old road to the Pali. The road through the outbound Pali Tunnel enters a deep cut in the cinders of the Pali cone. The volcanics near the lower edge of the forest reserve are about 300 feet thick, as determined by drilling, and are a complex of lava flows and cinder beds. The volcanics veneer the ancient alluvial floor of Nuuanu Valley, and the lava in the cannery district is overlain by two ancient coral reefs separated by 40 feet of clay, indicating that considerable time has passed since the lava flow occurred.

Origin of Koko Head, Hanauma Bay, and Koko Crater. Much of Hawaii Kai, the land along the south shore at the east end of Oahu, was built by a series of eruptions along a fissure. Most of the eruptions were violent explosions caused by sea water contacting hot lava rising in the fissure. Explosion clouds probably rose many miles into the air, and ash filled in all the ocean floor south of the steep Koolau spurs except Kuapa Pond (Fig. 5-8). Hanauma Bay, a state park, is easily accessible by auto, and one obtains an excellent view of the cross-section of tuff cone on the way to the beach.

A great number of white coral fragments stand in strong contrast to the black ash. The explosions blasted through an emerged coral reef of considerable thickness. A remnant of the reef is exposed in a gully just below the road along the coast just east of Hanauma Bay. C^{14} tests on coral fragments in the tuff indicate that the reef under the tuff was formed more than 32,000 years ago.[179] The tuff overlies marine deposits of the 25-foot stand of the sea in the valleys tributary to Kuapa. The explosions occurred about 35,000 years ago.[65]

Besides the ash cones built by the hydroexplosions, lava drooled out of the fissure northeast of Hanauma Bay, and Kalama cinder cone poured a flow into the sea between Koko Crater and Lighthouse Point (Fig. 5-8). The lava forms the black ledges along the beach east of Koko Head. Accretionary lapilli form a bed 2 feet thick under one of the small lava drools along the road. The eruptions along the Koko fissure were not simultaneous, but varied by a few thousand years.[65] The tuff beds form a spectacular coast line (Plate 8).

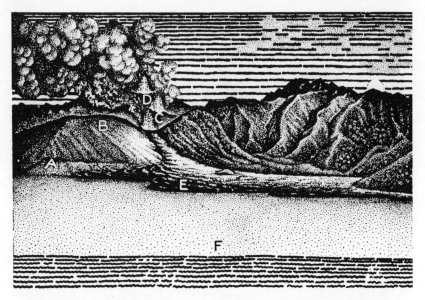

Figure 5-9—Round Top (B), Sugar Loaf (C), and Tantalus (D) fire-fountaining, and the Sugar Loaf-Round Top lava flow (E) pouring into Manoa Valley. Rocky Hill (A) and Waikiki (F). Ocean indicated by wavy lines.

As one drives around the east end of Oahu and descends the cliff to the windward shore, a reddish-colored island is seen. It is Kaohikaipu Island, the remnant of a recent cinder cone. On the shore is a fresh black lava, the Kaupo flow, named for an abandoned Hawaiian village that once existed there. The black lava issued from a crack at the foot of the cliff and flowed into the sea, presumably at the same time that the island erupted. It is the youngest lava flow on Oahu, and is the site of the interesting Sea Life Park. The lava has a K-Ar age of 32,000 years.[65]

Origin of Round Top, Sugar Loaf, and Tantalus. The most spectacular and one of the youngest eruptions on Oahu occurred about 67,000 years ago[65] when a fissure opened through Round Top and Tantalus (Fig. 5-9). High fire fountains played along the fissure, and glowing lava made huge firefalls down the steep valley walls into Pauoa, Makiki, and Manoa valleys. The Manoa branch crossed to the eastern valley wall and turned seaward under what is now the university campus. The flow is 40 feet thick where it terminates in the Moiliili District, where for years it was quarried. The lavas rest on emerged reef limestone. In the lava vesicles are many well-formed zeolite crystals, which made the Moiliili quarry a favorite mineral collecting ground in the past.

The Pauoa Valley flow stopped where Booth Road terminates. A vast quantity of "black sand," really fire-fountain debris, was deposited over the whole area. This sand was 10 to 50 feet thick in the abandoned quarries along the Round Top road (Fig. 3-8) and averaged about 5 feet in thickness over what is now downtown Honolulu. Although the "black sand" was cold when it fell, a similar eruption today would be disastrous because the weight and volume of the material would cause roofs to cave in and most vegetation to be destroyed.

The youth of the volcanics is shown by their stratigraphic position; also, the black sand is glassy and fresh, and the lava undecomposed. A peculiar ball-type lava is exposed in an abandoned quarry on Puuhonua Street in Manoa Valley.

Origin of the Kolekole Pass Sacrificial Stone. A paved road leads through Schofield Barracks to the scenic Kolekole Pass in the Waianae Range. The view from the rim at the pass rivals Nuuanu Pali, but is not on the regular tourist trips because it must be approached through Schofield Barracks. The road down into Lualualei Valley from the pass cuts across the ancient crater brec-

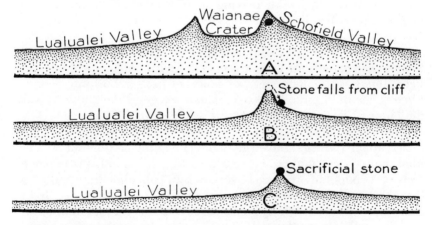

Figure 5-10—Diagram illustrating the history of Kolekole Pass, Oahu, and the Sacrificial Stone. A. Race between Lualualei and Schofield valleys to drain Waianae Crater; B. Lualualei drains the crater, and the Sacrificial Stone falls into Schofield Valley; C. Lualualei beheads Schofield Valley, leaving the Sacrificial Stone on the divide.

Figure 5-11—The Sacrificial Stone at Kolekole Pass, Waianae Range, Oahu, showing lapiés or grooves dissolved by rainwater. (Photo by H. T. Stearns.)

cias and dikes. A short trail from the pass leads up the hill to the Sacrificial Stone, where legend has it that sacrifices where made by the Hawaiians to their gods. The stone is a huge rain-fluted rock once part of a thick lava flow on the rim of the Waianae caldera. Erosion and weathering led to the partial destruction of the rim, and the stone fell into the talus pile at the head of the ancient Schofield Valley. The Lualualei Valley wall receded slowly into the talus pile, and the deeply rotted alluvium and talus surrounding the stone were removed, leaving it on the highest point of the divide (Fig. 5-10). Rainwater dissolved the rock to form the deep grooves or lapiés (Fig. 5-11).[139]

Origin of Makua Cave. Makua or Kaneana Cave (cave of the god Kane), one legends says, connects Oahu with Kauai, and Madame Pele, the Hawaiian goddess of volcanoes, after building Kauai, came to Oahu through this cave. Another legend states that it was the home of Kaneana, the shark-man deity.[230]

The cave is about 450 feet long and trends S. 25° E. In places the roof is about 100 feet above the floor. The entrance is about 50 feet high and 45 feet wide. The south wall of the mouth of the cave consists of 8 feet of olivine aa overlain by a pahoehoe flow about 25 feet thick, which in turn is overlain by aa. There may be a slight downthrow to the south on the south side of the 2½-foot dike forming the north side of the cave. The dike on the south wall running inland along the trend of the cave is about 4 feet thick, but it pinches out upward. Prior to the removal of the talus at the mouth, the cave was entered near the top of the present opening. The white line on the north wall marks the former upper limit of the talus that was removed during the excavation of the road. On the north wall, 20 feet above the floor of the cave, is coarse boulder conglomerate left on a ledge by the sea.

The cave resulted from the enlargement by wave action of a fault crack that runs nearly parallel to a cross-jointed dike. The vertical grain of the dikes has facilitated wave quarrying. The ridge in which the cave is situated is in the heart of the Waianae dike complex. Beyond the main opening is a series of chambers about 8 feet wide, on the floors of which are 2 to 6 feet of consolidated calcareous sand containing smooth, water-worn lava cobbles. The white coral sand is coated with a black opal that makes the deposit resemble basalt. Numerous holes several inches to a foot in diameter, and a foot or more deep, pit the floor. These holes have fluted walls. The grooves are due to percolating water dropping from the roof and dissolving the limestone. The walls and roof are coated in many places with several inches of opal that forms tiny blunt-ended stalactites. The floor at the mouth of the cave is about 55 feet above sea level, but a short distance inside it is estimated to be only about 30 feet. The cave was probably made during the rise and recession of the sea to and from the 95-foot level.

GEOLOGY OF OAHU

Waianae Range. The Waianae Range is composed of three groups of lavas erupted in Tertiary time from three rift zones (Fig. 5-12). The exposed part of the oldest lava is nearly 2,000 feet thick and consists largely of thin-bedded pahoehoe. The middle lavas are separated from the first series in most places by an angular unconformity and talus breccia, and in a few places by an erosional unconformity. The middle basalts are about 2,000 feet thick and closely resemble the lower ones, except that the later beds contain more aa. The upper lavas are about 2,300 feet thick and are mostly massive aa alkalic lavas issued from large cinder cones.

During the Pleistocene, a few secondary eruptions occurred on the Waianae Range near the ancient caldera.[5] These lavas and cinders are deeply weathered and nearly cut away by erosion. They crop out near Kolekole Pass and are named the Kolekole volcanics. They seem older than the secondary eruptions on the Koolau Range. The Waianae Volcano, like most of the others in the islands, produced only small amounts of ash, and most of the lavas were

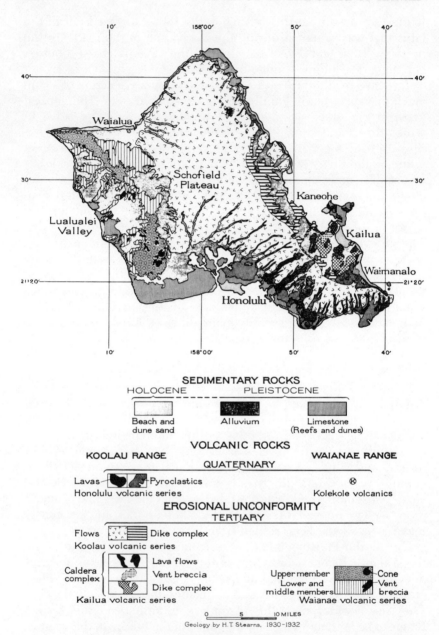

Figure 5-12—Geologic map of the island of Oahu. Faults and dikes omitted.

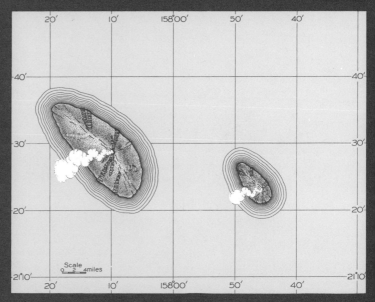

A. First stage showing the youthful Waianae (left) and Koolau (right) Volcanoes, each building lava domes over three rift systems intersecting at a central vent.

B. Silhouette of the first stage.

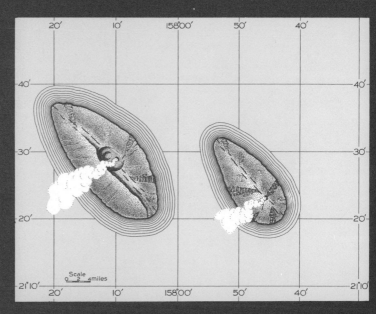

C. Second stage showing collapse or mature phase of the Waianae Volcano (left). A large caldera indents the summit and a high fault cliff prevents lava from flooding the newly established stream pattern on the southwest slope. The Koolau Volcano (right) is still in its youthful phase.

PLATE 4. DIAGRAMS SHOWING THE GROWTH OF OAHU

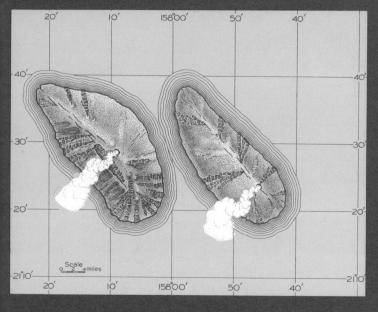

A. Third stage showing the Waianae Volcano (left) in the old age phase with the caldera practically filled and lava flows overtopping the northwest end of the fault cliff and plastering a few valleys on the southwest slope. The Koolau Volcano is building chiefly along the northwest rift.

B. Silhouette of the fourth stage.

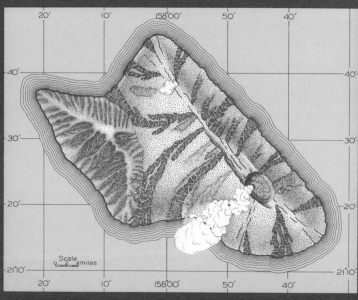

C. Fourth stage showing the Koolau Volcano (right) in its mature or collapse phase with a large caldera at its summit. The Koolau and Waianae Volcanoes are joined to form a single island. The amount of downfaulting along the northwest rift of the Koolau Volcano is unknown.

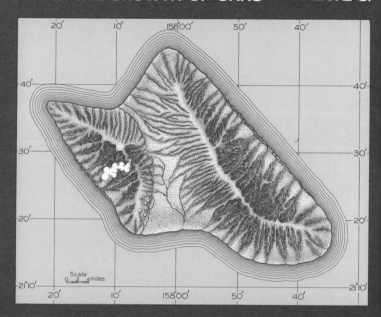

A. Fifth stage show-the Waianae (left) and the Koolau (right) Volcanoes deeply dissected by stream erosion. A small secondary cone erupts on the Waianae Range.

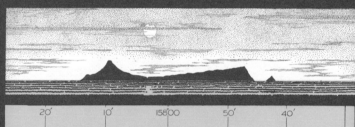

B. Silhouette of the sixth stage.

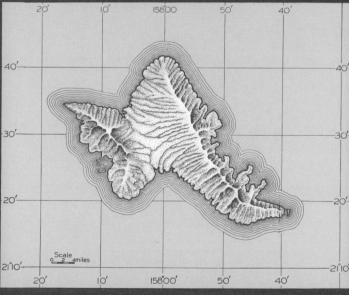

C. Sixth stage show-ing the Waianae (left) and Koolau (right) Ranges deep-ly submerged. The shore line is about 250 feet above the present sea level.

PLATE 6.   DIAGRAMS SHOWING THE GROWTH OF OAHU

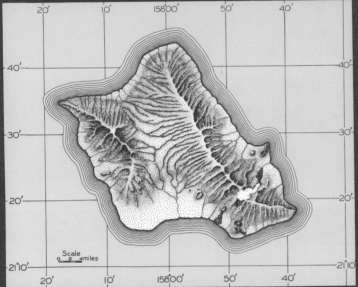

A Seventh stage showing the Waipio stand of the sea (about 350 ± feet lower than the present). Numerous secondary eruptions have occurred on the Koolau Range (right).

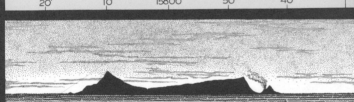

B. Silhouette of the seventh stage.

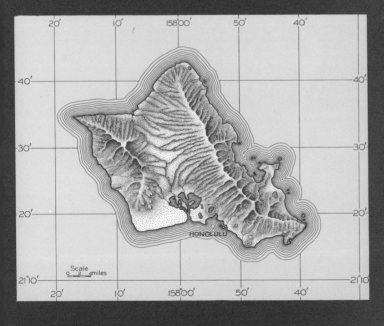

C. Eighth stage showing the sub-mergence of Oahu to present sea level.

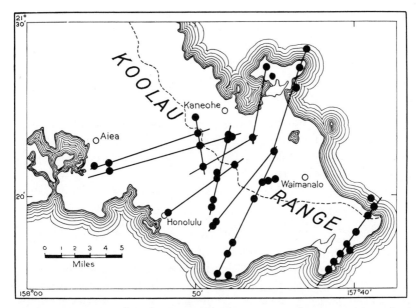

Figure 5-13—Map of southeastern Oahu showing secondary post-Koolau volcanic vents and dominant rift trends.

extruded from fissures a few feet wide, now indicated by dikes (Fig. 3-21). The caldera complex near Kolekole Pass, at the head of Lualualei Valley, was the center of volcanic activity. A rhyodacite flow 400 feet thick crops out in Lualualei Valley.

Koolau Range. The rocks of the ancient Koolau Volcano are chiefly thin tholeiitic basalts with minor amounts of ash, and their associated dike feeders. They have been divided into two groups (Fig. 5-12). The Kailua volcanic series lying at the foot of the Pali are the eroded rocks of the ancient Koolau caldera (Fig. 3-3). They are altered by hydrothermal action caused by steam rising in the vent area. They comprise a caldera complex of ponded downwarped lavas behind Lanikai, vent breccias now deeply weathered, and thousands of narrow dikes in the Kailua-Kaneohe area (Fig. 3-23). The Koolau volcanic series are those lavas and dikes lying outside the caldera and are altered only rarely by hydrothermal action. This group makes up the bulk of the Koolau Range and has an exposed thickness of 3,000 feet. The lavas were erupted from two main rift zones in Pliocene time (Fig. 1-1) and a third southwest rift zone passing through Diamond Head.

About 30 vents have erupted on Oahu since the great valleys were carved and filled with alluvium. They are called the Honolulu volcanic series (Fig. 5-12). The vents are aligned chiefly along northeast-southwest fissures at right angles to the two main rift zones of the Koolau Volcano, but some are close to the lesser third rift zone passing through Manoa Valley (Fig. 5-13). Soundings indicate that there may be many more cones off the windward coast along these or similar rifts. Quaternary eruptions are not found west of a line drawn from Aiea to Kaneohe, which means that the eruptions are closely related to the residual magma pods under the ancient Koolau caldera.

Sedimentary rocks. Only on Oahu do the sedimentary rocks cover a large area of the island (Fig. 5-12). Areas of emerged limestone are shown in Figure 2-15. They consist of layers of reef limestone alternating with beds of clay, tuff, and alluvium along the coastal margins, reaching depths of 1,200 feet at the periphery of the island. Extensive alluvial and talus deposits cover the valley floors. At Kahuku Point, and at other localities, beds of reef alternate with other sediments, indicating the complexity of the geologic history (Fig. 5-14). The extensive industrial and commer-

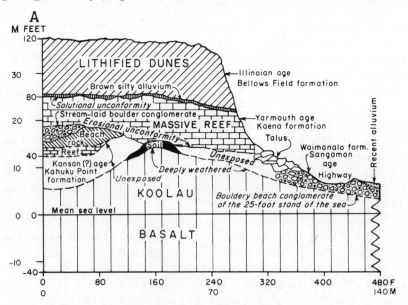

Figure 5-14—Geologic section at Kahuku Quarry, Oahu.

cial areas are built on the coastal plain deposits whereas housing climbs the hills of basalt or covers the valley floors. Highways and man's industrial activities avoid steep land.

The stratigraphic rock units on Oahu are given in Tables 6 and 7. The K-Ar ages of some of these rocks are given in Table 19.

STRUCTURE

The major structural feature of each of the Waianae and Koolau domes in cross-section is a gentle constructional arch with its axis coincident with the crest of the volcano. It is almost entirely the result of lava flows accumulating around a fissure vent. Dike rock occupies practically all of the heart of the Oahu rift zones. This means that the flow lavas have in part been displaced sideways with each injection, partly carried upward as fragments, and partly dropped into the magma reservoir and remelted.

Faults. The buried cliffs and their associated breccia in the Waianae Range may have been caused by faulting. A fault breccia 6 to 12 inches wide marks a fault of unknown displacement parallel to one of these cliffs in the Keaau-Makaha Ridge. Displacements of a few inches to several feet were noted in both ranges, but they are not large enough to justify individual description.

The only large fault seen in the Koolau Range crosses the abandoned winding road down Nuuanu Pali in two places. At an altitude of 750 feet in the lower exposure, the fault zone consists of a platy shear zone 4 to 6 feet wide with 3 to 6 inches of clay gouge in the center. The amount of the displacement could not be determined, but the conspicuously bedded pahoehoe on the west side could not be matched with any of the rocks exposed in the cliff along the road. The rock on the east side is a massive amydaloidal basalt that may be intrusive. Similar relations exist at an altitude of 950 feet. At 975 feet, where the fault crosses a small perennial stream, the dip decreases, and the fault is accompanied by much clay gouge and a wide strip of breccia. In one place, slightly displaced blocks in the breccia can be matched. About 300 feet up the road from the lower exposure of this fault, an irregular dike is displaced slightly by two parallel faults. This fault may be related to the ancient Koolau caldera. Thin streaks of breccia indicative of faulting were seen in several of the Waiahole tunnels in association with dikes.

Two faults are exposed along the road between the Maunawili Training School and Waimanalo; others occur in and near the

TABLE 6

Secondary Eruptions of the Honolulu Volcanic Series, Koolau Range, Oahu[a]

Middle and Late Pleistocene lavas and pyroclastics

Name	Location	Material erupted
ERUPTIONS DURING THE KAHIPA ($-300 \pm$ FOOT) STAND OF THE SEA		
1. Hawaiiloa	Mokapu Peninsula	Cinders and lava
2. Pali Kilo	Mokapu Peninsula	Lava
3. Pyramid Rock	Mokapu Peninsula	Lava
4. Moku Manu[b]	Islands off Mokapu Peninsula	Ash
5. Ulupau[b]	Mokapu Peninsula	Ash
6. Mokulea[b]	Kailua Bay	Lava
ERUPTIONS DURING THE KAENA ($+100$-FOOT) AND LAIE ($+70$-FOOT) STANDS OF THE SEA		
7. Rocky Hill and Manoa craters	Punahou St., Honolulu	Cinders and lava
8. Kalihi	Head of Kalihi Valley	Cinders, lava, and ash
9. Haiku	Head of Haiku Valley	Lava and ash
10. Aliamanu	Between Honolulu and Pearl Harbor	Lava and ash
11. Kaneohe	2 miles south of Kaneohe	Cinders and lava
12. Luakaha	Near head of Nuuanu Valley	Cinders, lava, and ash
13. Makuku	Near head of Nuuanu Valley	Cinders and lava
14. Pali	Pali Road	Ash, cinders, and lava
15. Makawao[c]	2 miles southwest of Olomana Peak	Ash, cinders, and lava
16. Kaau	Head of Palolo Valley	Ash and lava
17. Mauumae	Kaimuki, Honolulu	Cinders and lava
ERUPTIONS DURING THE WAIPIO (MINUS $350 \pm$-FOOT) AND WAIMANALO ($+25$-FOOT) STANDS OF THE SEA		
18. Salt Lake and Makalapa[73,162]	Northwest side of Honolulu	Ash
19. Ainoni	2 miles southwest of Olomana Peak	Cinders and lava
20. Maunawili	South side of Olomana Peak	Cinders and lava
21. Training School	North side of Olomana Peak	Cinders and lava
22. Diamond Head	Southeast part of Honolulu	Ash
23. Kaimuki	Kaimuki, Honolulu	Lava and spatter
24. Black Point	Southeast of Diamond Head	Lava
25. Kamanaiki	Kamanaiki Valley, branch of Kalihi Valley	Lava
26. Castle	3 miles east of Kailua	Cinders and lava
27. Punchbowl	Near center of Honolulu	Ash and lava

[TABLE 6 continued]

LATE PLEISTOCENE ERUPTIONS AFTER THE WAIMANALO
(+25-FOOT) STAND OF THE SEA

28. Tantalus fissure eruption:

Tantalus ⎱ On divide between Manoa and	Lava, cinders, and
Sugar Loaf ⎰ Pauoa valleys	great volumes of
Round Top	black "sand"

29. Koko fissure eruptions:

Manana	Manana (Rabbit) Island; 1¼ miles northwest of Makapuu Pt.	Ash
Koko	East end of Oahu	Ash and lava
Kahauloa	East end of Oahu	Ash and lava
Hanauma Bay	East end of Oahu	Ash and lava
Koko Head	East end of Oahu	Ash
Kalama	Northeast of Koko Crater	Cinders and lava
Kaohikaipu	Islet 1 mile northwest of Makapuu Pt.	Cinders and lava
Kaupo	1 mile west of Makapuu Pt.	Lava and spatter
30. Black Point	Southeast side of Diamond Head	Black ash[d]

[a]The age of some eruptions is not yet definitely established. The list is revised from the one published in Bull. 2 as the result of the work of Winchell.[252]

[b]Time of eruption uncertain.   [c]May be an ancient Koolau vent.

[d]The vent of the Black Point ash is unknown, but the ash is not the type produced by a submarine eruption.[5,239] It contains pisolites at Black Point, occurs as dunes in gullies on Diamond Head, and is interbedded with beach sand in the Kahala area. A sample collected on Diamond Head Drive contains olivine crystals, calcareous beach grains, and Pele's hair. R. L. Hay determined the refractive index of the glass grains to be 1.605±003. The only known vents young enough to have produced similar fresh ash are those along the Round Top-Tantalus fissure. Ash taken from the bottom of Round Top Drive has a refractive index of 1.623±003, which makes the Round Top vent seem an unlikely source unless alteration has affected the index.

Maunawili area and the northwest end of the range. All of them cause only small displacements.

Synclines. Two synclines occur on Oahu—one at Puu Kailio, at the center of the Waianae Volcano, and the other at Lanikai, near the eruptive center of the Koolau volcanic series. The fact that both the Lanikai and Kailio synclines occur at places of intense volcanic activity suggests that they are merely sags in the flows produced by local withdrawal of support.

The Kailio syncline forms Puu Kailio, near Kolekole Pass, at the head of Lualualei Valley. The rocks making up the syncline are the lower lavas of the Waianae volcanic series. The syncline occupies about three-quarters of a square mile at the eruptive center of the Waianae Volcano. The axis trends N. 70° E. The beds on the north

TABLE 7

STRATIGRAPHIC ROCK UNITS ON THE ISLAND OF OAHU

Age	Rock assemblage	
	Sedimentary rocks	Volcanic rocks
Holocene	Coral fills, younger alluvium, and unconsolidated beach and dune sand	
Pleistocene	Older alluvium, lithified dunes, and emerged marine limestones chiefly coralliferous	Honolulu volcanic series and the Kolekole volcanics
	Great erosional unconformity	
Pliocene		Koolau and Kailua volcanic series Erosional unconformity Waianae volcanic series { Upper member / Middle member / Lower member

side dip 28° S., and those on the south side dip 14° N. The syncline is terminated on the east side by a nearly vertical cliff against which rests talus breccia cut by dikes.

The Lanikai syncline forms the hills known as Kaiwa Ridge and Puu Papea, adjacent to Lanikai, near Kailua, on the northeast shore of the Koolau Range (Fig. 3-3). The rocks making up the syncline are Kailua amygdaloidal lavas cut by dikes. The axis trends N. 65° E., and plunges southwest away from the dike complex of the Kailua series, with the beds dipping toward it at angles of 5° to 10°.

GEOLOGIC HISTORY OF OAHU

Oahu began its geologic history as two separate submarine volcanoes (Fig. 5-15). They gradually built two islands (Plate 3, A). Both volcanoes were built over three sets of fissures intersecting at a summit crater, and both at frequent intervals erupted highly fluid basaltic flows that built up shield-shaped cones. The Waianae Volcano gradually developed both a large summit caldera near the present site of Kolekole Pass and a high, steep fault cliff that formed a wall bounding the southwest margin of the two main rift zones (Plate 3, C). Streams eroded the southwest slope after the fault cliff protected it from flows, and lava continued to accumulate in the great caldera until this depression nearly, if not entirely, filled up. Near the close of the epoch, lava overflowed the northwest end of the fault cliff and ran down some of the valleys northwest of the present site of Waianae, and a few bulky cinder cones were formed at the source of several of the flows along the two main rifts (Plate 4, A). In the meantime, the Koolau Volcano grew larger, with a pronounced elongation northwestward as a result of copious flows from the northwest rift zone. Finally, the Waianae Volcano died, the sea pounded back its shore into great cliffs, and torrential streams carved great valleys, especially on the southwest side, where the streams were older and the rocks weaker. These great valleys are now called Nanakuli, Lualualei, Waianae, Makaha, and Keaau.

Meanwhile, Koolau flows filled up the ocean between the Koolau and Waianae volcanoes and joined the two mountains into a single island (Plate 4, B). What is now called the Schofield Plateau resulted from the Koolau flows banking against Waianae Mountain. Simultaneously, a caldera about 6 miles across developed at the intersection of the rift zones near the present site of Kailua. Volcanic activity ceased, and streams carved deep amphitheater-headed canyons in the Koolau Volcano. The streams of the Waianae Range had nearly dried up because the moist northeast trades were cut off by the growth of the Koolau Volcano. Oahu was then much larger than it is now, and the mouths of the streams of that time are today more than 6,000 feet below sea level. The streams gradually

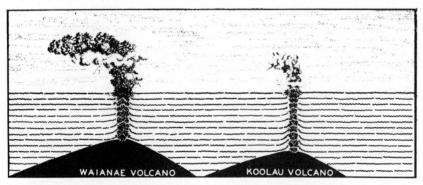

WAIANAE VOLCANO   KOOLAU VOLCANO

Figure 5-15—Submarine explosions of the Waianae and Koolau volcanoes just before they reached sea level. The cones consist chiefly of pillow lavas and ash in this phase.

destroyed the caldera, and today only the roots of the former firepits remain near Kailua. The magnificent canyons ate away much of their interstream divides and eroded headward so far that some even captured leeward-flowing streams. Plate 5, A shows Oahu when it stood 1,800 feet higher than it does now.

The great submergence was followed rather rapidly by a partial re-emergence. Consequently, few changes from wave attack are noticeable except the stripping away of the soil at the higher levels (Plate 5, C). The re-emergence, however, was not simple, but involved halts and partial resubmergence. Some of the later shorelines are well preserved in emerged reefs and beach deposits. The most important result of the shifting ocean level was the deep drowning of the great valleys and their subsequent sedimentation. This accounts for the ubiquitous flat valley floors. The complex history of the emergences and submergences is far from completely known; the shorelines so far deciphered, with their altitudes, are listed in Table 2.

During the late history of shifting sea level, volcanism was renewed near the old Koolau center of activity, and at intervals of a few hundred or a few thousand years down to the late Pleistocene, vents were blasted through the coral reefs, as at Diamond Head, Salt Lake, Punchbowl, or the Koko craters, and fire fountains played from cracks in the mountains and poured lavas into nearby valleys, as at Kalihi, Nuuanu, Kaneohe, Castle, Tantalus, or Sugar Loaf vents. Many erupted during the Waipio low stand of the sea (Plate 6, A). Thus, we find some lava flows that are interstratified with or lie upon gravel or coral reefs. Altogether 30 such secondary eruptions are now known on the Koolau Range, and there is no reason to believe that others may not take place in the future. One post-erosional eruption also occurred on the Waianae Range. Its age is not yet established, but it appears to be older than the post-Koolau eruptions.

6

ISLAND OF HAWAII

GENERAL STATEMENT

Hawaii has been built by lavas poured from five volcanoes, each with independent rift zones and individual geologic history. Their areas and the principal geomorphic features are shown above. Significant data regarding their forms are given in the following table:

TABLE 8
DIMENSIONS AND FORM OF THE DOMES OF HAWAII[240]

Name	Length (miles)	Width (miles)	Area (square miles)	Percent of island	Summit elevation
Mauna Loa	75	64	2,035	50.5	13,680
Kilauea	51	14	552	13.7	4,090
Hualalai	24	20	290	7.2	8,251
Mauna Kea	51	25	919	22.8	13,784
Kohala	22	15	234	5.8	5,505

The area of each dome is partly dependent upon its age. The southern slope of Kohala Mountain has been buried beneath Mauna Kea lavas. The western and southern slopes of Mauna Kea, the eastern and southern slopes of Hualalai, and the northwestern slopes of Kilauea have been buried by Mauna Loa lavas. The areas listed are present dimensions and make no allowance for buried slopes.

A map of Hawaii showing the subaerial and generalized submarine contours and profiles of the volcanic domes is shown in

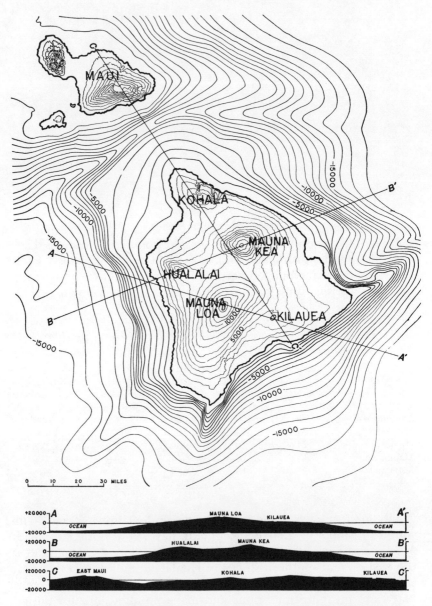

Figure 6-1—Map of the island of Hawaii showing subaerial and submarine contours and profiles of the volcanic domes. (After Stearns and Macdonald, 1946.)

Figure 6-2—Relief map of the island of Hawaii showing the historic lava flows. Numbers refer to descriptions of points of geologic interest in *Road Guide to Points of Geologic Interest in the Hawaiian Islands.* (Modified after Stearns and Macdonald, 1946)

Figure 6-1. Hawaii National Park Headquarters, the Museum, and the Hawaiian Volcano Observatory are located near the summit of Kilauea. The so-called round-the-island road does not encircle either Kohala Mountain or Kilauea; hence, large parts of the island are still inaccessible by auto. A jeep road was constructed to the summit of Mauna Kea in 1964.

During the past 132 years, Mauna Loa has averaged one outbreak in the caldera every four years, and has produced a lava flow every seven years. Kilauea has contained a lava lake for years at a time, and since 1800 has produced 30 flows outside of its caldera (Figs. 6-2, 6-3). The only recorded eruption of Hualalai was in 1800–1801. Mauna Kea and Kohala have not erupted in historic time. About 50 littoral cones exist on the shores of Kilauea and Mauna Loa but there are none on any of the other volcanoes in the Hawaiian Islands.[141]

Hawaii Island, except for the windward slope of Kohala, is little eroded. The only perennial streams are on the northeastern slopes of Mauna Kea and Kohala. The high permeability of the fresh lavas forming the surface of Kilauea, Mauna Loa, and Hualalai inhibit the development of permanent streams. Large areas on these moun-

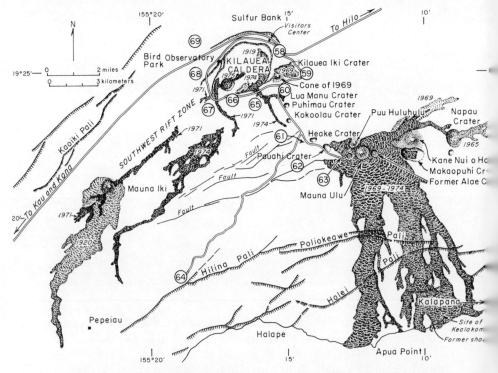

Figure 6-3—Map of part of Kilauea Volcano showing Chain of Craters and recent lava flows. Modified from Figure 8 in *Volcanoes of the National Parks in Hawaii.*

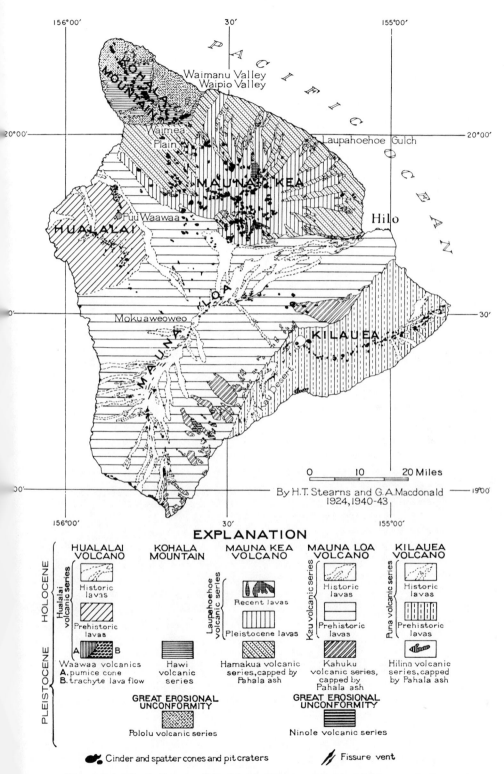

Figure 6-4—Geologic map of the island of Hawaii. Faults and dikes omitted.

TABLE 9

STRATIGRAPHIC ROCK UNITS IN THE ISLAND OF HAWAII

(The volcanic rocks of Mauna Loa, Mauna Kea, and Hualalai, those of Mauna Kea and Kohala, and those of Mauna Loa and Kilauea interfinger)

Age	Hualalai	Kohala Mountain	Mauna Loa		Kilauea	Mauna Kea
Historic	Historic member of the Hualalai volcanic series (1800–01)	Unconsolidated alluvium, dunes and landslides	Historic member of volcanic series (1832–1950)	Mud flow of 1868	Historic member of the Puna volcanic series (1790–1965)	Ribbons of gravel and small alluvial fans
Holocene	Prehistoric member of the Hualalai volcanic series	Fluvial conglomerates	Dunes; Prehistoric member of the Kau volcanic series		Dunes; Prehistoric member of the Puna volcanic series	Upper member of the Laupahoehoe volcanic series; Glacial debris and fluvial conglomerates
Late Pleistocene	Pahala ash (exposed on Waawaa volcanics only)	Pahala ash (not differentiated); Fluvial conglomerates	Pahala ash		Pahala ash	Lower member of the Laupahoehoe volcanic series; Local erosional unconformity; Pahala ash
Early and middle Pleistocene	Waawaa volcanics and lower unexposed part of Hualalai volcanic series	Hawi volcanic series; Great erosional unconformity; Pololu volcanic series	Kahuku volcanic series; unconformity; Ninole volcanic series		Hilina volcanic series	Hamakua volcanic series
Early Pleistocene						

tains are covered with black rock and are bare and devoid of vegetation. The southwestern side of Kilauea is a desert.

The lavas of Mauna Loa interfinger with the lavas of Kilauea, Hualalai, and Mauna Kea. The lavas of Mauna Kea interfinger with the latest lavas of Kohala Mountain. The 25-foot shoreline has been found on Mauna Kea but not on Hualalai, Mauna Loa, or Kilauea. Marine conglomerates are found at an elevation of 200 feet, and stream terraces reach a height of 1,100 feet on Kohala Mountain.

A broad shelf 1,200 feet below sea level (Lualualei stand) follows the coast of Mauna Kea, Kohala, and part of Hualalai, indicating a submergence of this amount following a long period of marine erosion. Apparently the lavas of Kilauea bury this shelf at Hilo. The deep canyons of Kohala Mountain were cut before this submergence, as indicated by deep fills at their mouths; hence, the Kohala Volcano appears to have become extinct before the other volcanoes. Radiogenic dates indicate that the Kohala lavas are late Pleistocene in age.[125]

Paleomagnetism surveys of lava flows in the old formations on the island indicate that, regardless of their age, none of the rocks shows reversed remanent magnetism, which occurred about 750,000 years ago. This finding agrees with radiogenic dating and indicates that all exposed rocks are Pleistocene in age.[45]

The great submergence of Kohala and Mauna Kea apparently occurred in the middle Pleistocene. The partly buried valleys on the southeast slope of Mauna Loa may have been cut during this long minus 1,200-foot stand of the sea. Most of Hualalai and all of Kilauea were formed later.

The stratigraphy is given in Table 9, and the distribution of the rock units is shown in Figure 6-4.

Mauna Kea

This mountain is the highest insular peak on earth. Snow usually remains throughout the year in one place on the summit. The dome is 30 miles across and studded with cinder cones, most of which are near the top and clustered into zones, indicating that the volcano was built over rifts trending eastward, southward, and westward (see map adjoining chapter head).

The lower slopes of the mountain, especially the high plains of Waimea, are blanketed with tan-colored ash deposits. Most of this material is fine-grained fire-fountain debris wafted from the numerous cinder cones nearby. Streams have cut narrow gashes in the windward slope, and Laupahoehoe Gulch contains an intracanyon flow. At its mouth is a flat of pahoehoe so recent that very little soil has formed on it. Mauna Kea poured out this lava after a canyon more than 400 feet deep had been cut.

The volcanics of Mauna Kea are divided into two series. The older or Hamakua volcanic series forms the major part of the mountain and is chiefly tholeiitic basalts with picrite-basalts carrying olivine and augite phenocrysts and a few alkalic basalts, hawaiites, and ankaramites in its upper part. It usually carries a blanket of tan-colored vitric Pahala ash 4 to 15 feet thick and is separated from the overlying Laupahoehoe volcanic series by the presence of the ash blanket and the porphyritic picrite-basalts. Capping the Hamakua lavas near the summit are several beds of glacial debris (Pohakuloa formation) reaching 90 feet in thickness. The upper lavas have K-Ar ages of 375,000 and 270,000 years, indicating that these lavas were being erupted after the Yarmouth interglacial

Figure 6-5—Section of Mauna Kea, Hawaii, showing hypothetical caldera filled with lavas of the Laupahoehoe volcanic series. (After Stearns and Macdonald, 1946.)

epoch.[169] The Laupahoehoe volcanic series is predominantly hawaiite with lesser amounts of alkali olivine basalt and ankaramite, but olivine basalts are also present. The lavas of this series form a thin veneer over the upper part of the cone, reaching a maximum thickness at the summit. They are characterized by many short flows and bulky cinder cones. The top of the mountain above 11,000 feet is a plateau that may be caused by the Laupahoehoe volcanic series filling a caldera in the Hamakua volcanic series (Fig. 6-5). Six flows are mostly black and bare and differ from the lavas in the lower member of the Laupahoehoe series only in their youthful appearance. Some are only a few thousand years old based on C[14] dating (see Table 10).[169,171] Those above 10,500 feet overlie glacial drift.

TABLE 10
Time-Stratigraphic Units, Rock-Stratigraphic Units, and Radiometric Dates for Mauna Kea Volcano (After Porter.[169])

Time-stratigraphic units			^{14}C and K/Ar dates	Rock-stratigraphic units			
	Holocene Series	Loaloan Stage	• 4400 ± 110 • 4790 ± 70 • 9080 ± 200				
	Pleistocene Series	Kaulan Stage		Laupahoehoe Group	Waikahalulu Formation	Younger drift	Makanaka Formation
		Kemolean Stage	• 29,700 ± 500 • 31,900 ± 550 • 37,200 ± 1400			?	
		Kuupahaan Stage	• 41,300 ± 8300			Older drift	
Quaternary System		Hanaipoean Stage	• 69,500 ± 2600 • 81,100 ± 23,600				
		Poliahuan Stage	• 171,900 ± 2800 • 174,000 ± 37,400 • 174,400 ± 26,500			Waihu Formation	
		Liloean Stage	• ≥ 94,500 ± 6100 • ≥109,800 ± 5600 • ≥114,100 ± 7600 • ≥122,400 ± 7300				
		Kilohanan Stage		Hamakua Group		Pohakuloa Formation	
		pre-Kilohanan rocks (undivided)	• 278,500 ± 68,500 • 382,100 ± 60,600			Hopukani Formation	
						lower member of Stearns and Macdonald (1946)	

Figure 6-6—Glacial striae on the south slope of Mauna Kea, Hawaii, prove that the mountain was once capped by a glacier. (Photo by C. K. Wentworth.)

A glacier about 250 feet thick covered the top of the mountain during the Wisconsinan glacial stage, as shown by moraines and glaciated areas above 10,500 feet (Fig. 6-6). The glacial evidence was discovered in 1909.[35] Three older drifts, the Early Makanaka, the Waihu, and the Pohakuloa, have been described, the oldest dating back about 250,000 years, as shown in Table 10.[169, 245] Fanglomerate outwash and tephra deposits are also present.

MAUNA LOA VOLCANO

Mauna Loa is a shield-shaped dome about 60 miles long and 30 miles wide. It is one of the most prolific lava producers on earth. A few cinder cones lie on its slopes and in the summit caldera, Mokuaweoweo. The caldera resulted from collapse and is growing broader through coalescence with adjacent pit craters (Fig. 6-8). It is now about 19,500 feet long, 9,200 feet wide, and 600 feet deep. During recent years, lava, poured from fissures and cones on its floor and rim, has been filling the depressions, and a few weak explosions have occurred.[224] The changes in the shape of the caldera between 1841 and 1965 are shown in Figures 6-7 and 6-8.

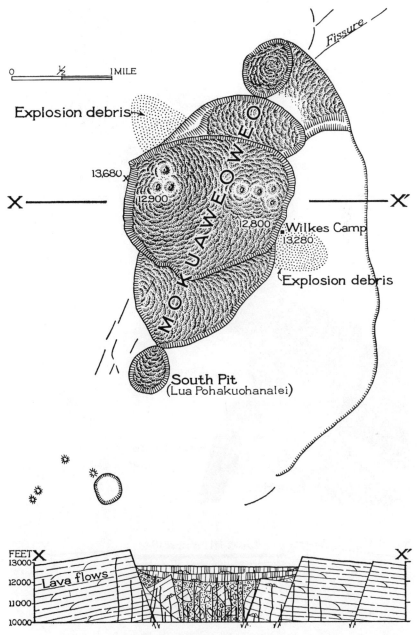

Figure 6-7—Plan and section of Mokuaweoweo caldera in 1841 (plan is after Wilkes). Areas of explosion debris added. Approximate altitudes in feet. The structure beneath the caldera is hypothetical. (After Stearns and Macdonald, 1946.)

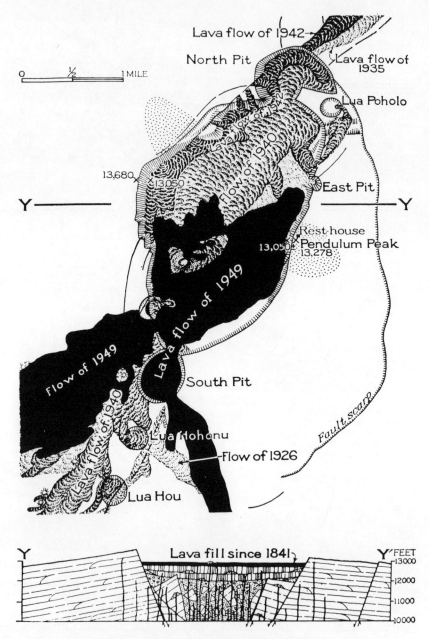

Figure 6-8—Map and section of Mokuaweoweo caldera after the 1949 eruption. Lua Poholo, East Pit, and Lua Hohonu are pit craters formed since 1841. (Modified after Stearns and Macdonald, 1946.)

Mauna Loa has well-defined southwest and northeast rift zones and a weakly developed north rift zone (Fig. 1-1). Most eruptions start as high, short-lived lava fountains in the caldera, then change to outpourings of lava from vents at lower altitudes along the rifts. The southwest rift probably produces submarine flows also. The south and southeast sides of the volcano are broken by echelon faults arranged in two patterns. The pattern distinguished by the northeasterly strike of the faults is the most common. The other,

Figure 6-9—Map of Hawaii Island showing visible faults (solid lines), concealed faults (broken lines), and names of fault systems. (After Stearns and Macdonald, 1946.)

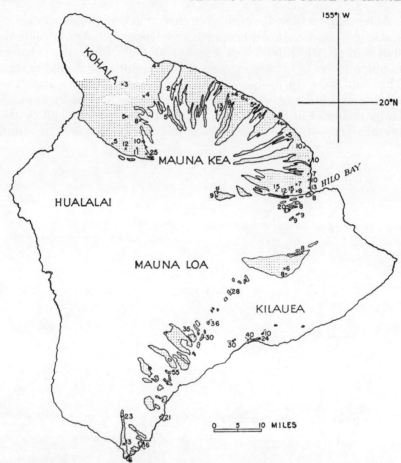

Figure 6-10—Map of Hawaii Island showing distribution and thickness in feet of Pahala ash. (After Stearns and Macdonald, 1946.)

with radial faults, is best developed in the southwest rift zone. Displacement along a few faults has occurred in historic time. Some of the scarps reach heights of 1,250 feet. The principal fault systems are shown in Figure 6-9. Two distinct epochs of faulting occurred.

Pahala ash.   The older rocks on the lower slopes of the mountain are blanketed with Pahala ash, which is named after a village in the Kau District.[224] The ash is a valuable horizon marker. It crops out over about 450 square miles (Fig. 6-10), but most of it has been buried by later lava flows. It is generally a fine yellowish to brownish-red vitric ash, forming an excellent soil and ranging from a few to 55 feet in thickness. Most of the sugar cane in the Kau District is grown on it. Near Kilauea, the Pahala ash also contains beds of lapilli and lithic ash. It was derived chiefly from tremendous explosions at Kilauea during periods of collapse when ground water entered the conduit. The phreatic explosions of 1924, which were caused by high-level water confined by dikes entering the hot conduit of Kilauea, were typical of the smaller types of explosions that generated the ash (Fig. 3-12). In spite of their relatively small size, the explosions threw out blocks weighing 10 tons, and the ash clouds reached a height of 4 miles.[192] They produced only lithic ash, because no magma was present.

Although essentially an ash derived from Kilauea, the Pahala ash has a composite origin, because all eruptions, especially from large cinder cones, make a little glassy ash. Thus the Pahala ash on Kohala and Mauna Kea was doubtless deposited in part from local eruptions. Much of it is secondary ash swept off the Kau Desert by strong winds following eruptions. Frazer thinks that most of the ash came from violent phreatomagmatic explosions accompanying the foundering of Kilauea caldera and the southwest rift.[63] Charcoal from the top of the bed of Pahala ash that lies at the bottom of the Kaone fault scarp on the south coast of Kilauea has a C^{14} date of $17,360 \pm 650$ years, and charcoal from the top of the ash on Maniania Pali south of Honuapo village, a date of $10,140 \pm 300$ years.[179] The dates indicate that the Pahala ash was being deposited in the late Wisconsinan glacial epoch. Perhaps additional rainfall on Kilauea summit during that epoch added to the ground-water supply and induced more hydroexplosions. It is possible that eruptions of some of the submerged volcanoes off the coast contributed to the Pahala ash (Fig. 2-11). Fossil bones of a flightless goose, *Geochen rhuax*, a new genus and species,[248] were found in Pahala ash beneath 100 feet of lava in a tunnel in Kau.[224]

Origin of the Ninole valleys. A number of radial ridges project above the general slope of Mauna Loa in the southeast slope. The ridges are believed to represent divides between canyons several thousand feet deep that were eroded in Mauna Loa and later partly filled with lava flows (Fig. 6-11). Fault scarps may have bordered the coast. Mauna Loa appears, therefore, to be an eroded mass probably as old as Kohala Mountain. The volcano may have been completely inactive during the erosion of the valleys, although a

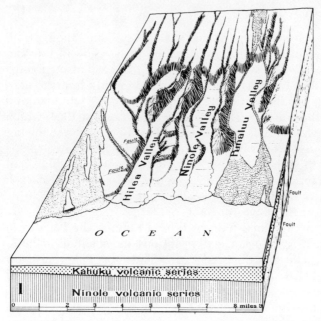

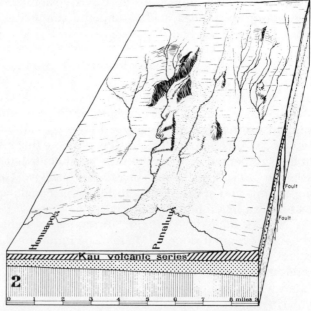

Figure 6-11—Diagrams showing the origin of the ridges composed of the Ninole volcanic series in the Kau District. *Stage 1* shows the ancient canyons cut in the Ninole volcanic series partly filled with lavas of the Kahuku volcanic series. *Stage 2* shows the present form after the valleys had been further filled with the lavas of the Kahuku and Kau volcanic series. (After Stearns and Macdonald, 1946.)

high fault escarpment might have bordered the summit caldera and for a long time shielded the district from lava flows. Because of the fairly high rainfall in the area and the originally steep gradients of the streams tumbling over fault escarpments, the valleys may have been cut in a relatively short time.

Rock units. The rocks of Mauna Loa are divided into three units. All are tholeiitic basalts. The oldest is the Ninole volcanic series. It forms the core of the mountain and is exposed in the ancient divide between the partly filled canyons in the southeast slope. One intercalated vitric tuff bed 15 feet thick lies 500 feet below the top of the series. A steep angular erosional unconformity separates the Ninole lavas from the overlying Kahuku volcanic series. The latter attains a thickness of 600 feet and is separated from the overlying Kau volcanic series by a mantle of Pahala ash 5 to 50 feet thick. A few of the Kahuku flows interfinger with the ash. The Kau volcanic series are fairly fresh lavas, commonly bare and rocky in dry areas and rarely more than 25 feet thick, except in the upper part of Mauna Loa, where they exceed 800 feet in thickness. The historic member of the Kau volcanic series comprises the lavas erupted since 1832.

Historic eruptions of Mauna Loa Volcano. Mauna Loa has been active less than 6 per cent of the time in the last 143 years. Most eruptions fall into two types: (1) summit eruptions without accompanying flank flows; and (2) flank flows accompanied by short-lived eruptions of a few minutes to a few days on the summit before the flank flow. The area and volume of the historic lava flows are given in Table 11.

The typical eruption. A typical eruption of Mauna Loa begins with a series of local earthquakes, which indicate the splitting open of the mountain and which enabled Finch in 1942 to predict the point of outbreak.[61] Sometimes the earthquakes are sharp and perceptible, but often they are weak and recorded by local seismographs only. Usually the eruption is accompanied by a fume cloud rising several miles into the air (Fig. 6-12) and lava fountains reaching a maximum height of 700 feet. The outbreak typically begins in Mokuaweoweo and extends down one of the rift zones either continuously along a fissure or by breaking out lower down along a newly opened fissure. Several days may intervene between the outbreak in Mokuaweoweo and that on the flank. Some eruptions occur in the caldera without any outbreak on the flank. During summit eruptions, lava commonly erupts from wall cracks and pours down the wall into the caldera. Where such flows plaster

TABLE 11
HISTORIC ERUPTIONS OF MAUNA LOA
(After Stearns and Macdonald, 1946)

Year	Month and day	Summit eruption (days)	Flank eruption (days)	Location of principal outflow	Altitude of main vent (feet)	Approximate repose period since last eruption (months)	Area of lava flow (square miles)	Approximate volume of lava (cubic yards)
1832	June 20	21	(?)	Summit	13,000(?)	......	......	....
1843	Jan. 9	5	90	N. flank	9,800	126	20.2	250,000,000
1849	May	15	....	Summit	[4]13,000	73	......	,..........
1851	Aug. 8	21	(?)	Summit	13,300	26	6.9	90,000,000
1852	Feb. 17	1	20	NE. rift	8,400	6	11.0	140,000,000
1855	Aug. 11	.....	450	NE. rift	10,500(?)	41	[2]12.2	150,000,000
1859	Jan. 23	<1	300	N. flank	9,200	26	[3]32.7	[3]600,000,000
1865	Dec. 30	120	..,.	Summit	13,000	73	......	....
1868	Mar. 27	1	[5]15	S. rift	3,300	23	[3]9.1	[3]190,000,000
1870	Jan. 1(?)	14	....	Summit	13,000	21	......	....
1871	Aug. 1(?)	30	....	Summit	13,000	18	......	....
1872	Aug. 10	60	....	Summit	13,000	11	......	....
1873	Jan. 6	2(?)	....	Summit	13,300	3	......	....
1873	Apr. 20	547	....	Summit	13,000	3	......	....
1875	Jan. 10	30	....	Summit	13,000	2	......	....
1875	Aug. 11	7	....	Summit	13,000	6	......	....
1876	Feb. 13	Short	....	Summit	13,000	6	......	....
1877	Feb. 14	10	[7]1	W. flank	−180±	12	......	....
1880	May 1	6	....	Summit	13,000	38	......	....
1880	Nov. 1	.....	280	NE. rift	10,400	6	24.0	[3]300,000,000
1887	Jan. 16	.....	10	SW. rift	5,700	65	[3]11.3	[3]300,000,000
1892	Nov. 30	3	....	Summit	13,000	68	......	....
1896	Apr. 21	16	....	Summit	13,000	41	......	....
1899	July 4	4	19	NE. rift	10,700	38	16.2	200,000,000
1903	Oct. 6	60	....	Summit	13,000	50	......	....
1907	Jan. 9	<1	15	SW. rift	6,200	37	8.1	100,000,000
1914	Nov. 25	48	....	Summit	13,000	94	......	....
1916	May 19	.....	14	SW. rift	7,400	16	6.6	80,000,000
1919	Sept. 29	Short	42	SW. rift	7,700	40	[3]9.2	[3]350,000,000
1926	Apr. 10	Short	14	SW. rift	7,600	77	[8]13.4	[3]150,000,000
1933	Dec. 2	17	<1	Summit	13,000	91	2.0	100,000,000
1935	Nov. 21	<1	42	NE. rift	12,100	23	[9]13.8	[1]60,000,000
1940	Apr. 7	133	<1	Summit	13,000	51	[10]3.9	100,000,000
1942	Apr. 26	2	13	NE. rift	9,200	20	[11]10.6	100,000,000
1943	Nov. 21	3	....	Summit	13,000	18	(?)	(?)[12]
1949	Jan. 6	145	2	Summit	13,000	61	5.6	77,000,000
1950	June 1	<1	23	SW. rift	8,000	12	[13]35.0	[13]600,000,000
1975	July 5	2	....	Summit	13,000	181	5.2	32,500,000
1984	Mar. 25	Short	[14]22	NE rift	9,400	108	4.1	[13]232,000,000
Total		1,330	1,374				260.1	4,301,500,000

TABLE 11 continued

[1]The duration for most of the eruptions prior to 1899 is only approximate. Heavy columns of fume at Mokuaweoweo, apparently representing copious gas release accompanied by little or no lava discharge, were observed in January 1870, December 1887, March 1921, November 1943, and August 1944. They are not indicated in the table.

[2]Upper end of the flow cannot be identified with certainty.

[3]Area above sea level. The volume below sea level is unknown, but estimates give the following orders of magnitude: 1859—300,000,000 cubic yards; 1868—100,000,000 cubic yards; 1887—200,000,000 cubic yards; 1919—200,000,000 cubic yards; 1926—1,500,000 cubic yards. These are included in the volumes given in the table.

[4]All eruptions in the caldera are listed at 13,000 feet altitude, although many of them were a little lower.

[5]Flank eruption started April 7.

[6]Activity in the summit caldera may have been essentially continuous from August 1872 to February 1877. Only the most violent activity was visible from Hilo.

[7]Submarine eruption off Kealakekua, on the west coast of Hawaii.

[8]2.5 square miles of this is the area of the thin flow near the summit. An unknown area lies below sea level.

[9]About 0.5 square mile of this is covered by the thin flank flow above the main cone and 0.8 square mile is in Mokuaweoweo caldera.

[10]2.8 square miles is in Mokuaweoweo caldera and 1.1 square miles outside the caldera.

[11]2.8 square miles of this is covered by the thin flank flow near the summit, and 0.5 square mile is in the caldera.

[12]Amount of lava liberated was probably small; eruption was largely a liberation of gas.

[13]Preliminary determination.

[14]Kilauea erupted while Mauna Loa was in eruption in 1984. Seismographs indicated no effect on each other.

coarse talus and clinker, curious hummocky and bumpy lava surfaces are formed. The cracks, usually a few inches to several feet wide, are enlarged at the main vents to fissures 10 to 25 feet wide by stoping, fluxing, and subsequent collapse. In other places pit craters develop by stoping.

At first the sudden gas release causes intense fountaining, which commonly merges along the crack into veritable "curtains of fire." Cones are not produced at first because the lava of the fountains is sufficiently liquid when it falls to the ground to flow away as very frothy pahoehoe. Highly cellular tan pumice clots up to one foot across are carried upward in the hot, rapidly ascending fumes. At various heights up to 1,000 feet the updraft becomes insufficient to support the clots, and they fall, smashing into bits on the hard rocky surface. Some fall into the lava streams and are floated off. Pele's hair, delicate threads of glass spun by the lava fountains, drifts leeward for miles, causing the ground to glisten as though covered with jewels. The crust of pahoehoe formed close to the fountains where glass spinning is rapid may consist of welded mats of Pele's hair and coarser strands of spun glass.

Great volumes of very fluid pahoehoe lava are poured out during the first few days. The lava flows down the slope in two or more rivers at rates of 10 to 25 miles per hour (Fig. 6-12), at times merging below the vents to form a single flow. A short distance from the lava fountains, these pahoehoe flows usually change to thin clinkery aa

flows. The flows near the source on the upper part of the mountain
are commonly only 6 inches to 3 feet thick. On the lower slopes
they are generally 10 to 15 feet thick, and where they pool in flats,
they attain a thickness of 50 feet or more.

Generally, the bulk of the gas is released in a few days and the
fountains gradually die down, building chains of spatter cones,
spatter ramparts, and cinder cones along the fissures. The lava out-
flow typically becomes restricted to a single river issuing at the
lower end of the cone chain.

During long eruptions, the rivers of pahoehoe crust over and
build one or more feeding tubes that conduct the lava many miles
down the mountain with only slight loss of heat. The 1859 flow is 33
miles long, the longest historic flow. It lasted 10 months, and pillow
lava may have formed where it ran into the sea.[66] During some
eruptions, pahoehoe advances over and extends beyond the earlier
aa. These pahoehoe flows are potentially the most destructive;
someday they may fill and destroy Hilo Harbor. The 1881
pahoehoe stopped in the outskirts of Hilo after flowing 29 miles.

Diverting lava flows by bombing. The first attempt to stop a
lava flow by bombing was made by the U.S. Army during the 1935
eruption of Mauna Loa at the lower tube outlet at an altitude of
8,800 feet. The writer rode in one of the planes from which bombs
were dropped and later examined the area where the bombs fell.
The bombs weighed only 500 pounds. Many fell on already hardened lava and had little effect. The few that fell into the molten
lava threw out small clots of pahoehoe but otherwise had no effect.
Bombing was tried again during the Mauna Loa eruption of 1942.
One bomb broke the lava channel levee and caused the lava to form
a new channel, but the terrane was unfavorable to the new channel
and the lava stream rejoined the main stream a short distance
downslope.[104] It is believed that the huge bombs now available
might divert lava flows by precision bombing of spatter ramparts
and levees on steep slopes, and thus possibly prevent lava rivers
from reaching Hilo. However, a legal problem would develop if the
lava were diverted onto private land that might otherwise have
remained safe from the flow.[62]

Barriers to divert lava flows. Serious consideration has been
given by the state and federal governments to building rock barriers
above Hilo to protect the city from lava flows. They would be very
expensive, as shown by expenditures for walls, built by bulldozers,
that failed near Kapoho during the 1960 eruption. However, the

Figure 6-12—Air view of the flank eruption of Mauna Loa Volcano, Hawaii, November 22, 1935, showing one of the main streams of the flow disappearing in a steaming fissure. Another stream sinking into an ancient crater caused the column of steam below the main vent. Snow-clad Mauna Loa caldera is in the background. (Photo by U.S. Navy.)

rock used there was chiefly highly vesicular and light in weight,
and the terrane too flat. Arguments for and against walls have been
published.[90, 107, 244]

HUALALAI

Hualalai Volcano is about 17 miles in diameter and is one of the
most symmetrical cones in the Hawaiian Islands. The mountain is
studded with about 120 cinder and spatter cones, and near the
summit it is pockmarked with craters. Some of the cones reach a
height of 200 feet. One pit crater near the summit has an incomplete
veneer of lava less than 2 feet thick, caused by a lava pool draining
away while still very fluid (Fig. 6-13). The volcano is built over a
northwest rift, a southeast rift, and a poorly developed northeast
rift.

Its rocks have been divided into historic, prehistoric, and
Waawaa members of the Hualalai volcanic series. The Hualalai
volcanic series comprise all the rocks in the mountain. The Waawaa
volcanics comprise Puu Waawaa, a trachyte cone, and the lava flow
from it. The rocks of the Hualalai volcanic series are chiefly olivine
basalts with an incomplete veneer of olivine-rich basalts carrying
augite phenocrysts. Several flows of alkalic basalt have been found.
The lavas of the Hualalai volcanic series definitely interfinger with
the lavas of the Kau series of Mauna Loa on the southern and eastern slopes. The entire mountain appears to have been built in the
Pleistocene.

Collapse has shattered about half a square mile around an unnamed cone near the saddle between Hualalai and Mauna Loa.
Such collapse is unusual except at Kilauea. Much of the coffee in
the Kona District is grown on the ½ to 2 feet of ash soil derived from

Figure 6-13—Sketch of pit crater, with remnants of lava veneer on its walls, in the southeast rift zone of Hualalai Volcano, Hawaii. (After Stearns
and Macdonald, 1946.)

the cones on Hualalai. The ash forms the Kona tuff formation.[240] Evidence of only one paroxysmal explosion has been found on the entire mountain.

Puu Waawaa, on the north slope, is a cone 1,220 feet high composed of trachyte pumice containing a noticeable amount of obsidian. The writer interprets as a lava flow a ridge of trachyte several hundred feet thick that extends northwest from the cone (Fig. 6-14). This trachyte ridge was first noted by Cross.[32] It is overrun in places by later aa flows from Hualalai, a fact that indicates basalt sometimes follows trachyte in the closing phase of a Hawaiian volcano.

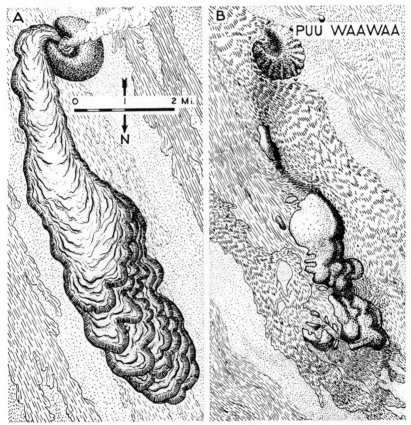

Figure 6-14—Two stages in the geologic history of Puu Waawaa, Hawaii. A. Massive trachyte lava flow overlying thin basalt flows at close of the eruption. B. Present stage showing cone eroded and lava flow weathered and nearly buried by later basalt flows.

The only other soda trachytes are on Kohala Mountain, but Puu
Waawaa does not lie on the extension of any Kohala rift; hence, it is
likely the result of local differentiation in the Hualalai hearth. Its
radiogenic age is 0.4 m.y.[254] The cone is quarried extensively for
lightweight aggregate.

Historic eruption.   Hualalai was last active in 1800–1801, when
voluminous lava flows poured from a long crack on the northwest
flank. Known as the Kaupulehu flow, it is remarkable for its cognate
inclusions. The lava contains thousands of tons of angular and subangular dunite and gabbro xenoliths, mostly less than a foot in
diameter. Feldspar crystals, some of gem quality, and some reaching three-quarters of an inch in length, also occur. Near the source
vent, small xenoliths coated with lava of 1801 are piled up like
cobbles. These dunite xenoliths look like green candies dipped in
chocolate. Before eruption, apparently, the magma stoped away a
large precooled mass of dunite and gabbro. The xenoliths have
been the subject of intensive study because they shed light on the
character of rocks at depth.[178] Also remarkable are the lava stalactites on the sides of the channels in the flow.

A line of spatter cones below the main belt road in the same area
marks the source of a black flow known as the Huehue flow, which,
according to the Hawaiians, also erupted in 1801.[89] The olivine
basalt contains pieces of partly charred wood in its tree molds, as
does the Kaupulehu flow.

Gravimetric measurements fail to show a circular high under
Hualalai, but show an elongated high stretching toward Mauna Loa
from a point 3 miles south of the summit.[93] All the other volcanoes
have a circular high just south of their summits, indicating dense
rock bodies at shallow depth. The stations are few and far between
on the south slope of Hualalai, and further work may change the
shape of the gravity map contours. Aeromagnetic surveys indicate
that the main magma reservoir is under Hualalai (Fig. 13-1).

Kohala Mountain

Kohala Volcano was built over a northwest rift, a southeast rift,
and a poorly developed southwest rift. Along the northwest and
southeast rifts, numerous cinder cones are clustered. The mountain
is 21 miles long and 13 miles wide. Much of the south slope is
buried under lava flows from Mauna Kea. Deep gorges are incised
in the east slope. Faults are responsible for the direction of the

headwaters of Waipio and Honokane streams. A sphagnum swamp lies to the east of the summit. A traverse revealed numerous small, deep, narrow, collapsed pits along fault cracks and holes in aa flows, hidden in the swamp and in the adjacent jungle.

Streams have barely cut into the west slope of the mountain, whereas the canyons on the east side are more than 2,000 feet deep and the sheerness of their walls is unsurpassed anywhere in the islands (Fig. 3-5). Near the coast, bedrock floors of the gorges are drowned to a depth of nearly 1,000 feet, as noted long ago by Branner.[22] Remnants of gravel terraces rise in these canyons to 1,100 feet and indicate an even greater submergence succeeded by a later partial emergence. The west or lee coast is not cliffed and, except near the several large cones, has only a thin soil covering, in contrast to the east coast, where sea cliffs are 1,200 feet high and soil as much as 20 feet deep. This great difference is not due solely to dissimilar conditions of rainfall and roughness of seas on windward and leeward sides of the volcano, but is attributable at least in part to difference in age. The lava beds on the west slope are younger than most of those on the east. Four stages in the geologic development of Waipio and Waimanu valleys are shown in Figure 6-15.

The rocks of Kohala Mountain are divided into two volcanic series. The older Pololu series is composed of thin-bedded tholeiitic basalts with alkalic basalts at the top in most places. The younger Hawi series is composed chiefly of mugearites, a few soda trachytes, and one Hawaiite flow. Some of the more viscous flows formed bulbous domes, but bulky cinder cones lie on the fissure vents of most of the flows. The Hawi lavas lie mostly at the top of the mountain and are usually from 1 to 3 flows thick. A thin red soil bed from a few inches to several feet thick separates the Hawi from the underlying Pololu lavas, except in the wet windward slope, where the lavas are separated by an erosional unconformity.[199] A Hawi flow several hundred feet thick spilled into Pololu Valley (Fig. 6-16). The later Hawi lavas interfinger south of Waipio Valley with the lavas of the Hamakua series from Mauna Kea. A late flow in the Hamakua series spilled into the southeast side of Waipio Valley.

A graben half a mile wide and 3 miles long crosses the summit of Kohala Mountain. It is bordered by faults arranged *en échelon* (Fig. 6-17). The faults cut both volcanic series. They appear to outline a

Stage 1. Waipio Stream flows along the margin of
the heavy alkalic basalts of the Hawi volcanic
series. The rest of the block consists of older,
easily eroded, thin-bedded basalts of the
Pololu volcanic series. The locations of
the upper tributaries of Waipio and
Waimanu streams are determined
partly by fault scarps. The line AA'
is the north boundary of a dike
swarm.

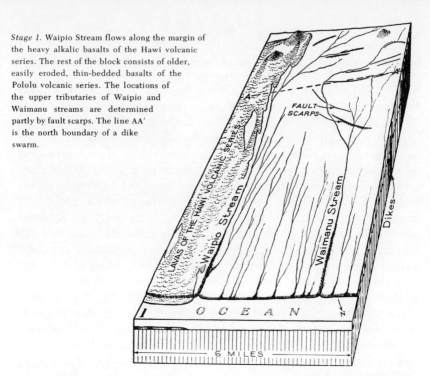

Stage 2. Waipio and Waimanu streams have cut
deep canyons in the carapace of the mountain.
Hiilawe, Waimanu, and Waihilau streams tap
water confined between a few stray dikes,
whereas the headwaters of Waipio Stream
have tapped water confined in the main
dike swarm that trends parallel to the
line AA'. The sea has cut high cliffs
along the shore. The spur on the
left side of Waipio Canyon, which
is armored by thick alkalic basalts, has resisted wave erosion better than the rest
of the block consisting
of basalt.

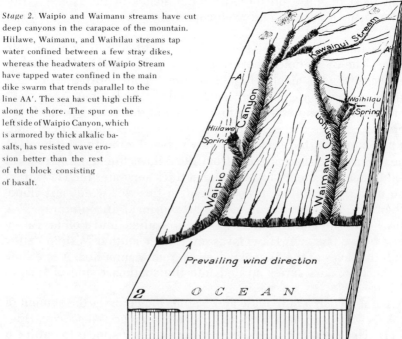

Figure 6-15—Four stages showing the development

Stage 3. The large volume of spring water tapped in the main dike swarm by Waipio Stream has caused its tributaries to cut headward faster, so that the ancestral Kawainui stream has been captured by Waipio Stream. A lava flow from Mauna Kea has spilled into Hiilawe cove and flowed down Waipio Valley. Others have spilled over the sea cliff left of Waipio Canyon, slowing down marine erosion in this sector. High cliffs have been cut by the sea on the weak basalts.

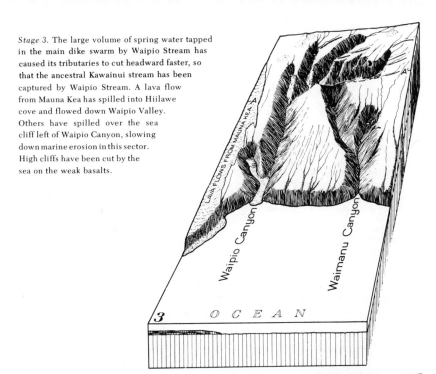

Stage 4. A submergence of the island by more than 1,200 feet has partly drowned the sea cliff and main canyons. Alluvium floors Waipio and Waimanu valleys. Landslides are filling the head of Waimanu Valley as a result of the decrease in flow from loss of more ground water to Waipio Stream.

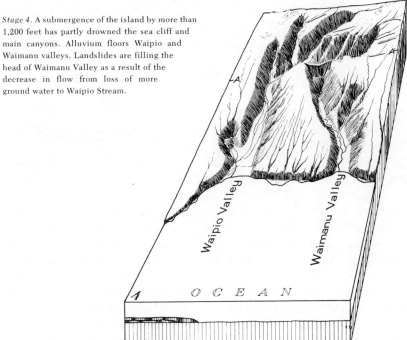

of Waipio and Waimanu valleys, Hawaii.

Figure 6-16—Sketch of Pololu Valley, Hawaii, showing late valley-filling flow. (After Stearns and Macdonald, 1946.)

caldera 2 miles wide and 3 miles long that was largely filled by the Hawi volcanic series. The Hawi lavas did not overtop the walls of the graben; hence, most of the late lavas flowed northwestward and southeastward before fanning over the slopes. This fault-controlled distribution left two large areas of Pololu lavas uncovered, one to the southwest and the other to the northeast of the summit graben.

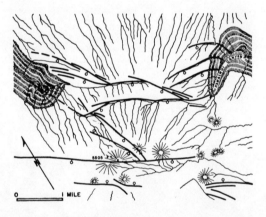

Figure 6-17—Map of the summit of Kohala Mountain showing how the drainage has been influenced by faulting. The downthrown side of the faults is indicated by small circles where the summit collapsed. (After Stearns and Macdonald, 1946.)

Two hundred and fifty dikes are exposed in the canyons in the windward slope. They range from a few inches to 40 feet in width, and average about two feet. The widest basalt dike is 15 feet. Three hornblende biotite soda trachyte dikes, 18, 30, and 40 feet wide respectively, are also exposed. An olivine basalt intrusive a mile long, possibly a stock, is exposed in the Kawainui Branch of Waipio Valley. A few feet of Pahala ash overlies the Hawi volcanic series on the southern slope. Vitric ash beds are common near the summit in this series but scarce in the periphery of the mountain and in the Pololu series. No lithic explosion breccias were found.

Kilauea Volcano

Kilauea Volcano nestles on the southeast slope of Mauna Loa and merges so imperceptibly with its giant neighbor that significant dimensions cannot be assigned. Lava flows from Mauna Loa pass over the slopes of Kilauea, and it is possible that some day a flow from Mauna Loa may enter the caldera of Kilauea.

The notable features of Kilauea are: the summit caldera 2.93 miles long and 1.95 miles wide; the active pit crater of Halemaumau, which for years at a time contains a lava lake (Fig. 3-1); the high echelon fault escarpments on the south coast; the chain of pit craters on the southeast rift zone; and the long cracks in the southwest rift zone.

A dense forest covers the windward slope of Kilauea, but the Kau Desert on the lee side is nearly devoid of vegetation. There, drifting sand dunes 10 to 20 feet high are formed largely of reworked ash.

It is believed that Kilauea lies on the main volcanic rift passing through Kohala and Mauna Kea, and originated when the great faults on the south side of Mauna Loa tapped the magma in this rift. The basement of Kilauea is probably composed of lava from Mauna Loa. Figure 6-18 is a diagram showing a hypothetical relation of these volcanoes to the interior of the earth.

Kilauea is an ash producer. At least 11 different ash eruptions can

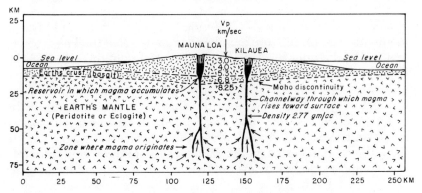

Figure 6-18—Schematic section of Mauna Loa and Kilauea volcanoes, island of Hawaii, based on seismic data. The magma rises through permanently open conduits from a source about 60 kilometers deep and collects in reservoirs of unknown dimensions beneath the calderas. Eruptions take place when the magma splits the mountain and forms a fissure eruption. Note the relatively slight depression of the Moho discontinuity beneath the volcanoes. (Modified after Macdonald, 1961, and Eaton and Murata, 1960.)

be recognized in its surficial deposits,[224] and not all came from Halemaumau. Both phreatic and phreatomagmatic explosions occur. Heavy rainfall causes water to be confined at high level in the summit area by dikes and fault barriers.

Lava flows from Kilauea, except those that pool in depressions, range from a few inches to 15 feet in thickness, and average 8 feet. They vary in length from a few feet to several miles. Some lavas chilled so quickly when they came in contact with vegetation that molds of even delicate fern fronds and grass were formed. In the tube of the flow of 1920, lava stalactites 3 feet long and no thicker than a lead pencil are the result of secondary melting. Within historic time, some small flows have issued so quietly that they were not discovered until the lava had cooled, even though the staff of the Hawaiian Volcano Observatory is constantly watching for them.

Rocks of Kilauea. The rocks of Kilauea have been divided into two units: The oldest, the Hilina volcanic series, comprises the lava flows and pyroclastic rocks laid down by the volcano prior to the deposition of the Pahala ash. They crop out only in Hilina fault escarpments on the south slope of the volcano (Fig. 6-4), where they have an exposed thickness of 1,000 feet. They consist of thin-bedded flows and thin ash beds. The formation is capped with 30 feet of Pahala ash.

The Puna volcanic series covers most of Kilauea and was erupted in Holocene and latest Pleistocene time. The rocks are correlative with the Kau volcanic series on Mauna Loa, as both series overlie Pahala ash. The Puna series is divided into prehistoric and historic members. The prehistoric member has an exposed thickness of 410 feet in Uwekahuna Bluff, on the western edge of the caldera. The flows noticeably thicken at the base of fault scarps (Fig. 6-19). Lava tubes are numerous. Thurston lava tube in the National Park is most accessible (Fig. 3-15). Some of the flows were poured out of the caldera and others from flank fissures. About 60 cinder and spatter cones on the east rift and 40 along the southwest rift gave vent to flank flows (Fig. 6-4). Ten littoral cones exist where flows ran into the sea and exploded. These rootless cones are distinguished from vent cones by the presence of much dense black glass sand. Kalapana black beach sand consists of glass particles produced by lava exploding on contact with sea water. Pit craters are numerous. The thick ash deposits around the caldera belong to the Puna series (Fig. 6-20). The deposits contain numerous humus horizons and were derived chiefly from Kilauea caldera by phreatic and phreatomagmatic explosions.[174] A carbon[14] test (sample W-201) by the U.S.G.S., collected in the excavation for the Volcano House, indicates that hot basaltic pumice burned a fern forest there about 2,500 years ago. The mode of eruption of the prehistoric member did not differ from that of the historic member, although great diversity has been recorded in historic eruptions.

Historic eruptions of Kilauea. The eruptions of Kilauea Volcano from 1823 to 1983 are listed in Table 13. The duration of the flank eruptions was about 1 per cent of the time Kilauea has been active. Native legend records about 40 to 50 eruptions from about A.D. 140 to 1823.[77] The history of Kilauea caldera since 1823 has been essentially one of slow infilling, punctuated by occasional collapses (Fig. 6-21).

Types of eruptions. Eruptions of Kilauea fall naturally into four types: (1) flank flows; (2) lava lakes in the caldera; (3) short-lived eruptions in Halemaumau resembling flank flows; and (4) paroxysmal explosions.

Two major kinds of paroxysmal explosions have occurred in historic time, phreatomagmatic and phreatic. Phreatomagmatic explosions probably occurred in prehistoric time also. The phreatomagmatic explosions are characterized by violent blasts that hurl out

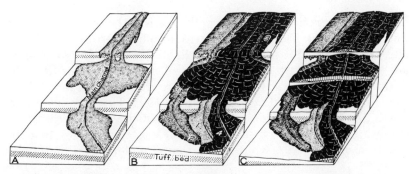

Figure 6-19—Diagram illustrating the relation of faulting to successive lava flows. A. Lava flow spills over two fault scarps, forming narrow cascades on the scarps and fans at their bases. The front block is tilted down to the right, which deflects the lava in that direction. B. Four lava flows have cascaded over the scarps. The inner scarp has been nearly buried. C. A new fault has split the middle block in two; the innermost fault has moved while the outermost fault has remained stationary. The two epochs of faulting are distinguished by the hanging plasters and cascades of lava on the innermost scarp and their absence on the newly formed scarp.

Figure 6-20—Bedded explosion deposits and crack in the southwest rift zone of Kilauea Volcano, Hawaii. (Photo by G. A. Macdonald.)

both blocks of solidified lava from the walls and clots of magma, as they did in 1790. This explosion was accompanied by a great collapse or engulfment of the caldera floor. The phreatic explosions are also violent blasts that hurl out wall rock, but differ from the phreatomagmatic explosions in that they are free from liquid lava. The only one recorded occurred in May 1924. Thick explosion deposits about Kilauea are mute testimony of the many unrecorded explosions in the late history of Kilauea. Legend states that the eruption of 1620 was explosive and more violent than the one in 1790.[78]

Flank flows issue from fissures in the east and southwest rift zones either above or below sea level. The flows of 1832, 1868, and 1959 issued from fault cracks in the subsiding block between Kilauea caldera and the pit crater of Kilauea Iki. They are questionable flank flows.

Lava lakes are formed when the Kilauean lava column rises into a pit crater in the floor of the caldera. Lava may be added to the

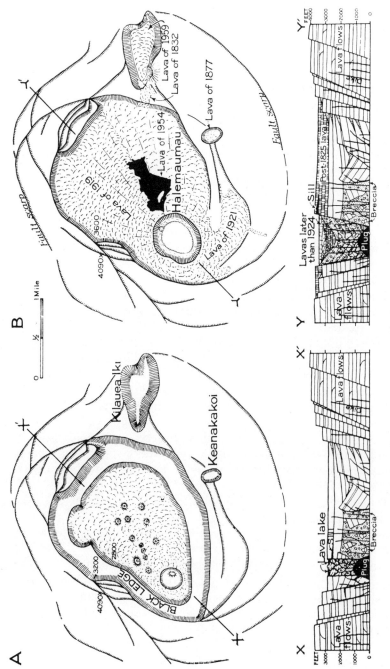

Figure 6-21—Maps and sections of Kilauea caldera (A) in 1825 (after Malden), and (B) in 1961. Note that the large central pit of 1825 has been entirely filled with new lava. The structure beneath the caldera is hypothetical. (Modified after Stearns and Macdonald, 1946.)

caldera floor, or it may rise and fall alternately within the lake or lakes for months or years without appreciable additions to the floor, much as a column of mercury rises and falls in a barometer. In 1921 the lava reached its high for the century and overflowed the caldera rim. The lake phase usually ends with rapid collapse of the floor of Halemaumau. The lava disappears underground and the vents become intakes.

The short-lived eruptions in Halemaumau since June 1924 are difficult to classify. They resemble flank flows in that the lava breaks out of cracks in Halemaumau with strong lava fountains, pours a flow into the pit, and in a few days or a few weeks is dead. These eruptions are like the 1832 and 1868 flows in Kilauea Iki Crater or the flank flow of 1964 in Makaopuhi Crater. However, because of the confinement of the flows within Halemaumau, a lava lake temporarily develops. Why the post-1924 eruptions have not re-established the lava lake is not apparent. It may be due to an insufficient supply of gas.

The lava lake. Throughout much of the nineteenth century and the first quarter of the twentieth, the most spectacular feature at Kilauea was the lava lake. Our detailed knowledge of its nature and activity is largely due to the work of Jaggar and his associates at the Hawaiian Volcano Observatory.

The principal lava lake of Kilauea occupied Halemaumau pit, which appears to mark the position of the principal conduit, although lakes have existed for shorter periods at other places on the caldera floor. When Halemaumau lake is active, magma is present in two distinct, although probably intergradational, physical states. The lake proper consists of fluid, freely flowing pahoehoe, called lake magma. This freely fluid portion of the lake is generally shallow, however, and rests on semisolid material resembling pasty aa, called bench magma.[87]

The feature that distinguishes the true lava lake from ordinary ponds of lava accumulated by overflow on the caldera floor or in other depressions, is the system of circulation that connects the lake magma with the magma column at depth. Lake magma rises through fissures and "source wells" in the bench magma, and descends again through sinkholes. Both the inlets and the outlets commonly persist for long periods.

Crusts form continuously on the lava lake, but movement generally tears them apart. The fragments are swept into the sinkholes or are overflowed at the edges and sink. Some are remelted; others become pasty and fuse in the lake bottom, becoming part of the bench magma (Plate 8).

Lava fountains a few inches to 30 feet high play on the surface of the lake. Some of them are nearly constant in position and activity and mark underlying source wells or sinkholes. Others are evanescent and shift frequently, playing briefly at places where a crust fragment has just sunk carrying down air. Burning gases liberated at some of the vents result in so-called "blowing cones." The only ejecta carried away from the lava lake by the wind are pumice, Pele's hair, and Pele's tears. At times both magmas may drop rapidly, as much as several hundred feet in one night. Such rapid sinkings are generally accompanied by collapse of the walls, and the island pinnacles crash down in great rock slides, revealing red-hot rock in their cores. Great quantities of dust-laden fume rise from the pit and generally obscure its floor.

Much has been published regarding the means by which high temperature and fluidity are maintained in the lava lake for long periods. Daly believed that a two-phase convection is the chief mechanism—gas-rich magma rising to the lake, losing its gases, and descending again as gas-poor and consequently denser magma.[33] Still another probable mechanism is heating by exothermic reactions between gases.[42] Temperature measurements at the lake appear to support the latter mechanism, although not to the exclusion of others. These measurements show the temperature to decrease from about 1,175° C. at a depth of 43 feet to about 860° C. at a depth of 3 feet, and then rise again to about 1,000° C. at the lake surface. Temperatures of about 1,120° C. were measured in lava fountains, and still higher temperatures, reaching 1,350° C., in cupolas over sinkholes and in the blasts of blowing cones, where the gases had free access to atmospheric oxygen.[86]

Lava rings commonly develop from lava fountains around the margin of a lava lake. At times they serve as dikes to hold the lake higher than the crater floor. The lava ring of 1892 held the lake 40 feet above the floor, and a lower one in 1894 is shown in Figure 3-9.

Unusual Eruptions of Kilauea

Explosions of 1790. The 1790 explosion, which was fatal to a whole company of Keoua's army marching across the Kau Desert, is recorded by Dibble.[43] Fossil footprints left in the soft ash in the desert are still visible (Fig. 6-22). The distribution of the blocks indicates that the focus of the explosions was north or northeast of the present Halemaumau. During the early phases, the explosions were magmatic; blocks of the ejected wall rock were coated with fresh lava. Halemaumau probably was enlarged greatly by the explosions and by engulfment. The explosions were apparently phreatomagmatic, caused by the influx of ground water. No paroxysmal explosions were recorded at Kilauea between 1790 and 1924.

Eruption of 1823. The eruption of 1823 occurred along a large crack in the southwest rift zone. The lava was very fluid and did not built spatter cones. It reached the sea so quickly that the Hawaiians were unable to move their canoes. In most places only a coating exists on the ground and a loose crust on top, indicating that the liquid lava between drained completely away even though there is evidence that the lava flow was originally 10 to 30 feet thick. Clots flung from the fissure landed like soft cowdungs and cooled so quickly that they molded the grass on their undersurfaces.

The walls of the fissure are lined with lava balls—fragments of wall rock and clots of new lava that fell back into the magma and became coated with lava. Small phreatic explosions occurred at two places along the source crack immediately after the lava was erupted. Small fragments of detrital limestone were ejected, indicating that the prehistoric flows extended the coast and buried coral beach rock. The lava ran seaward as a great flood, leaving crust shorelines as high as 34 feet above the present top of the flow on cinder cones that lay in its path.[193]

Eruption of 1840. The 1840 flow in the Puna District is the first flow on record to destroy a village. It buried the village of Nanawale on June 3, 1840. The flow is a picrite-basalt containing abundant olivine phenocrysts.[105] It built three littoral cones, ranging from 150 to 250 feet in height, rich in olivine sand. Wave action has completely destroyed one, and the highest point of the remaining two is only 78 feet above sea level.

Eruption of 1868. The 1868 eruption is the first one in historic time that occurred simultaneously with an eruption of Mauna Loa. Strong earthquake shocks did great damage that year. Subsidence of the Puna coast near Kaimu buried palm trees to a depth of 8 feet. A church at Kalapana was nearly buried by beach sand. Eruptions occurred in the southwest rift of Kilauea and in the wall of Kilauea

Figure 6-22—Fossil footprints of prehistoric Hawaiians in the ash on the southwest slope of Kilauea Volcano, Hawaii. (Photo by Hawaiian Volcano Observatory.)

Iki. The lava at the latter place cascaded to the bottom of the crater and covered the entire floor. The underside of some of this lava cooled so quickly that it molded fern leaves.[161] The lava in the southwest rift rose in a fissure 3 feet wide and 1½ miles long. It formed 9 small patches and four driblet spires, and, where it did not overflow, it congealed to form a dike, the top of which is visible.[224] During 1868, a submarine eruption occurred on the east rift zone off Cape Kumukahi.

Eruption of 1920. The lava flow of 1920 built the first secondary lava cone in historic time. The cone is called Maunaiki and covers the fissure over which it formed. A pahoehoe lava flow spread 6 miles seaward from it and in one place rare arborescent lava formed.[224] One unusual feature of this flow is that the lava lake in Halemaumau remained active throughout the period of the flank flow, although its surface fell as a result of the flank eruption. The lava was seen to pour southwestward from the lake through a tube in a dike, filling one of the rift-zone fissures. Thus we have evidence of horizontal flow through a vertical dike. A daily account of this eruption was published in the Bulletin of the Hawaiian Volcano Observatory for that period.

Explosions of 1924. During May 1924, the first explosions at Kilauea to be witnessed by Caucasians occurred, and the writer was fortunate enough to be present.[192] They resulted from ground water pouring into the hot vent of Kilauea immediately following a period of extensive collapse. Doubtless, this water came from storage between dikes rather than from the basal water table.

The height of the molten lava in Halemaumau had fluctuated rapidly for two months prior to its disappearance from view on February 21, 1924. On the date of its disappearance the bottom of the pit was 380 feet below the northeast rim station. Until April 29, Halemaumau continued to be a fuming empty pit, in practically the same condition as it was on February 21. On the night of April 22, pronounced cracking and faulting of the ground began at Kapoho, 30 miles east of Kilauea. It probably resulted from collapse accompanying the downward drainage of the magma in the northeast rift of Kilauea. On April 29, the bottom of Halemaumau began to drop, accompanied by avalanches from the walls of the pit. By the end of the first week in May the bottom of Halemaumau was more than 700 feet below the rim,[72] ample evidence that the lava column of Kilauea was rapidly sinking. By May 10, large clouds of dust began to rise from the pit, as avalanching went on unabated, and during the night of May 10–11 a small explosion occurred that threw out rocks. Small explosions occurred on May 12 and continued at frequent intervals with increasing violence until they reached a maximum on May 18. Some of the cauliflower explosion clouds that were caused by these explosions are estimated to have reached a height of more than 4 miles (Fig. 3-12). Explosions continued at more or less regular intervals with decreasing intensity until May 27, when the pit returned to a condition of steaming, avalanching, and dust-making similar to that of the period before May 11.

During May, 3,961 local earthquakes and 1 teleseism were registered at the observatory. Lightning and heavy downpours of rain frequently accompanied the explosions. No magmatic or essential ejecta, pumice, cinders, or Pele's hair were thrown out during the explosions. The projectiles consisted entirely of blocks of rock torn from the throat of Halemaumau or old talus debris. The fine material consisted entirely of pulverized rock: no vitric ash could be found even by microscopic examination. Halemaumau increased in diameter from 500 to 3,000 feet.

The explosions were low-temperature steam explosions, and because no magmatic ejecta accompanied them, they were phreatic explosions.

Only two persons have descended into Halemaumau and returned since 1924, when the crater was deepened by explosions. Two lovers jumped to their deaths in the pit on June 2, 1932. A Mr. Konishi was lowered in a basket suspended from a cable stretched across the crater to recover the bodies. In 1968, an Englishman, Ralph J. Emmerson, 37, made nine descents into Halemaumau under cover of fog in order to elude national park rangers.

Eruption of 1955.   One of the most voluminous eruptions of Kilauea broke out of a fissure on the east rift zone extending from an altitude of 1,310 feet down to 150 feet, on February 28, 1955. About 120,000,000 cubic yards of lava were extruded in the 88 days the eruption lasted. A chain of spatter cones was built along the fissure, erupting lava which passed through cane fields, covered paved roads, and tumbled over a cliff into the sea (Plates 1 and 2). The lava covered 6.1 square miles.

Eruption of 1959.   Kilauea Iki (little Kilauea), the pit crater, a mile across, near the summit and the scene of the 1868 eruption, again erupted on November 14, 1959 (Plate 1).

Many things were unusual about this eruption, which lasted until December 20, 1959 (Fig. 6-21). The seismograph at the observatory recorded 2,200 earthquakes on November 13 and 14. The lava erupted from a fissure half-way up the crater wall. The fire fountains, small at first, gradually grew larger. The activity soon built a pumice and spatter cone 150 feet high and covered an area for several miles to the south and southwest with pumice. Olivine crystals trailing long strands of Pele's hair drifted far to the south. On November 20 lava was being poured into the pit at a rate exceeding 1,000,000 cubic yards per hour. On November 21 the fountain suddenly died, but it started again on the 26th. Activity continued only 16 hours and then stopped abruptly. This activity was the first of 15 eruptive phases, each lasting only a few hours and each ending with the lava draining back into the vent with a spectacular whirlpool at the surface. On December 17, the lava fountain reached the height of 1,900 feet, the greatest ever recorded in Hawaii.[177] The rapid backflow of lava into the vent on December 19 lowered the surface of the lava lake about 20 feet. The total lava emplaced was about 51,000,000 cubic yards and the thickness 365 feet. Slow cooling after the eruption led to a shrinkage of 12 per cent, with slump scarps on the surface of the former lake. Estimates of maximum rates of lava out-pouring are given in the following table compared with other eruptions since 1940.

The temperature of the erupting lava ranged from 1120° to 1190° C., the highest temperature ever reported for erupting lava in Hawaii.[177] The silica content ranged from 46.3 to 49.5 per cent

TABLE 12
ESTIMATED MAXIMUM RATES OF LAVA EXTRUSION DURING RECENT ERUPTIONS OF HAWAIIAN VOLCANOES

Eruption	Volume (cubic yards per hour)
1940, Mauna Loa	2,600,000
1952, Kilauea	1,800,000
1955, Kilauea	800,000
1959, Kilauea	2,600,000
1960, Kilauea	650,000
1967, Kilauea	1,500,000

during the eruption. A mile from the vent the blanket of pumice was nearly three feet deep. During July, 1960, a core hole was drilled in the crust of the lava pool and penetrated the still liquid lava beneath. It welled up into the casing. Since then several more holes have been drilled to determine the rate of cooling. It is estimated that it will take 50 years for the lava lake to cool. The rate of crustal thickening for a 13-month period after the eruption ceased was 0.94 foot per month.

Eruption of 1960. The eruption began in the evening of January 13 in a sugar cane field northwest of the center of Kapoho village. A line of fountains half a mile long soon developed. Steam blasts from the ingress of brackish ground water showered the surrounding area with wet black ash containing abundant salt. The people had been evacuated to Pahoa village nearby, but Kapoho village was destroyed (Plate 8). On January 15, the lava flow entered the ocean in a front nearly 1,000 feet wide. Great clouds of steam rose from the water. The chilling of the lava front caused a dam that diverted the lava sideways. Observers in airplanes saw glowing lava about 25 feet underwater still not crusted over. By January 18, the main fountain had reached a height of about 800 feet, and lava was pouring out at the rate of 6,500,000 cubic yards per day. During this time dozers were mobilized and walls were built to try to stop and divert the lava. In some places the lava overtopped the walls, and in others it was intruded under the walls. An old cinder cone, Puu Kukii, was fissured, part of it uplifted, and a small thin lava flow issued on its side. It may have been either a secondary or primary vent. On February 10, a series of loud explosions lasting 3 minutes threw ash and cinder nearly 2,000 feet in the air, accompanied by much

Plate 7 —————▶

Above. Nuuanu Pali behind Kaneohe, Oahu, is fluted by stream
erosion and has a complex origin.
The low green hill behind the houses
is a cinder cone of the Honolulu volcanic series. *Photo by H. T. Stearns.*

Right. Iao Needle in Iao Valley,
Maui, is an erosion remnant in the
ancient caldera of the West Maui
Volcano. *Photo by Sawyer's, Inc.*

Left. Youthful cones and flows of the
Hana volcanic series march across
Haleakala Crater, Maui. The far rim
is seven miles away. *Photo by Sawyer's, Inc.*

Upper. A small fountain in the lava lake of Halemaumau Crater, Kilauea Volcano. *Photo by Pacific Film Corp.*

Lower. Night view showing fountains and cracks in the pahoehoe crust.

Upper. Tuff beds exposed along coastal highway at the foot of Koko Head Crater, Oahu. *Photo by H. T. Stearns.*

Lower. Remains of Kapoho Village and a 400-foot firefountain during the 1960 eruption of Kilauea Volcano. *Courtesy Lewis Cooksey.*

Below. Waimea Canyon, Kauai. The horizontal basalt beds in the distance solidified in an ancient caldera 12 miles across. The beds in the foreground are thin, steeply dipping basalts which made the former rim of the caldera. *Photo by Robert Wenkam.*

steam. During the next three days other explosions followed. This type of explosion, producing vitric ash, had not been witnessed before, although with abundant ground water it is surprising that larger explosions did not occur. Lack of large-scale collapse probably saved the area from devastating explosions. On February 18, a ball of burning gas rose from the crater followed by a billowing black cloud of ash, and the lava fountain resumed, shooting up 1,000 feet in the air. On February 19, wet black ash was deposited over the village area. On February 20, the eruption ceased. The olivine crystal content of the lava changed during the eruption. The cone built at the main vent was 3,300 feet long, 1,000 feet wide, and 360 feet high, indented by a row of seven craters. About 155,000,000 cubic yards of lava was erupted. About half a square mile of new land was built beyond the shoreline. The flow covered 2.7 square miles and in places had a depth of 50 feet. So much toxic fume drifted to Oahu during this eruption that plants were killed in the yard of the writer on the Schofield Plateau. For days, the sun was a dim sphere in the sky. (The preceding descriptions of the 1959 and 1960 eruptions were taken from Macdonald.)[111]

Eruptions of 1961. Lava erupted on February 24 in Halemaumau. This eruption was accompanied by fire fountains 100 feet high. Within three hours, the pool was 110 feet deep and activity began to slacken as lava started pouring down one of the vents. By mid-afternoon the eruption was over and about 30,000 of the 300,000 cubic yards of lava had drained away. The eruption resumed on March 3 and ended March 23 with the production of about 350,000 cubic yards of lava.

An eruption that began on July 10 had formed a lava lake 140 feet deep by July 12. A fire fountain 800 feet high built a pumice and spatter cone against the southwestern wall of Halemaumau. The eruption ended July 17 with a pool 210 feet deep and a volume of 17,300,000 cubic yards.

Earthquakes in the east rift zone in September and the collapse of the summit indicated that magma was moving into fissures east of the caldera. Early in the morning of September 23, lava broke out 12 miles east of Halemaumau and in three places 5 miles east of Napau Crater. Three explosions on March 23 indicated an eruption 15 miles from the summit. Fountains reached a height of 400 feet and lava poured into a nearby crack. The eruption ceased on March 24. Altogether, 13 small flows were erupted with a volume of only about 3,000,000 cubic yards, yet the sinking of the summit area indicated a movement of about 70,000,000 cubic yard of magma into the rift zone.

Eruption of 1962. An eruption began at 1:10 A.M. on December 7 in Aloi Crater, where fountains 40 feet high played along a fissure 500 feet long. Two hours later a pool containing 350,000 cubic yards had formed. Then the fountains died down and three-quarters of the lava drained down the vents. Soon lava was erupting on Kane Nui o Hamo cone and at two points farther east. By December 8, more small vents had opened near Aloi and Alae craters, but they soon ceased; by the evening of December 9 the activity was over. About 425,000 cubic yards was erupted, but only 155,000 cubic yards did not drain away. About 10,000,000 cubic yards of lava was transferred from the summit area into the east rift zone, causing the ground near Alae Crater to rise 2½ feet.[143]

Eruption of 1963. On August 21, lava fountains 30 feet high with a temperature of 1093° C broke out from a fissure crossing Alae Crater and flowed into the adjacent forest. Lava poured out at the rate of 150,000 cubic yards per hour and formed a lake 62 feet deep by August 22. Then lava started to drain down the vents and the surface of the pool dropped 12 feet; the eruption ceased the next day.[166]

Eruptions of 1965. Lava erupted on March 5 along a series of fissures extending from Makaopuhi Crater through Napau Crater for 8 miles. More than 20,000,000 cubic yards of lava was erupted in 8½ hours. Pools were formed in Makaopuhi and Napau craters, but soon much of the lava had drained back into the fissures. After 16 hours of quiet, activity was resumed on March 6, and during the next four days, 2 to 3 million cubic yards of lava was erupted along the rift in the 6 miles east of Makaopuhi Crater. Then, on March 10, a new surge of magma arrived and fountaining in the crater reached 200,000 cubic yards an hour. A lake 340 feet deep formed, containing about 9,000,000 cubic yards of lava. During the next four days, about 2,500,000 cubic yards of lava drained down the fissures; the lake dropped 50 feet and the eruption stopped.

On Christmas Eve, fountains broke out along a fissure for 2 miles eastward of Aloi Crater, and some lava poured into the crater. The eruption stopped in 6 hours, and the summit area began to collapse.

Eruption of 1967–1968. Lava broke out in Halemaumau on November 5, 1967, at 2:30 A.M. Fire fountains reaching 200 feet in height extruded lava at the rate of about 1,500,000 cubic yards an hour. By midnight a pool 100 feet deep had formed. The eruption stopped at 1:00 A.M. November 6, and lava poured back down the vents, lowering the lake 45 feet. Fountaining started again on November 9, and a leveed lake 30 feet above the surrounding floor was built. The eruption ceased on November 19, and the lake dropped 20 feet as lava drained back into the vents.

Lava fountains 100 feet high began again on November 21, and then 30 successive phases of fountaining, lake filling, and drainback occurred. During the 29th phase, on February 27, 1968, the entire floor was elevated, carrying the lake upward. Lava oozed out of cracks along the walls of Halemaumau. The eruption lasted a total of 261 days and produced about 110,000,000 cubic yards of lava. Halemaumau was filled to within 150 feet of the rim by the time the eruption stopped on July 13, 1968.

Lava erupted in the east rift zone in Hiiaka Crater on August 22, 1968 and migrated eastward 12.5 miles in the next four days, venting in six different places. Only 45,500 cubic yards remained at the surface when the eruption stopped.

Another eruption began on October 7, 1968, along a fissure 4 miles long northeast of Makaopuhi Crater, and stopped about October 22. A lake 16 feet deep formed in Napau Crater. About 9,000,000 cubic yards of lava remained on the surface, which was less than 25 per cent of the lava erupted.[81]

Eruptions of 1969–1974.

Between May 1969 and July 1974, Kilauea was virtually in continuous eruption, with most activity localized in the upper east-rift zone at Mauna Ulu, a new lava shield approximately 6 miles from Kilauea's summit. During this interval, Mauna Ulu activity and four short-lived eruptions elsewhere on Kilauea produced about 480,000,000 cu. yds. of lava. By late July 1974, activity at Mauna Ulu ceased. On July 19, lava erupted from fissures in the southern part of Kilauea's summit region, covered the floors of Keanakakoi and Lua Manu pit craters and the southeastern part of the caldera floor, and flooded adjacent areas. Vigorous activity lasted only about a day, but feeble activity continued until July 22. Two months of summit inflation followed; then a brief summit eruption occurred on September 19 within Halemaumau and on the nearby caldera floor. The new lava in Halemaumau reached a maximum depth of about 61 ft. and a final depth of 33 ft. after some drainback into the eruptive fissures.

Inflation of the summit resumed immediately; its center was located

approximately 1.86 miles south of Halemaumau. Early on the morning of
December 31, lava began fountaining from *en échelon* fissures located near
the inflation center. Fountains attained maximum heights of 325 ft. and fed
flows that travelled as far as 7.5 miles southwestward. Visible eruptive
activity lasted only 6 hours, but continuing earthquakes and ground defor-
mation for several days indicated that magma was draining from the summit region and being intruded into the southwest flank.[232,234]

The areas covered by late lava flows in the summit area are
shown in Figure 6-23, and in the Chain of Craters area in Figure
6-3. A plan and section of the newly formed Mauna Ulu and Alae
shield volcanoes are shown in Figure 6-24. Lava flows entered the
sea in 1969, 1970, 1971, 1972, and 1973. Some flows built fragmental lava deltas, as shown in Figure 6-25.

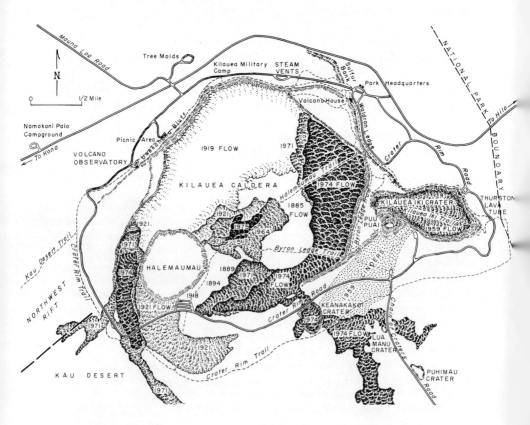

Figure 6-23—Map of the summit of Kilauea Volcano showing areas of recent
lava flows.

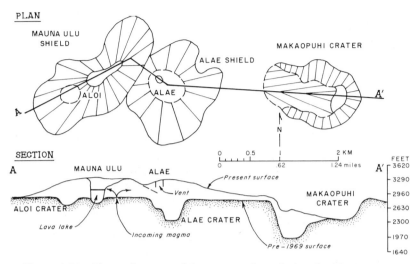

Figure 6-24—Plan and section of the Mauna Ulu and Alae shield volcanoes.
After Tilling *et al.*[233]

Eruption of 1975.   Lava fountains erupted from fissures on the
floor of Kilauea and in Halemaumua on November 25, and poured
out 332,000 cubic yards of lava, as shown in Figure 6-23. The eruption ceased that night.[233]

Eruption of 1977.   The eruption began on September 13 and
ended October 1. It broke out from a fissure 4.3 miles long in the
east rift zone above Kalapana. It built numerous spatter cones along
the fissure. The largest one, Puu Kia'i (Guardian Hill), is 115 feet
high. The longest flow came to within 1,300 feet of homes in
Kalapana. About 45,780,000 cubic yards of lava was extruded and
covered 3.09 square miles, according to records of the Hawaiian
Volcano Observatory.

Eruption of 1983. The eruption began at 12:31 A.M., January 3, in
Napau Crater. It reappeared in several locations during the next
nine-and-a-half hours, moving eastward to Puu Kamoamoa, before
halting at 10:02 A.M. It flared to the surface again at 2:25 P.M. a half
mile west of Kalua Crater. Fountaining reached 250 feet and continued intermittently throughout the year. One outbreak fountained
900 feet high and built a cinder cone. Two flows reached Royal
Gardens subdivision near Kalapana, destroying homes there.*

Drilling in lava lakes.   Drilling into the deep lava lakes in
Kilauea Iki, Alae, and Makaopuhi craters gave scientists an oppor-

---

*The vent Puu O erupted thirty times between January 3, 1983, and February 4, 1985. It built
a cone 400 feet high and fountained up to 1,500 feet.

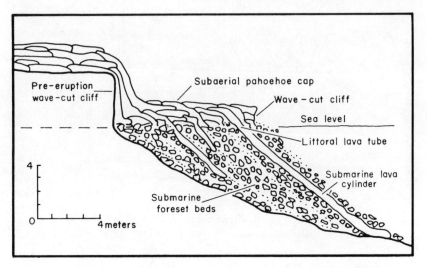

Figure 6-25—Cross-section of an advancing lava delta, diagrammatically showing subaerial pahoehoe cap that covers the mainly fragmental, poorly sorted, submarine foreset beds. (Modified from Moore and others, 1973, Fig. 4 by Peterson.)[167]

tunity to determine the rate of cooling and the forming of different minerals in the cooling lava. The crust thickens at a rate of about 3 feet per month. The maximum temperature beneath the crust is about 1140° C.[165]

Volume of historic lava flows.   The volume of historic flank flows, excluding submarine eruptions, is given in Table 13. The volume of lava added to the floor of the caldera from the 1823 collapse to April 1924 was about 2.6 billion cubic yards. The explosions of 1924, together with the accompanying and succeeding engulfment, caused a loss of about 264 million cubic yards.[9]

The total production of lava by Kilauea Volcano since the beginning of the 1823 eruption, including flank flows above sea level, has equaled about 5.5 billion cubic yards or about one cubic mile, which is more than that produced by Mauna Loa since 1832 (0.7 cubic miles). However, about 4 billion cubic yards of this total was confined to the caldera, which added little to the bulk of the mountain, whereas the quantity engulfed in Mokuaweoweo caldera is unknown. Mauna Loa probably produced as much as Kilauea, if this quantity were known. The rate of extrusion from the rift zones of Kilauea has greatly increased in the last 10 years.

Summary of Kilauea activity.   The following summarizes much of our knowledge about Kilauea: (1) A lava lake commonly persists for a period of 6 to 10 years. (2) Rapid rise and much activity in the lake are accompanied by tumescence in the mountain. This phase often is terminated by fissuring of the mountain and a flank flow lasting from less than a day to 7 months. (3) Most flank flows last less than a month. (4) Collapse of Halemaumau follows most flank flows, the lava generally, but not always, disappearing from sight through outlets in its bottom. (5) Heavy fuming accompanies the disappearance and reappearance of the lava in Halemaumau. (6) The lava disappears for periods ranging from 3 days to more than 10 years, and the duration of periods of dormancy is unpredictable. (7) The lava lake is usually shallow, about 50 feet in depth. (8) On a few occasions, low domical lava cones have been built, partly by over-flow, and partly by tumescence and bodily uplift of the plastic bench magma. (9) The temperature of the lava lake is hotter at the surface, where oxidation takes place, than at a depth of 3 feet. (10) The temperatures range from 860° C. to 1175° C. in a vertical sec-tion of the lake. (11) The hottest temperatures are at fountains and blowing cones, where the most gas is being discharged. (12) Northerly tilt at the Volcano Observatory accompanies a rising lava phase, and southerly tilt indicates a sinking lava phase. (13) Lava may rise into the pit quietly with little or no fountaining, or it may burst out in fountains 200 feet high. (14) The lava lake sometimes pulsates slowly, as much as a foot every 6 hours. (15) Some evi-dence exists of lunar tides with double amplitudes of an inch or so. (16) Kilauea has paroxysmal phreatic explosions at rare intervals, induced by ground water percolating into the vent following rapid recession of the lava column. (17) Cycles may exist, but their dura-tion and causes are obscure. (18) The magma reaches the surface through narrow fissures, usually less than 3 feet wide, and some-times cascades into the pit from cracks high on the walls. (19) At times of magmatic subsidence, great quantities of broken rock fall into the vent. It forms a vent breccia filling a pipe, the lower end of which is probably being melted slowly and stoped where it is in contact with the magma chamber. (20) After the mountain is fis-sured, the lava may form a dike by lateral injection from the lava lake, and the lava may flow through the dike in a tube of its own making. (21) Sills and other irregular intrusive bodies are injected into the walls of Halemaumau. Similar lateral intrusions lower in

TABLE 13
ERUPTIONS OF KILAUEA VOLCANO[1]

Year	Date of outbreak	Duration (days)	Altitude (feet)	Location	Approximate repose period since last eruption (months)	Area (sq. miles)	Volume (cu. yards)
1750 (?)	.....	.....	1,700	East rift	.....	1.57	19,500,000
1790 (?)	.....	.....	1,100–750	East rift	.....	3.04	37,670,000
1790*	November (?)		......	Caldera	.....	No lava flow	No lava flow
1823	Feb.-July	Short	1,700–250	Southwest rift	.....	3.86*	15,000,000*
1832	Jan. 14	Short	3,650	East rim of caldera	.....	(?)	(?)
1840	May 30	26	3,100–750	East rift	.....	6.60*	281,000,000*
1868	April 2	Short	3,350	Kilauea Iki	.....	.07	(?)
1868	April 2 (?)	Short	2,550	Southwest rift	.....	.04	250,000
1877	May 4	1 (?)	3,500 (?)	Caldera wall	.....	.04	(?)
1877	May 21 (?)	.....	3,450 (?)	Keanakakoi	.....	.04	(?)
1884	Jan. 22*	1	−60 (?)	East rift	.....	(?)	(?)
1885	March	80 (?)	3,640 (?)	Caldera	14	(?)	(?)
1894	Mar. 21	6+	3,690	Caldera	108	(?)	(?)
1894	July 7	4 (?)	3,690	Caldera	3.5	(?)	(?)
1918	Feb. 23	14	3,700	Caldera	283	.04	250,000
1919	Feb. 7	294*	3,000	Southwest rift	11	1.60	34,500,000 (?)
1919	Dec. 21	221	3,000	Southwest rift	1	5.00	62,000,000
1921	Mar. 18	7	3,700	Caldera	7.5	.77	8,800,000
1922	May 28	2	2,650–2,400	Makaopuhi and Napau	14	.04	(?)
1923	Aug. 25 (?)	1	3,000	East rift	15	.20	100,000
1924*	May 10	17	......	Caldera	8	No lava	No lava
1924	July 19	11	2,365	Halemaumau	2.5	.02	320,000
1927	July 7	13	2,400	Halemaumau	35	.04	3,160,000*
1929	Feb. 20	2	2,500	Halemaumau	19	.06	1,920,000
1929	July 25	4	2,560	Halemaumau	5	.08	3,600,000
1930	Nov. 19	19	2,600	Halemaumau	15.5	.09	8,180,000
1931	Dec. 23	14	2,700	Halemaumau	12.5	.12	9,640,000
1934	Sept. 6	33	2,800	Halemaumau	44	.16	9,500,000

Year	Date		Elevation (ft)	Location			Volume (m³)
1952	June 27	136	2,870	Halemaumau	212.5	.23	64,000,000
1954	May 31	3	3,180	Halemaumau and caldera	18.5	.44	8,500,000
1955	Feb. 28	88	150–1,310	East rift	8.9	6.10	120,000,000
1959	Nov. 14	36	3,500	Kilauea Iki	53.5	.24	51,000,000
1960	Jan. 13	36	100	East rift	0.8	4.1	155,000,000
1961	Feb. 24	1	3,100	Halemaumau	12	....	30,000
1961	Mar. 3	22	3,100	Halemaumau	0.2	....	350,000
1961	July 10	7	3,110	Halemaumau	3.5	.16	16,000,000
1961	Sept. 22	3	2,600	East rift	2.2	.02	1,860,000
1962	Dec. 7	2	3,150	East rift	14.2	.03	155,000
1963	Aug. 21	3	3,040	East rift	8.5	.10	830,000
1963	Oct. 5	2	2,800	East rift	1.5	1.25	9,070,000
1965	Mar. 5	10	2,600	East rift	17.0	3.00	23,000,000
1965	Dec. 24	<1	3,150–3,000	East rift	9.5	.23	1,160,000
1967	Nov. 5	251	3,150	Halemaumau	23.3	.25	110,000,000
1968	Aug. 22	5	2,900–1,900	East rift	1.3	.01	[10]500,000
1968	Oct. 7	15	3,000–2,400	East rift	1.3	.8	9,000,000
1969	Feb. 22	6	3,100–2,900	East rift	4.0	2.3	22,000,000
1969	May 24	875	3,150	East rift	2.0	19.3	240,500,000
1971	Aug. 14	<1	3,660–3,600	Caldera	[2]10	.8	12,400,000
1971	Sept. 24	5	3,740–2,730	Caldera and Southwest rift	0	1.5	10,500,000
1972	Feb. 4	455	3,150	East rift	4	13.5	162,500,000
1973	May 5	<1	3,340–3,250	East rift	0	.1	1,600,000
1973	May 7	187	3,340–3,250	East rift	0	.1	2,600,000
1973	Nov. 10	30	3,250–2,900	East rift	0	.4	3,700,000
1973	Dec. 12	222	3,150	East rift	1	3.1	39,300,000
1974	July 19	3	3,600–3,520	Caldera and East rift	0	1.2	13,000,000
1974	Sept. 19	<1	3,680	Caldera	2	.4	14,000,000
1974	Dec. 31	<1	3,600	Caldera	3	2.9	14,300,000
1975	Nov.	<1	3,600	Caldera	11	.01	332,000
1977	Sept.	17	2,000	East rift	22	3.09	45,780,000
1979	Nov. 16	2	3,280	East rift	26	.10	785,000
1982	April 30	2	3,620	Caldera	29	.11	650,000
1982	Sept. 28	1	3,620	Caldera	5	.27	4,500,000
1983	Jan. 3	100	2,600	East rift	3	5.0	180,000,000
						Total	1,785,307,000

[1]Asterisks indicate footnote explanations given in reference 9. Data from 1965 to 1983 supplied by Hawaiian Volcano Observatory.

the mountain or submarine flank flows may account for most if not all of the unexplained abrupt subsidences of the lava lake. (22) The lava lake may fall as much as 600 feet in a few hours. (23) The lava lake surface may lie from 400 to 1,500 feet below the highest point of the rim of the caldera. (24) Lava may break out several hundred feet above the lake on the adjacent caldera rim while the lake is full of lava. (25) Masses of aa and partly remelted crusts commonly form islands that rise and fall, usually at a slower rate than the lake surface. (26) Most of the lava in the lake is pahoehoe. (27) The Kilauea caldera is the result of collapse due to stoping and melting of its underpinning and to explosions. (28) The pyroclastic deposits from the lake phase consist of Pele's hair, Pele's tears, and very cellular pumice, which form a thin cover of vitric ash to the leeward (southwest) side of the caldera. (29) The pyroclastic deposits of the paroxysmal phreatomagmatic explosions consist of essential bombs and lapilli, fragments of wall rock ranging from tiny pellets to 10-ton blocks, and vitric and lithic ash. (30) The phreatic explosions produce blocks and dust of solidified wall rock. (31) Fragments of partly crystallized hot intrusive bodies were ejected in 1924, the uncrystallized portion apparently congealing quickly into blebs of glass. (32) Earthquakes are more abundant during a collapsing phase than during an erupting phase. (33) Flank eruptions have been followed by phreatic and phreatomagmatic explosions. (34) The lava lake sometimes shows a tendency to sink when an eruption of Mauna Loa ceases. This is thought to be a response to local earth forces, not an indication of a connection between the magma chambers of the two volcanoes. (35) The geologic history, as determined from geologic mapping, indicates that the main bulk of Mauna Loa is older than Kilauea, and that the latter probably came into existence in the late Pleistocene.

STRUCTURE OF KILAUEA

Rift zones. Kilauea is an asymmetrical shield-shaped dome of stratified thin-bedded lavas, with thin intercalated ash beds making up a small part of the bulk. The dome is transected by two zones of dikes, identifiable on the surface by fissures (Fig. 6-20) and cone chains. Most of the fissures show no displacement parallel to the plane of the fissure. One zone trends southwest from the caldera into the Kau District; the other trends southeast for 4 miles and then turns N. 65° E. and extends to Cape Kumukahi (East Point) in the

Puna District. This change in trend is unusual for rift zones in Hawaiian volcanoes. The southwest rift lies parallel to, and about 2 miles south of, the Kaoiki fault system, along which the southern edge of Mauna Loa has been downthrown. It has been suggested that Kilauea originated at the intersection of the Kaoiki fault system with the Eastern Fundamental Fissure of the Hawaiian Archipelago, which passes through Mauna Kea.[224] The east rift zone of Kilauea may have been determined by an ancient line of faulting similar to the Kaoiki system.

Faults. The faults may be grouped into three large classes: (1) circular and curved concentric faults associated with pit craters and the caldera; (2) faults in and bordering the rift zones, along which the downthrow is generally on the side toward the rift; and (3) faults along the southern coast, many with large downthrow on the southern or coastal side. The faults, with few exceptions, are normal. Two are rotational. The faults are characterized by echelon patterns and often rise in steps. The faulting started in late Pleistocene time at the close of the laying down of the Hilina volcanic series and Pahala ash, and has continued to the present. Along the faults, the Hilina lavas and Pahala ash are displaced hundreds of feet, but the Puna lavas are displaced only tens of feet. The rocks of the Puna series are displaced by faults in many other places. Some faults moved as much as 6 feet in 1868. A graben, or fault trench, subsided 12 feet near Kapoho in 1924.[59] Cracking and movement along a series of fractures crossing the Chain of Craters Road near Pauahi Crater began in May 1938,[88] and are still occurring intermittently.

The average trend of the faults along the southern coast is slightly north of east (Fig. 6-9). Nearly all fault planes dip southward from 30 to 45 degrees. The aggregate displacement amounts to 1,500 feet in places. It is greatest due south of the caldera and dies out both eastward and westward. The greatest displacement is where the dome is the highest. Many cascades of late Puna lavas over earlier fault scarps have been displaced by subsequent movement (Fig. 6-19). The oldest scarps have been little eroded. Faults concealed by later lavas were inferred by the presence of abnormally steep slopes. The fact that less veneering has taken place in the region due south of the caldera indicates that a protective southern caldera rim existed during the extrusion of most of the Puna lavas.

Some of the faulting has resulted in the formation of grabens and horsts. Kalapana lies in a graben[23] and Puu Kapukapu is a typical horst. The small graben just north of Kapoho was deepened as much as 12 feet in 1924.

The zone of normal faulting on the southern coast probably was caused by the instability of the dome and landsliding on a huge scale,[9,58] as Kilauea rises about 20,000 feet above the ocean floor to the south (Fig. 6-1). The faults appear to be superficial, and although they are tensional, no lava has erupted along them. They may flatten at depth and merge with the bedding planes, and never cause eruptions.[114]

Faults dipping seaward along the coast of Kilauea and Mauna Loa as a result of failure of the huge volcanic piles by landsliding have been termed "seaward slip faults."[191,224] The blocks slipping seaward at times leave lower blocks or grabens behind. It is likely that the Hilina-Kapukapu fault system will cause the fires of Kilauea to migrate to the intersection of the system with the southeast rift of Kilauea.[224] The Koae fault system bounds the seaward side of the southwest rift zone graben of Kilauea Volcano. Moore and Krivoy[143] have presented convincing evidence that the Koae system of faults intersecting the rift zone is the source of the magma in the southeast rift zone, and that the magma is moving from the summit vent to the lateral vents more or less horizontally along the faults[143] (Fig. 6-26). Seismic data indicate that the 1960 lava at Kapoho moved horizontally 30 miles from the summit reservoir to the surface vent and moved upward 1.8 miles, an average upslope of 3°. It is believed that the rift does not extend deeper than the old sea floor beneath the volcano.[143]

The rift-zone faults usually bound grabens. Because of repeated filling of the grabens by lavas and burial of the marginal faults, the total movement is not measurable. The displacement of blocks not yet buried seldom exceeds 25 feet and is mostly vertical or nearly so. The subsidence appears to be due to the spreading of the dome under the influence of gravity and dike injection, probably aided by the melting and absorption of the rock in the grabens by the magma.

Crustal structure. According to Ryall, et al., the earth's crust under Kilauea consists of 3 well-defined layers.[182] The uppermost varies from 1.2 to 2.6 km in thickness and is composed of vesicular, fractured basalt flows. The second layer, much less even in thickness, probably consists of olivine basalt. It is about 5 km thick at Hilo and Kalae (South Point) and elsewhere fills in the crustal section between the lavas at the top of the column and the denser rock

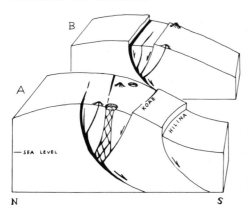

Figure 6-26—Generalized block diagrams of the east rift zone of Kilauea Volcano looking east. *A.* shows the general relations between eruptive fissures, cones, pit craters, Koae fault system, and Hilina fault system on the upper part of the rift zone near Aloi Crater. *B.* shows the relations of eruptive fissures, grabens, and cinder cones on the lower part of the rift zone near the east cape of the island. (After J. G. Moore and H. L. Krivoy, 1964.)

below. The third layer averages about 6 km in thickness and corresponds to the principal layer of the Pacific oceanic crust. They believe this layer to be faulted under the summit with an offset of the top of the layer of about 7 km. Depths to the Moho discontinuity are 11.0 km at Hilo and 12.5 km at Kalae, with a maximum thickness of about 14.5 km between Hilo and the summit.

Intrusive rocks in Kilauea.   Few intrusive rocks are exposed in Kilauea because of the small amount of dissection. A 10-inch dike trending N. 50° W. cuts half-way up the sea cliff of Puu Kapukapu, and a 6-inch dike striking N. 45° W. cuts an interstratified ash bed in Hilina Pali. Both dikes cut lavas of the Hilina volcanic series. Dikes striking parallel to the east rift zone are exposed in the southwestern wall of Makaopuhi Crater, and several dikes are exposed in the north wall of Kilauea caldera. They range from 1 to 3 feet in width and belong to the Puna volcanic series. Several historic dikes and intrusive bodies are exposed in the walls of Halemaumau. Sill-like bodies in the wall glowed when first exposed by explosions in 1924. The largest of these bodies, known as the Uwekahuna laccolith, originally intruded as a tholeiite differentiated into a picrite, gabbro, and a rock approaching quartz-basalt, as a result of the initial gravity settling of the heavy olivines and the final filter pressing of the residual liquid.[151]

Lava from a later lava lake in Makaopuhi Crater has filled the joint cracks in the lava fill from the top downward. Some of the rootless dikes are a foot wide.[137]

Mechanism of Kilauean eruptions.   Seismic work shows that magma originates at a depth of about 60 km (37 miles), and finds its way to the surface every few years through dikes only a few feet wide during the rapid building of the volcano, pausing at a shallow reservoir within the crust (Fig. 6-18). Tumescence or swelling, measured by tilt meters at the summit of Kilauea, accompanies the intrusion of the magma into the rift system. Measurable collapse or detumescence usually follows the extrusion of a flank flow. Magma moves from the reservoir through the rifts to a flank flow at a rate of about 3,000 feet per hour.

Swarms of local earthquakes with progressively higher epicenters, sometimes numbered in the thousands per day, indicate the rupturing of the edifice as the magma rises to the surface. These cease and harmonic tremor begins when the lava is erupting. When the eruption ceases, local earthquakes recur as the volcano collapses.

The reservoir is shown as a laccolith-like body by Macdonald,[109] after whom Figure 6-18 was partly constructed. However, the dike complexes in eroded cores of Hawaiian volcanoes have closely spaced dikes, resembling hundreds of vertical parallel concrete walls, which would prevent emplacement of a horizontal or laccolith-shaped intrusion.

The magma reservoir is more likely to be bounded by nearly vertical walls, except locally, where dikes have been removed by melting or stoping. A gravimetric study made by Woollard indicated that rock in the eroded Koolau caldera is too dense, at a depth of 4,000 feet below sea level, to be intrusive basalt.[253] Possibly olivines and pyroxenes have settled out during the long cooling period to form large bodies of olivine and clinopyroxene holocrystalline rocks. The occurrence of large quantities of xenoliths of these rocks in many late lava flows supports this hypothesis.[178]

Typical composition in volume per cent of the gases collected at Kilauea are: H_2O, 79.31 (62.50);[a] CO_2, 11.61 (20.20); SO_2, 6.48 (13.20); N_2, 1.29; H_2, 0.58 (1.90); CO, 0.37 (1.66); S_2, 0.24 (.42); Cl_2, 0.05; and A, 0.04. Copper chloride (CuCl) was detected in the volcanic flames of Kilauea in 1960.[150] They are all or in part elements reaching the surface of the earth for the first time. However, some of the H_2O is probably rainfall derived from ground water stored in the edifice between dikes and absorbed by the magma on its way to the surface.

*Values in parentheses are the quantities of primary magmatic gases from the best Kilauea samples computed by Naughton and Barnes.[254]

The temperature of the basalt magma as it reaches the surface ranges from 1,050° C. to 1,200° C.; the magma has a viscosity of 2 to 4×10^3 poises and a gas content ranging from 1 to 2 weight per cent at the beginning, to 0.5 per cent during the later stages. Below the level at which gas bubbles start to form in it, the magma has a specific gravity of about 2.73. Lavas continue to flow at temperatures far below the liquidus of similar dry melt in the laboratory—in some cases probably to less than 800° C.[112] Drill holes into the lava lakes formed in Kilauea Iki in 1959 and in Alae Crater in 1963 indicate that it takes six months to form a crust 19 feet thick. The isotherm at the base of the crust was 1067° C.[165]

Interconnection between Mauna Loa and Kilauea. Considerable literature exists on the subject of the interconnection of Kilauea and Mauna Loa volcanoes. It fascinates every geoscientist who works in the area to find lava erupting from the giant Mauna Loa at an altitude of 13,000 feet, while a lava lake bubbles away quietly at 3,100 feet altitude in Halemaumau. The time interval between a Kilauean flank flow and a Mauna Loa outbreak was less than 3 months for 3 flows and for the other flows ranged from 5 months to 9 years. The only coincidences of eruption were in 1868 and 1984. However, 1868 was the most intensive seismic year in Hawaii during the last century. Gravimetric data now available indicate that the vents have reservoirs which have formed sufficiently high in the crust to be independent of each other,[93] a fact supported additionally by chemical analyses[231] and by seismograph records.

The Hawaiian Volcano Observatory. No text would be complete without reference to the Hawaiian Volcano Observatory and to Dr. T. A. Jaggar, its founder. Dr. Jaggar, then Professor and Head of the Department of Geology of Massachusetts Institute of Technology, persuaded the trustees of the estates of Edward and Caroline Whitney of Boston to give $50,000 for research or teaching in geophysics. Some of the money was used by Dr. A. L. Day and E. S. Shepherd of the Geophysical Laboratory of the Carnegie Institution for special resistance thermometers and for designing a cableway across Halemaumau in order to measure the temperatures of the lava lake. Frank Perret and Shepherd reached Kilauea on July 2, 1911, and built an observation station on the rim of Halemaumau and succeeded in measuring a temperature of 1,000° C. in the lava lake. Jaggar reached Kilauea on January 17, 1912, and began his life's work. The observatory was very short of funds for many years and depended solely on local contributions. At times Jaggar served without salary. The U.S. Weather Bureau assumed operation of the observatory in 1919, and in 1924 it passed to the U.S. Geological Survey. Jaggar worked hard for the creation of Hawaii National Park, which for a few years took over the operation of the observatory.[106]

Jaggar's contributions to volcanology in Hawaii were the foundation for all subsequent work. He retired in 1940 and died on January 17, 1954, at the age of 82. The observatory is now equipped with the latest type of seismographs and other instruments for studying volcanic action, and has personnel trained in various fields of geoscience.

GEOLOGIC HISTORY OF HAWAII ISLAND

Much of the geologic history of the island is not decipherable because of the lack of deep dissection and because so much of the island lies below sea level. How long ago the first lava issued from a fissure on the ocean floor at the present site of Hawaii, and which of the great domes was born at that time, are unanswered questions. The permanence of rifts makes it likely, but not certain, that the island was built from the ocean floor by the coalescence of the five volcanoes we now see. Only tholeiitic basalt, the undifferentiated parent magma of the basaltic substratum, is exposed in the base of all five volcanoes. No indication exists of other buried volcanoes, although numerous submarine cones lie adjacent to Hawaii (Fig. 2-11). The stratigraphic units shown in Figure 6-4 can be dated only approximately, by means of eustatic shorelines, evidences of glaciation on Mauna Kea, and radiogenic methods. The history of the island as summarized below relates to the part above present sea level.

Early and middle Pleistocene time. Tholeiitic basalts were poured out rapidly to build shield-shaped islands over the Western Fundamental Fissure at the sites of Mauna Loa and Hualalai, and over the Eastern Fundamental Fissure at the sites of Mauna Kea and Kohala Mountain. Apparently, most of the Ninole, Hualalai, Pololu, and the lower part of the Hamakua volcanic series had been erupted by the end of the middle Pleistocene. A caldera caused chiefly by collapse had probably developed on Kohala Volcano, and faulting had produced scarps in the southeastern slope of Mauna Loa. Lava flows were erupted chiefly from fissures bordered by spatter ramparts or marked by chains of small cinder and spatter cones.

Coalescence of the several separate island domes served to form a single island. Cessation of volcanism on Kohala Volcano and probably on Mauna Loa, at least on its southeastern slope, took place. There was weathering and vigorous stream erosion of the northeastern slope of Kohala Volcano and the southeastern slope of Mauna Loa, and a long period of marine erosion, when a broad shelf was cut on Mauna Kea and Kohala. The shelf is now submerged 1,200 feet. Eruption of the Hamakua volcanic series on Mauna Kea continued. Kilauea was probably born at the intersection of the faults on the southeastern slope of Mauna Loa with the Eastern Fundamental Fissure, resulting in the eruption of the Hilina volcanic series. Eruption of the Haulalai volcanic series continued, and differentiation in the Kohala magma reservoir took place.

Canyons reached a depth of about 3,000 feet in Kohala Mountain and in Mauna Loa, and high sea cliffs were cut. Eruption of the Waawaa volcanics occurred on the north rift of Hualalai. Renewed volcanism on Kohala Volcano led to the outpouring of the Hawi volcanic series. The renewed volcanism on Mauna Loa laid down the Kahuku volcanic series. The Hawi and Kahuku lavas in places spilled into and nearly filled some of the canyons cut in the preceding repose period. There was a progressive decline in the rate of volcanism on Mauna Kea and possibly on Kilauea, as the upper parts of the Hamakua and Hilina volcanic series were laid down.

Submergence of the island an unknown amount, perhaps as much as 2,400 feet, caused alluviation of canyon mouths, especially those in Kohala Mountain.

Rapid re-emergence of the island took place, perhaps as much as 1,500 feet. Concurrent stream erosion removed the alluvium in small canyons but left high gravel terraces in the large canyons on Kohala Volcano. A short halt occurred, forming the Olowalu shoreline 250 feet above present sea level. There was continued volcanism on Mauna Loa, Mauna Kea, Kilauea, and Hualalai, and dying volcanism on Kohala Volcano. The re-emergence halted about 300 feet below present sea level. Marine erosion made high cliffs along shores exposed to strong wave action, and streams began to cut gulches into the wet northeastern slope of Mauna Kea.

Rapid resubmergence of 400 feet to the Kaena shoreline about 100 feet above present sea level was followed by renewed alluviation in the large canyons of Kohala Volcano. Kohala Volcano became extinct.

Late Pleistocene time. Accumulation of the Pahala ash occurred on all five volcanoes on slopes not being overflowed by lava. With an increase in the explosive activity of Mauna Kea and Kilauea, there was a decline in the volcanic activity of Hualalai and probably Mauna Loa. The earliest flows of the Kau and Puna volcanic series on Mauna Loa and Kilauea were laid down. Extrusion of the lower member of the Laupahoehoe volcanic series took place on Mauna Kea, some of the flows filling stream valleys and others spilling over sea cliffs. These volcanics probably also filled a caldera in the summit of Mauna Kea. About 250,000 years ago, a glacier formed on the summit of Mauna Kea. The ocean simultaneously receded to a shoreline about 350 feet below present sea level, then rose and cut benches and sea caves 25 feet above present sea level. It then receded again about 350 feet below present sea level. A glacier again formed on the top of Mauna Kea and the sea fell below present level. Eruptions occurred on Mauna Kea, melting the glacier and causing great floods.

Holocene time. During Holocene time, the last glacier on Mauna Kea melted. Weathering and erosion continued on Kohala Mountain. Mauna Loa and Kilauea were very active and continued to lay down rocks in the Kau and Puna volcanic series. Occasional phreatic and phreatomagmatic explosions occurred at Kilauea and Mauna Loa. Activity on Hualalai and Mauna Kea continued to wane. The upper member of the Laupahoehoe volcanic series was erupted on Mauna Kea. The sea rose to present level as the polar ice caps melted.

During historic time Mauna Kea has not erupted; Hualalai erupted in 1800–1801; Mauna Loa has poured out numerous flows; Kilauea exploded violently in 1790 and 1924, has had a lava lake part of the time in its summit crater, and has poured out many flank flows. Mauna Ulu, a new vent along the Chain of Craters Road, became more active than Halemaumau.

7

ISLAND OF MAUI

Maui from the Air

In the distant soft, blue, velvety haze, a huge dark mass that seems to be sailing eastward rises through a limitless sea of white downy clouds. Faint green tinges the eddy in its wake. Projecting through the cloud-foam on the north side of the eddy is a sharp black pinnacle. Thus appear the bulky dome of Haleakala and Puu Kukui, the pinnacled top of the dissected West Maui Volcano, from an airplane approaching Maui at an altitude of 5,000 feet. The three lower neighboring islands of Molokai, Lanai, and Kahoolawe are not yet visible, but on the far distant horizon like three pale-blue phantom mountains in a mirage rise the tops of the domes of Mauna Kea, Mauna Loa, and Hualalai on the island of Hawaii. As the plane rises higher and higher above the flat roof of the trade-wind clouds, their unbrokenness proves to be an optical illusion, for they are isolated cottony tufts with azure patches of sea between. The red-ochre surfaces of Lanai and West Molokai now become visible through the clouds.

Farther away, and extending for miles over the sea from Kahoolawe, is a red dust streamer of earthy filings in the sky, scraped from the surface of the island and borne seaward by the wind.

Still higher and eastward the plane flies and there, far below, the narrow steep concordant ridges of the West Maui Mountains lie like gaunt and weatherbeaten ribs on the projecting prow of a partly sunken old ship. To the east, and seeming to be a different island, is the roughly triangular mass of Mount Haleakala, which from this height appears very smooth except for great, deep, dark scars which

203

look as if four huge landslides had sloughed off the eastern side of the summit.

The plane circles downward and a green flat isthmus can be seen connecting Haleakala to the West Maui Mountains. To the north stretches pale-green water, separated from the sapphire-blue ocean by a white fringe where the surf breaks at the edge of the coral reef. Elsewhere, the white fringe hugs the shore. As the plane descends, more features become visible. A yawning depression bordered by steep rocky cliffs broken by two side notches indents the summit of Haleakala (Plate 7). Across this hole march smooth red and black cinder cones on a black carpet of stiff, stark lava. A black strip extends from the depression down the great Keanae Valley, one of the scars seen from higher up. Seaward the blackness changes to grayness, then to gray-green, and finally to dark-green as the lava flows become cloaked with jungle.

Another black strip stretches from the summit depression southward through Kaupo Valley and fans into a black and green polka dot pattern. There, scattered trees and patches of grass struggle valiantly to cover the nudity of the lava on the dry leeward slope. The other two great scars, now distinguishable as Kipahulu and Waihoi valleys, have the same form as the first two, but the late lava that covers their head walls and floors is completely masked with dense dark-green vegetation.

A belt of rocky brownish land spotted with green brush and yellow grass surrounds the high summit depression. This belt lies too high to catch the almost constant drizzle of the trade-wind rains. Below it lies a dark-green band of forest that extends unbroken to the sea on the north and east slopes, but pinches out longitudinally to the south and west into light yellow-green areas of pasture and darker fields of the egregious weed, pamakani, Hawaiian for "blown by the wind."

Below the pasture land on the broad west slope of Haleakala is a narrow strip of gray-green pineapple fields in checkerboard patterns. Below them, and extending across the Isthmus to the very base of the precipitous slopes of the West Maui Mountains, is a great expanse of a brighter green—fields of sugar cane. Glittering among them are numerous small circular mirrors—sunlight reflected on nearly round storage reservoirs. From the mirrors extends a vast network of narrow gleaming ribbons—the main irrigation ditches. Three larger ditches extending eastward to the jungle bring the thirsty Isthmus the flow of streams from the rainy wind-ward northeast slope.

Dusty, unirrigated, arid lands, being overgrown slowly by the keawe tree, stretch southward from the cane fields in a belt of spotted red and yellow-green. South of these arid lands and spreading eastward to Kaupo Valley are fields strewn with black flows of fresh and forbidding lava. They are arranged in pennants that stream from a line of cinder cones and shallow craters that march northeastward across the summit depression. These cones lie in the southwest and east rift zones of the volcano. The flows from these rifts take on the green clothing of the jungle at the east end of the island as they march down into the sea. "Here the mouths have been stopped with earth. A silky turf lies snug over the curves of the volcanoes, all is suavity in the scene. Each fissure in the crust is sutured up by this tender flax. The earth is smooth, the slopes are gentle; one forgets the travail that gave them birth. The turf effaces from the flanks of the hillocks the sombre sign of their origin."[183]

Scattered hills, the upper ones forested and the lower ones checkered with pineapple fields, crown the bulge of the older rift that extends northward from the summit.

The West Maui Mountains, with their deep, dark, foreboding canyons, are tightly belted by a road that skirts the sea, crowded there by the steep slopes behind. Indenting the summit area is a nearly circular green depression through which silvery streams of water find their way to a common outlet on the east side, where they run through a deep gorge into the sea. This circular valley head, the ancient caldera of the West Maui Volcano, is now cool and clothed with the forest verdure and is famous for its pinnacle, called Iao Needle (Plate 7).

On the summit and to the northward are swampy flats in which small pools of water gleam. These are peat swamps, so acid that they support only stemless plants, stunted trees, and silversword. They look like extensive landing fields awaiting a squadron of planes.

Sugar cane and pineapple fields cover the narrow coastal flats and the fans of gravel dropped hurriedly by great floods on their way to the sea. Some of the fields creep daringly up the interstream divides but are beaten back by the jungle or stopped abruptly by declivities that no animal or machine can cultivate.

The southeast slope of the greatly dissected dome is semiarid and

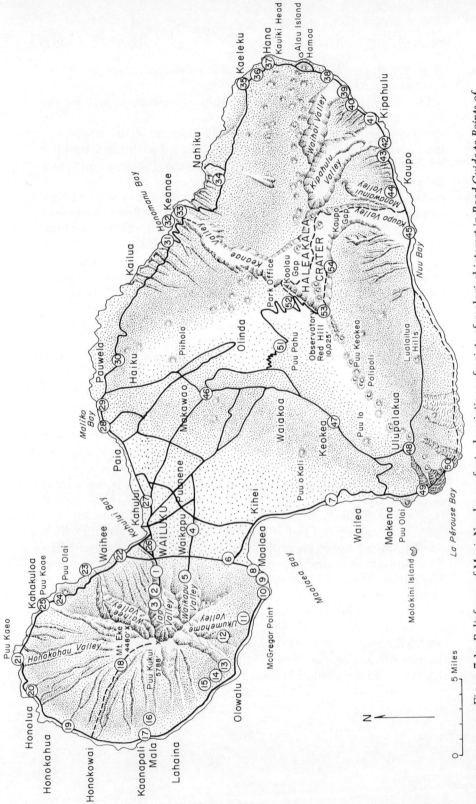

Figure 7-1—Relief map of Maui. Numbers refer to descriptions of points of geological interest in *Road Guide to Points of*

the layers of lava rock paralleling the steep slopes resemble layers in a cake that puffed too high in the middle, was baked to a crisp, and then cracked radially. Capping the ridges like a white frosting are the later silica-rich lavas, which weather light gray in contrast to the darker, underlying basaltic lavas. Interstratified with the darker layers are yellowish thin ones of weathered fire-fountain ash resembling cream filling in the cake. Narrow dark dikes cut across all layers.

One realizes at this height that glistening streams pour forth, some small, some large, from nearly all the canyons in the West Maui Mountains, but, on the great expanse of Haleakala, the sparkle of running water is visible in very few places, and those are near the coast. In spite of its great stretches of rain forest, the surface of Haleakala is covered with lava flows still sufficiently young to be very porous. Much of the vast quantities of rain, amounting in some places to 500 inches a year, sinks without difficulty.

Descending still farther, groups of buildings with their clumps of scarlet bougainvillea and red and green roofs mark the sites of camps on pineapple and sugar plantations. Clustered around the harbor on the north side of the Isthmus are the buildings and wharfs of Kahului, and a short distance to the west at the foot of the West Maui Mountains lies Wailuku. Like a narrow ribbon waving in the air, a solitary road can be seen winding in and out of the ravines along the north and east slopes near the coast, and connecting the lonely but charming village of Hana on the east tip of the island with the main settlement on the Isthmus. Roads avoid the barren lands, the jungle, the lava fields, and the sands. They all lead to the smooth land where man has made water abundant.

The plane lands amid the sugar cane on the Isthmus. Small sheds housing wells from which pipes discharge great quantities of irrigation water are seen here and there. The cool air of the clouds is gone. The persistent warm humid trade winds of the tropics meet the passenger as he disembarks. A broad stubby rainbow brilliantly colors an oncoming squall. Then the rain falls softly.

LOCATION, GEOLOGY, AND GEOLOGIC HISTORY

Maui, the second largest island, is 48 miles long, 26 miles wide, and covers 728 square miles (Fig. 7-1). The principal towns are Wailuku, Kahalui, and Lahaina. Haleakala (house of the sun), forming East Maui, is 10,025 feet above sea level, and Puu Kukui on

West Maui is 5,788 feet high. Sugar, pineapple, and cattle are the principal products, but the tourist business is growing rapidly.

Like Oahu, Maui is composed of two volcanic mountains. East Maui, or Haleakala Volcano, famed for its gigantic summit depression of unusual shape, is 10,025 feet high and 33 miles across (Plate 9). West Maui, 5,788 feet high and 18 miles across, is distinguished for the Needle, a rock pinnacle in the spectacular Iao Valley. The stratigraphic rock units on the island are given in Table 14 and their distribution is shown in Figure 7-2. Eight stages in the geologic history of Maui are shown in Plates 9 to 12.

West Maui. The West Maui Mountains are incised by deep amphitheater-headed valleys (Fig. 7-3), and on the east are overlapped by lava flows from Haleakala that have built a saddle known as the Isthmus. Iao Valley is an old caldera tapped by the Wailuku River and enlarged by erosion. Vent breccia at the head of the adjacent Waikapu Canyon indicates that this stream also tapped the caldera or an adjoining crater. Although rift zones are known (Fig. 7-4), this volcano approaches the "central type," in contrast to the

TABLE 14

STRATIGRAPHIC ROCK UNITS ON THE ISLAND OF MAUI

Major geologic unit	Major rock units				
	East Maui	West Maui			
Historic volcanic rocks	Volcanics erupted in 1790(?) near Makena[a]				
Holocene sediments	Unconsolidated deposits	Unconsolidated deposits			
Pleistocene sediments	Calcareous dunes Consolidated earthy deposits Kaupo mudflow	Calcareous dunes Consolidated earthy deposits			
Pleistocene and Holocene volcanic rocks	Hana volcanic series (includes Kipahulu member in Kipahulu Valley)	Lahaina volcanic series			
	Great erosional unconformity				
Pleistocene volcanic rocks	Kula volcanic series	Honolua volcanic series			
	Honomanu volcanic series	Wailuku volcanic series			

[a] Formerly thought to be 1750(?).

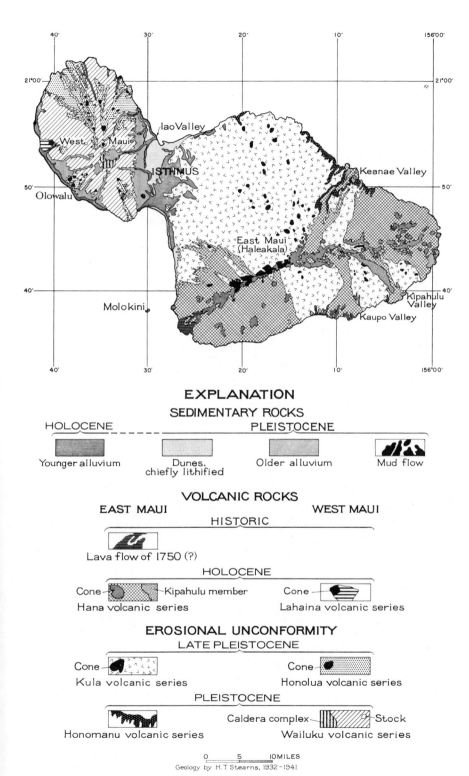

EXPLANATION

SEDIMENTARY ROCKS

HOLOCENE — — — — — — — — — — PLEISTOCENE

Younger alluvium

Dunes,
chiefly lithified

Older alluvium

Mud flow

VOLCANIC ROCKS

EAST MAUI   WEST MAUI

HISTORIC

Lava flow of 1750 (?)

HOLOCENE

Cone — Kipahulu member
Hana volcanic series

Cone
Lahaina volcanic series

EROSIONAL UNCONFORMITY

LATE PLEISTOCENE

Cone —
Kula volcanic series

Cone —
Honolua volcanic series

PLEISTOCENE

Honomanu volcanic series

Caldera complex — Stock
Wailuku volcanic series

0   5   10 MILES
Geology by H.T. Stearns, 1932-1941

Figure 7-2—Geologic map of the island of Maui. Faults and dikes omitted.

"fissure type," because dikes radiate in all directions from the ancient caldera, almost all the lava beds are steep, and many were poured from the central vent. Single basaltic dikes as much as 24 feet across, the widest basaltic dikes yet found in the islands, crop out on West Maui. Typically, the basalt is thin-bedded aa and pahoehoe, erupted chiefly through narrow cracks so that only a few cinder cones were produced. Toward the close of the basaltic eruptions, violent explosions are indicated by interstratified beds of lithic tuff and agglomerate containing large blocks.

Extrusion of the basalts, which constitute the mass of the mountain, was followed by a rest period during which a few inches to several feet of soil formed. These basaltic volcanics form the Wailuku volcanic series. Then alkalic lavas and stiff trachyte from fissures and local vents almost completely veneered the dome (Fig. 7-2). These rocks form the Honolua volcanic series. The light color produced by the weathering of the trachyte, in contrast with the darker product from the decomposition of basalt, gives the mountain the appearance of a brown cake partly covered with white frosting. Trachyte cones are prominent, and many of them are bulbous domes (Fig. 3-11). The presence of soils 20 feet or more thick indicates that the volcano probably became extinct in middle Pleistocene time.

Pit crater fills, some containing lake sediments (Fig. 7-5) and numerous faults are exposed in the deep canyon behind Lahaina. A caldera complex is exposed in Iao and Waikapu valleys, and 762 dikes were mapped but thousands more exist. Fewer than 100 of these dikes were more than 3 feet in width and only 27 exceeded 6 feet in width, indicating that highly fluid lava reached the surface through narrow fissures, as on Kilauea Volcano today. More large intrusive plugs are exposed in West Maui than in any other Hawaiian volcano.

During the erosion cycle, when the great canyons were carved, extensive fanglomerates were laid down along the east side of the mountain and smaller ones along part of the leeward coast. Some of these deposits are probably marine; in the later Pleistocene time, the island passed through a series of submergences and emergences similar to those of Oahu, as shown by the presence of fossiliferous conglomerates up to an altitude of 250 feet near Olowalu, and by the loss of soil through marine erosion at much higher elevations.[195] Near the southern coast, a few flows and cones

Figure 7-3—Air view of Lahaina and the deep canyons incising the ancient West Maui Volcano. The small reservoir in the center lies in the crater of Laina cone, the site of one of the latest eruptions. Note how this cone and the larger one upslope to the right divert the streams from their normal courses. (Photo by R. M. Towill Corp.)

of olivine-rich basalt and nepheline basanite were erupted in late Pleistocene time and rest upon, and in places are interstratified with, the fanglomerates. These rocks form the Lahaina volcanic series. Explosions in Iao caldera spread tephra over the adjacent slopes. Test borings by the writer north of Wailuku in 1975 indicate a widespread mudflow correlative with the Lahaina volcanic series, and one lava flow interbedded with the older alluvium.[221]

East Maui or Haleakala. The summit depression of East Maui or Haleakala Volcano is 7½ miles long and 2½ miles wide, and its floor is covered with bare flows and large cinder cones (Plate 7). The flanks of the mountain are covered with flows, some of which are black and bare. One flow was erupted as recently as 1790(?), apparently between the visits of La Pérouse in 1786 and Vancouver in 1793.[155] The volcano was built over three rift zones (Fig. 7-4), and is unlike West Maui because these rifts are studded with large cinder cones. Most of the lava flows, except those on the Isthmus, dip about 12°. In many places, three series of lavas can be distinguished. The lower units, the Honomanu volcanic series, consists of thin-bedded, typical tholeiitic basaltic pahoehoe and aa. Overlying this unit conformably is the Kula volcanic series, composed chiefly of thicker alkalic aa flows, which issued in a more viscous state and which contain many interstratified, thin ash-soil layers. Because many of the large cinder cones were built during the Kula epoch, ash beds are more numerous than in the lower underlying Honomanu basalts. Some olivine basalts and picrite basalts occur in the Kula series.

Evidence exists that the south slope of Haleakala has been shortened in relation to the other slopes by seaward slip faults, probably

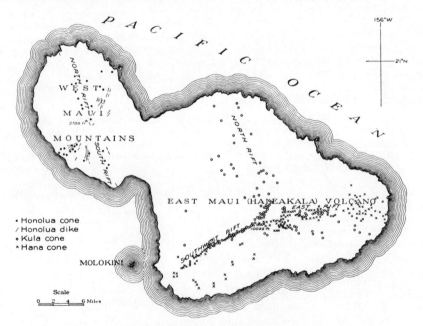

Figure 7-4—Map of Maui showing vents of the Hana, Kula, and Honolua volcanic series. (After Stearns and Macdonald, 1942.)

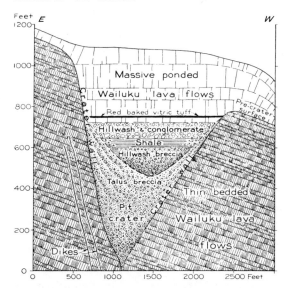

Figure 7-5—Section of pit crater in Kanaha Valley near Lahaina, West Maui. (After Stearns and Macdonald, 1942.)

indicating large landslides from that part of the cone (Plate 9). A pronounced angular unconformity is exposed in the south wall of the summit depression (Fig. 7-6), where Kula lavas bury a former cliff in the Honomanu lavas.

A long quiescent period followed, during which canyons were carved in the volcano, although a few eruptions may have occurred during this erosion interval. By the end of the cycle, the amphitheater heads of the canyons were several thousand feet deep. Apparently most of the canyons were cut back to the summit (Plate 10).

After this rest period, copious flows once more issued, but only along the southwest and east rifts. These lavas partly filled the canyons and veneered most of the mountains except tracts adjacent to the northwest rift. The third and upper rock unit is the Hana volcanic series. Its lavas range in composition from ultrabasic olivine augite porphyries to nonporphyritic alkalic basalts.

Bulky cinder cones marking many of the vents form prominent hills along the rift zones (Fig. 7-7). An unusual type of intercanyon lava, called "plastering" lavas because of the way they cooled as thin veneers on the canyon walls, is found in steep valleys in East Maui. The veneer ranges from a few inches to a few feet in thickness and extends for miles along the valley walls. The plastering lavas preserve a record of the changes in sea level at the mouth of Keanae Valley (Fig. 7-8). Some were so fluid that they reached velocities of about 20 miles an hour, tumbled wildly over water-falls, and behaved somewhat like a flood of thin mud. They built deltas of lava upon reaching the sea, where they cooled rapidly, but upstream only the bottom foot or so remains where the lava was chilled in contact with the ground.

Some of the waterfalls over which the lava flowed were so steep and high that the plastering lava did not cover them entirely, but formed thin horizontal sheets at their lips and parallel vertical sheets, resembling gigantic pieces of upturned plywood, at their feet. The plunge-pool fills are generally dense, columnar-jointed, nearly circular masses resembling intrusive plugs. Talus debris, which slid from the canyon wall into the lava, and bands of sand-textured clinker are found in a few places. The lava plaster is missing entirely from the walls in some places, where the only remnant is a slick hard veneer of blue rock on the canyon floor. Presumably the loose clinker was removed from the surface of the plaster by the stream after water returned to its channel.

Some of the vents in the summit depression are unusual. Fissure vents opened on the face of cliffs so that spatter and thin flows are found plastering former gullies in the talus fans. Other eruptions from similar vents produced enough cinders to form thick fans, such as those under Haleakala Peak. Some of the spatter cones have been named for their bizarre forms, such as Pele's Pig Pen (Ka Puaa o Pele) and the Bottomless Pit, both located on the trail across the floor. The pit has a crater about 75 feet deep, shaped like a well. It

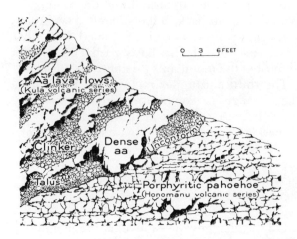

Figure 7-6—Angular unconformity in the south wall of the summit depression of Haleakala, Maui. (After Stearns and Macdonald, 1942.)

Figure 7-7—Looking northeastward to the cones of the southwest rift zone of Haleakala Volcano from the 1790 (?) lava flow near Makena, Maui. (After Stearns and Macdonald, 1942.)

was explored in 1940 by Frank Hjort, then ranger-in-charge, Haleakala National Park. He found sealed jars containing umbilical cords of infants, evidently dropped into the crater by superstitious Hawaiians in early days.

During the early part of the last eruptive period, a voluminous mudflow, carrying blocks of consolidated cinders up to 50 feet in diameter, moved down Kaupo Valley to the sea. In the deep amphitheater heads of Kaupo and Keanae valleys, flows and large cones of the Hana epoch practically masked the interstream divide between the adjacent canyons. The low interstream divide between Kaupo and Kipahulu valleys still projects above this sea of lavas. Thus, the so-called crater of Haleakala is chiefly, if not entirely, the result of erosion by Kaupo and Keanae streams, their two great amphitheaters coalescing to form the depression[203] (Plate 12).

Because so much of the surface of Haleakala Volcano has been covered by flows in Holocene time, few traces of emerged shorelines remain. The oldest recognized gravels were apparently graded to a sea about 100 feet higher than the level of the sea at present. Emerged fossiliferous marine deposits have been found up to 50 feet above sea level. Extensive lithified calcareous dunes lie on the Isthmus. The sand was blown inland when the sea stood about 350 feet lower in the Pleistocene. A 4-foot layer of brown soil separates two ages of lithified dunes at the south end of the Waihee Golf Course on West Maui.

In 1974, bones of two species of flightless rails and a flightless ibis were found in a lava tube near Hana.

PLATES 9 TO 12. EIGHT STAGES IN THE DEVELOPMENT OF MAUI

9A. *Stage 1* shows the East Maui and West Maui volcanoes as separate islands erupting tholeiitic basalts.

9B. Silhouette of Stage 1.

9C. *Stage 2* shows East Maui Volcano with a caldera on its summit and faults on its south side, and West Maui Volcano erupting Honolua lavas and joined to Lanai and Molokai volcanoes.

10A. *Stage 3* shows East and West Maui joined with Kahoolawe, Lanai, and Molokai. East Maui Volcano is erupting Kula lavas. Present outline of Maui is indicated by a dotted line.

10B. Silhouette of Stage 3.

10C. *Stage 4* shows the canyon-cutting period of middle Pleistocene time, with all volcanoes dormant. Present outline of Maui is indicated by a dotted line.

11A. *Stage 5* shows the development of Maui after the great submergence during the Olowalu 250-foot stand of the sea. East and West Maui are separate islands. The valleys have been deeply filled with alluvium.

11B. Silhouette of Stage 5.

11C. *Stage 6* shows East and West Maui united during the Kahipa minus 350±-foot stand of the sea. Hana lavas started to fill the canyons on East Maui, and the Kaupo mudflow has just been emplaced.

12A. *Stage 7* shows the island during the Waipio minus 350±-foot stand of the sea, with the Hana and Lahaina lavas being erupted and dunes forming on the Isthmus.

12B. Silhouette of Stage 7.

12C. *Stage 8* shows Maui at the present time.

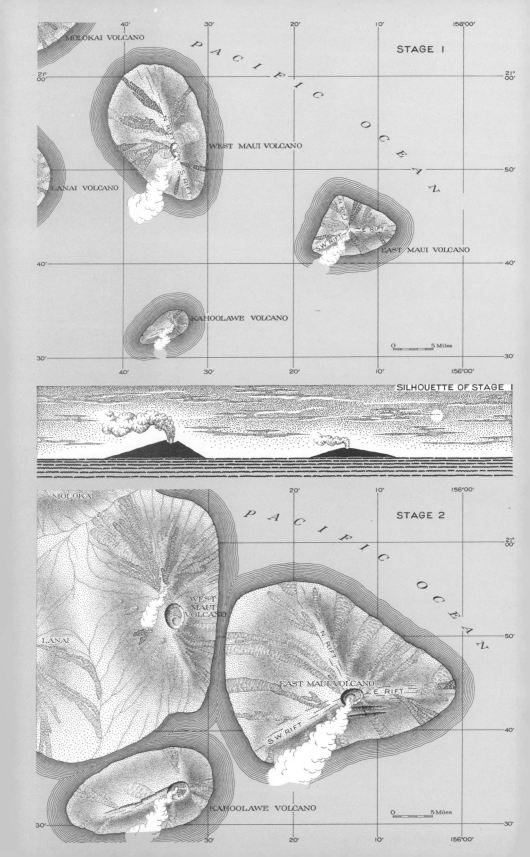

STAGE 1

MOLOKAI VOLCANO

PACIFIC OCEAN

WEST MAUI VOLCANO

LANAI VOLCANO

N. RIFT

S.W. RIFT

N. RIFT

E. RIFT

S.W. RIFT

EAST MAUI VOLCANO

KAHOOLAWE VOLCANO

0   5 Miles

SILHOUETTE OF STAGE 1

MOLOKAI

PACIFIC OCEAN

STAGE 2

WEST MAUI VOLCANO

LANAI

N. RIFT

EAST MAUI VOLCANO

E. RIFT

S.W. RIFT

KAHOOLAWE VOLCANO

0   5 Miles

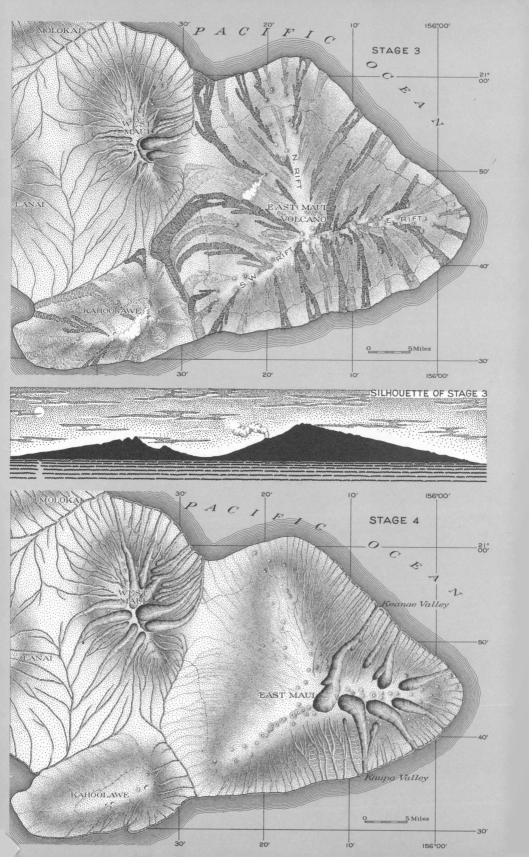

STAGE 3

PACIFIC OCEAN

MOLOKAI

WEST MAUI

LANAI

N. RIFT

EAST MAUI VOLCANO

E. RIFT

S.W. RIFT

KAHOOLAWE

0   5 Miles

SILHOUETTE OF STAGE 3

STAGE 4

PACIFIC OCEAN

MOLOKAI

WEST MAUI

LANAI

Keanae Valley

EAST MAUI

Kaupo Valley

KAHOOLAWE

0   5 Miles

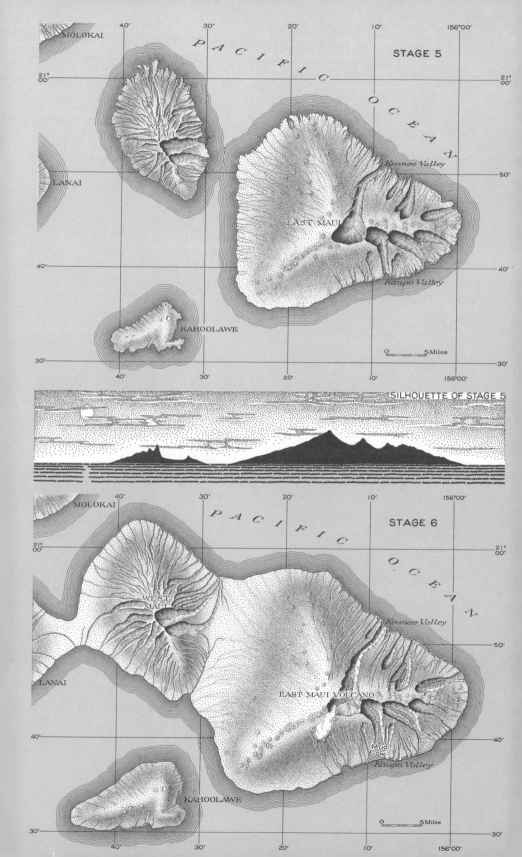

STAGE 5

P A C I F I C   O C E A N

MOLOKAI

WEST MAUI

LANAI

EAST MAUI

Keanae Valley

Kaupo Valley

KAHOOLAWE

0   5 Miles

SILHOUETTE OF STAGE 5

MOLOKAI

P A C I F I C   O C E A N

STAGE 6

WEST MAUI

LANAI

EAST MAUI VOLCANO

Keanae Valley

Mud flow

Kaupo Valley

KAHOOLAWE

0   5 Miles

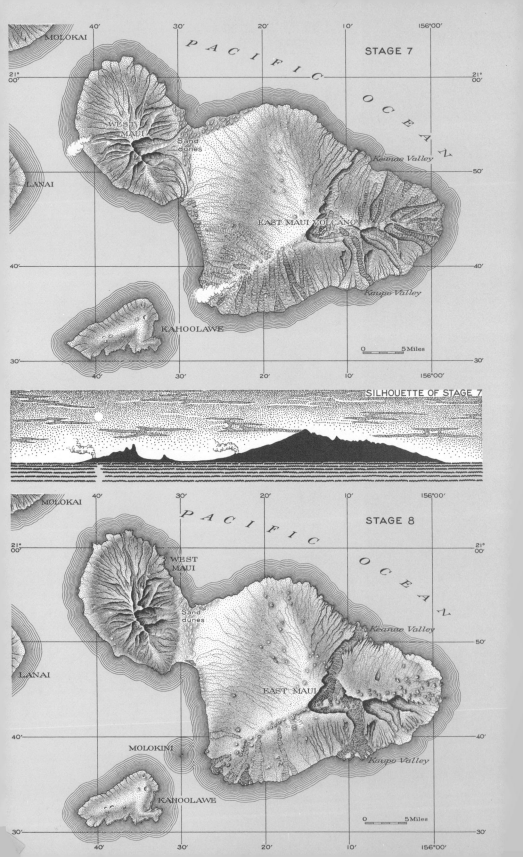

STAGE 7

MOLOKAI

PACIFIC OCEAN

40'   30'   20'   10'   156°00'

21°00'

WEST MAUI

LANAI

Sand dunes

Keanae Valley

50'

EAST MAUI VOLCANO

40'

Kaupo Valley

KAHOOLAWE

0   5 Miles

30'

SILHOUETTE OF STAGE 7

MOLOKAI

40'   30'   20'   10'   156°00'

PACIFIC OCEAN

STAGE 8

21°00'

WEST MAUI

LANAI

Sand dunes

Keanae Valley

50'

EAST MAUI

40'

MOLOKINI

Kaupo Valley

KAHOOLAWE

0   5 Miles

30'

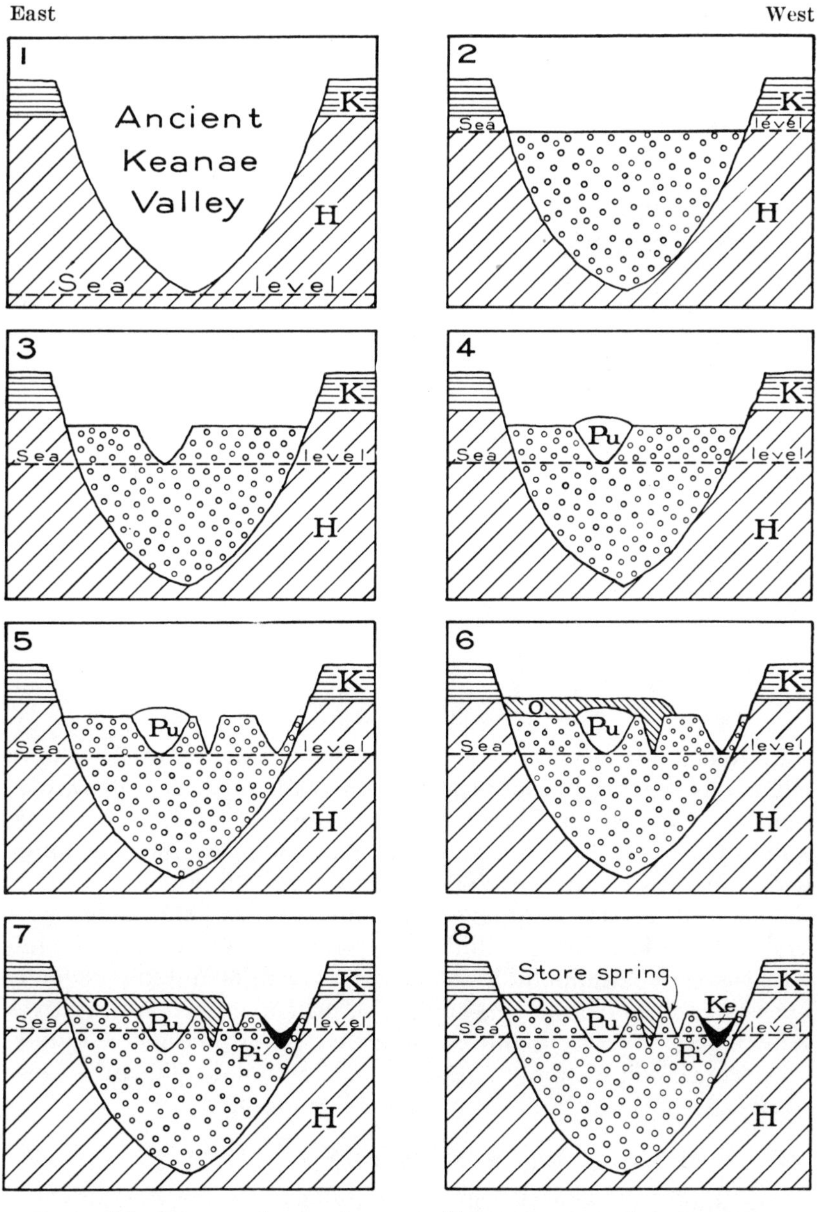

Figure 7-8—Stages in the development of lower Keanae Valley, East Maui. (1) Cutting of Keanae Valley through the Kula lava, K, and into Honomanu lavas, H, probably near the end of Kula time. (2) Alluviation of the lower part of Keanae Valley due to deep submergence of the valley mouth. (3) Relative fall of sea level, and cutting of a small gulch into the older alluvium. (4) Filling of this gulch by the Pauwalu lava, Pu, the oldest Hana lava in the area. (5) Cutting of small gulches into the older alluvium west of the Pauwalu lava. (6) Burial by the Ohia lava, O, of the eastern part of Keanae Valley, and the more easterly of the post-Pauwalu gulches. (7) Further erosion, and partial filling by the Piinaau lava, Pi, of the more westerly gulch. (8) Eruption of Keanae lava, Ke, partly burying the Piinaau lava. (After Stearns and Macdonald, 1942.)

8

ISLAND OF MOLOKAI

Location and Area

Molokai, in the county of Maui, fifth in size of the Hawaiian Islands, is separated from Oahu by Kaiwi Channel, 25 miles wide, from Maui by Pailolo Channel, 8.5 miles wide, and from Lanai by Kalohi Channel, 9 miles wide. Molokai is 38 miles long, 10 miles wide, and has an area of 260 square miles. The highest point is Kamakou Peak on East Molokai, with an altitude of 4,970 feet. West Molokai is a low dome called Mauna Loa, but to avoid confusion with the active Mauna Loa Volcano on Hawaii Island, this name is not used on Molokai in this book. The principal town and wharf is Kaunakakai. Pineapple and cattle are the chief products. Cinders, rock, sand, and pineapples are shipped to Honolulu. The pineapple plantation on West Molokai has been abandoned.

Geomorphology

All flights between Honolulu and the islands southeast of Oahu either carry passengers over or close to Molokai, or make a stop there. The great sea cliff (Fig. 8-1) along the windward side of this island is the highest in the world, according the *Guinness Book of World Records*. The extensive areas of pineapples neatly laid out in rows in the red soil are best seen from the air. A long band of drifting yellow sand dunes, the dirty shallow red water off the lee-ward shore, the projecting Kalaupapa Peninsula with its crater and

222

Figure 8-1—The great cliff on the north side of East Molokai. The peninsula in the foreground is the extinct Kalaupapa Volcano and the site of the leper colony. It is younger than the cliff. Note the dikes forming walls in the cliff in the right. They lie in the south side of the rift zone of the ancient East Molokai Volcano. (Photo by U.S. Navy.)

remnants of its leper colony, and the lack of cities are important features. Vancouver, the early French explorer, left cattle with the King of Hawaii and they were protected on Molokai by a tabu. As a result, the forest, which formerly covered the area around the airport on central Molokai, was devastated by overgrazing, and the King's fishponds, along the leeward shore, were filled with mud by subsequent erosion. The cattle were killed for their bones and fats long ago, but axis deer were introduced and now roam the country. Wild goats still do much damage to the forest on East Molokai. The airport is on the Hoolehua plain, formed by the lavas of the East Molokai Volcano ponding against the old West Molokai Volcano. The prominent geomorphic areas of Molokai are shown in Figure 8-2. The canyon country of East Molokai was once a caldera 2 miles wide and 4½ miles long. Although the great sea cliff along the windward side may be due to the recession of a former fault cliff, profiles based on existing soundings do not indicate faults of large displacement. Moore has proposed that a huge submarine landslide caused the cliff.[136]

One mile off the eastern end of Molokai lies the eroded remains of a tuff cone formed by the contact of sea water with rising hot lava. The cone is 203 feet high and forms the island called Mokuhooniki. It is a favorite nesting ground for sea birds and is much younger than Molokai.

The writer spent the summer of 1935 camping with strong young Hawaiian men in the huge canyons of East Molokai, which were accessible only by water at that time. Our supply boat came once a week. We lived on wild goats and fish most of the time. We ascended each tributary stream to the great cliff at its head; the Hawaiians scaled the waterfalls barefooted and assisted the writer up the steep slippery cliffs with ropes. Hundreds of dikes and dozens of faults were carefully mapped, and evidence of a former caldera was found.[197]

Spectacular cream-colored "coral" sand dunes stretch 5½ miles southwestward from Moomomi Beach on West Molokai. They reach heights of 60 feet, but are remarkable for the movement of the sand over a cliff 600 feet high before the dunes became cemented. Near Ilio Point, the dune rock extends below sea level, indicating that most of the dunes drifted inland during the Waipio low stand of the sea. They contain abundant fossil shells of land snails. The dunes are notched by both the 5- and 25-foot stands of the sea.

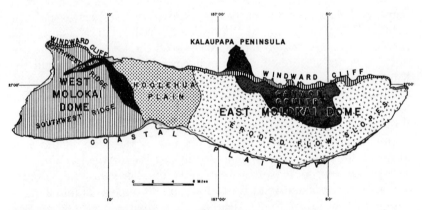

Figure 8-2—Map of Molokai showing the major geomorphic areas on the island. (After Stearns and Macdonald, 1947.)

Several stages of cementation occur. Some of the dunes are loose and the sand appears to have been blown chiefly from the older dunes. Bones of a flightless goose were found in a lithified dune at Moomomi Beach.[214]

Much lithified beach rock occurs along the shores of West Molokai. It has been quarried and shipped to Oahu for building stone. It was used in the beautiful Honolulu Academy of Arts building on Beretania Street in Honolulu.

The shortage of water has always held back the development of West Molokai. Water is abundant on the uninhabitable steep windward side of East Molokai, but is scarce elsewhere on the island. The shortage was remedied at last by the State Division of Land and Water Development through the "Stearns Plan tunnel," which was driven from an altitude of 900 feet in South Kaunakakai Gulch through the backbone of the island to Waikolu Valley, a distance of 26,825 feet.[16] Pipelines were laid in 1965 to the dry Hoolehua plain from the long-delayed tunnel, which was first projected in 1954.

A sign on the road at 15.5 miles east of Kaunakakai points to the Bell Stone (Kulahaloa). The stone is about ¼ mile inland, near the

TABLE 15

STRATIGRAPHIC ROCK UNITS ON THE ISLAND OF MOLOKAI

Age	Rock assemblage	
	Sedimentary rocks	Volcanic rocks
Holocene	Younger alluvium and unconsolidated beach and dune deposits	
Late Pleistocene	Lithified dunes, emerged reef limestone, and older alluvium	Kalaupapa basalt
	~~Great erosional unconformity~~~	
Pleistocene		East Molokai volcanic series — Upper (differentiated) member / Lower (basalt) member / Caldera complex member
		~~Erosional unconformity~~
		West Molokai volcanic series

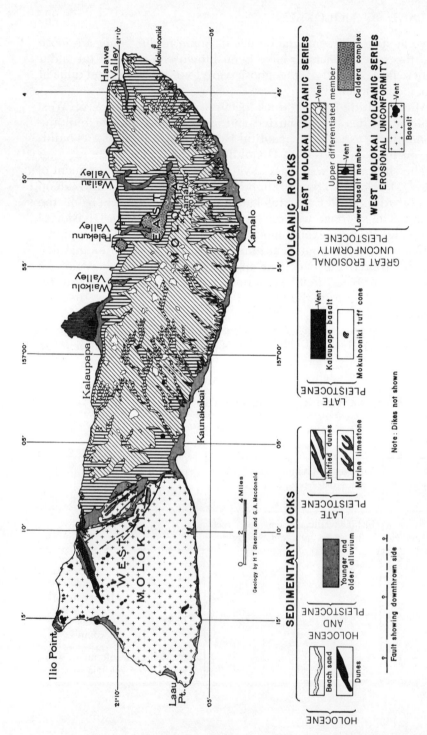

Figure 8-3—Geologic map of the island of Molokai.

eastern rim of a small gulch. It is a slab of lava 8 feet long, 4 feet wide, and 2 feet thick, resting loosely on another boulder. When struck, it gives out a loud bell-like tone. Half a mile west of the Kalaupapa lookout is the ancient volcanic vent called Puu Lua. The eastern part is a cinder cone, but the western part is a dome of lava on which is situated the ancient phallic temple called Kauleonanahoa. Here is the large phallic rock on which childless Hawaiian women used to sit and pray for children.

GEOLOGY OF MOLOKAI

Three volcanoes built Molokai. The western one, known as West Molokai, is 1,381 feet high and about 12 miles across. The eastern one, East Molokai Mountain, is 4,970 feet high, 27 miles long from north to south, and 8 miles wide from east to west. A smaller and much later volcano forms the Kalaupapa Peninsula on the north coast of the eastern volcano. The stratigraphic rock units on the island are given in the accompanying table and their distribution is shown in Figure 8-3.

West Molokai. Most of West Molokai is covered with lateritic soil 10 to 50 feet thick, indicating long extinction. The center of former volcanic activity lies just south of the summit and is barely exposed in a narrow gorge draining the area. Most of the lava was extruded from a rift zone that extends 10 miles to the southwest and plunges under the sea. Penguin Bank, the most extensive submarine shelf adjacent to the main islands, stretches 27 miles to the southwest of Molokai (Figure 1-1). The average depth of water over the bank is about 180 feet. At the edge of the shelf is a sheer submarine cliff 1,800 to 3,600 feet high. This bank trends southwestward along the submarine extension of the southwest rift zone of West Molokai and, therefore, may be a marine platform that was planed across the rift zone ridge during a low stand of the sea. A veneering reef less than 100 feet thick exists.[96] Another possible explanation is that the bank was originally a separate volcano leveled by the sea and capped by coral reef. If there was an older volcano, it is possible that West Molokai was built on the northeast rift zone of that mountain.

West Molokai consists almost entirely of thin-bedded aa and pahoehoe basalt flows, named the West Molokai volcanic series. The volcano has a flatter dome than most in the Hawaiian group. A few eroded and weathered cinder and spatter cones lie on the rifts.

On the east side are numerous fault blocks, indicating collapse of the northeast slope. The most prominent scarp is 500 feet high.

In the gulch draining southward from the main vent, the West Molokai lavas, covered with three feet of soil and underlain by six feet of spheroidal weathered basalt, can be seen disappearing under the flows from the eastern volcano. Therefore, West Molokai Volcano must have become extinct a long time before its large eastern neighbor did.

Most of the lower slopes are covered with the shingle of former beaches. The surface has been swept bare of soil. These indications of former high sea level have not yet been studied in detail.

East Molokai. The large eastern dome is cut into great amphitheater-headed valleys on the windward side and smaller ones on the leeward side. A spectacular cliff, reaching a maximum height of 3,600 feet, forms the entire north coast of the mountain (Fig. 8-1). Faulting and landsliding may have played a part in the origin of this cliff.[136]

A survey of the heads of Wailau and Pelekunu valleys revealed that these valleys tapped a caldera about four miles across and that the size of their amphitheater heads is only partly attributable to erosion.[197]

The eastern volcanic dome is composed chiefly of thin-bedded tholeiitic aa and pahoehoe having an average dip of about 12°, except where the flows bank against West Molokai. They constitute the lower member of the East Molokai volcanic series. Most of the dome is veneered by alkalic basalts and trachyte poured out mainly from large cinder cones and bulbous domes, which are now prominent topographic features. These rocks constitute the upper member of the East Molokai volcanic series. The volcano was built over eastward- and northwestward-trending rift zones, but some of the alkalic basalt and trachyte cones are not associated with the rifts. The easterly rift passes out to sea under Kalaupapa.

The leeward shore is bordered by a live fringing reef a mile wide, and the slopes are stripped by marine erosion to an altitude of 1,000 feet. Fossiliferous marine conglomerates crop out in a series of narrow discontinuous terraces up to an altitude of 280 feet. The drowned windward valleys and emerged marine deposits offer clear evidence of the complex emergences and submergences on both East and West Molokai.

Kalaupapa. In the late Pleistocene, a small volcano was formed at the foot of the great windward cliff, and flows from it have built a low peninsula about four square miles in area and 405 feet high. These lavas are named the Kalaupapa basalt. The Leper Settlement, called Kalaupapa, is located on the peninsula (Fig. 8-1). The submarine part of the volcano is huge and may represent the young stage of a great new dome. A crater 400 feet deep indents the summit of the dome. Some of the loose coral debris along the shore is apparently in a higher position than storm waves could have thrown the fragments, and seems to indicate an emergence of 5 feet or more. Conglomerate overlying the basalt on the southeast side of the peninsula seems to be graded to a stand of the sea 25 feet higher than the present level. On the basis of this evidence, the Kalaupapa basalt is assigned to the late Pleistocene. Mokuhooniki, an island off the east end of Molokai, also belongs to the Kalaupapa epoch of volcanism.

STRUCTURE

The East Molokai Mountain is an asymmetrical shield dome, elongated eastward and westward and built about an ancient caldera in Wailau and Pelekunu valleys. The elongation was due to extrusion of lavas along northwest and east rift zones. The beds dip 2° to 15° away from the volcanic center, except in the lower part of the high northern sea cliff, where they dip 8° to 25° S. The apex of the dome is missing, owing to collapse and erosion. The caldera complex is bounded by normal faults. Faults are numerous near the mouth of Pelekunu Valley and in the cliffs bounding Haupu Bay. The presence of a former fault depression 6 miles long and 2 miles wide, on the north shore of the volcano, is suggested by faults (Fig. 8-4, Stage 3) and ponded lavas in the north side of the mountain. Faults dipping toward the center of the mountain lie 3 miles south of the caldera. These scarps have caused abnormally thick flows because of ponding.

West Molokai Mountain is made up of two broad fairly flat constructional arches, one extending southwestward and the other northwestward from the summit as a result of lavas pouring from rift zones with the trends. The northeastern side of the dome is terminated in a set of echelon fault scarps 100 to 500 feet high, facing northeastward. The downthrown part of the dome lies under

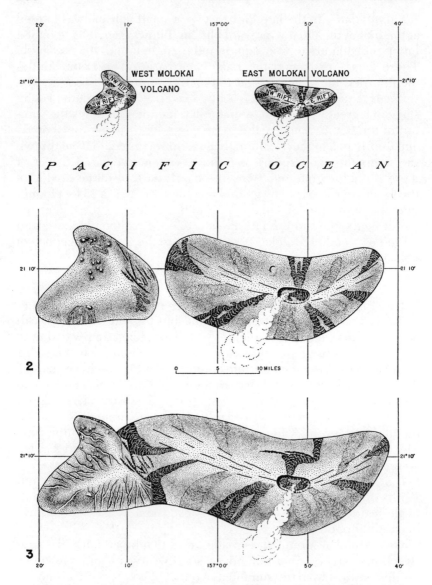

Figure 8-4—Drawings illustrating six stages in the development of the island
of Molokai (see explanation in text). *Stage 1* shows the appearance of two
separate islands above sea level in early Pleistocene. In *Stage 2* they are much
enlarged, and a caldera has formed on East Molokai. In *Stage 3* the two islands
have merged, and West Molokai Volcano has become extinct. *Stage 4*, in

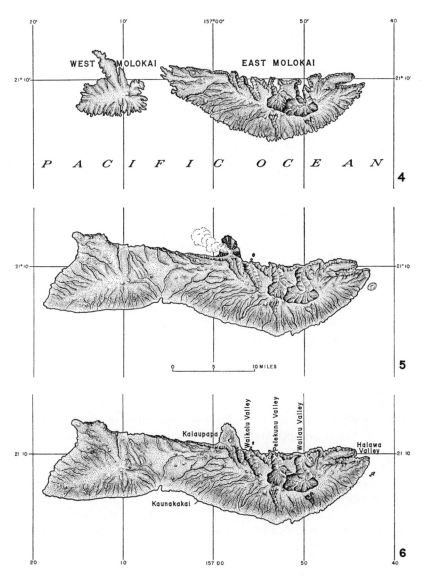

middle Pleistocene time, shows a new separation into two islands by submergence. *Stage 5*, in late Pleistocene time, shows a minor renewal of volcanism on East Molokai, and *Stage 6* shows the present condition of the island. Penguin Bank has been omitted on the west end of Molokai. (After Stearns and Macdonald, 1947.)

Hoolehua plain and is buried by lavas from the East Molokai Volcano.

GEOLOGIC HISTORY OF MOLOKAI

Early Pleistocene time. The geologic history of Molokai began with the building of a shield- or dome-shaped island of thin-bedded tholeiitic basalts at the site of West Molokai Mountain about 1.84 million years ago.[125] Then East Molokai Volcano grew above sea level with the eruption of the thin-bedded basalts in the lower member of the East Molokai volcanic series, about 1.47 million years ago (Fig. 8-4, Stage 1). Next came the extinction of the West Molokai Volcano and downfaulting of its northeastern side. Weathering began and a soil cover developed. Streams began to erode its slopes (Fig. 8-4, Stage 2). Eruptions continued at the East Molokai Volcano, and as its vent area collapsed, a caldera 4½ miles long and 2 miles wide developed. Faulting may have dropped part of the north side of the volcano during this or later stages. Lavas of East Molokai gradually filled the channel between East and West Molokai islands, and the Hoolehua plain was formed.

The East Molokai Volcano became almost extinct during the next stage, allowing the magma reservoir to differentiate (Fig. 8-4, Stage 3). Oligoclase basalts (mugearites) and a little trachyte, of the upper member of the East Molokai volcanic series, were erupted from bulky cinder cones and bulbous domes about 1.4 million years ago. The upper lavas were more viscous than the basalts and did not spread far from their vents. The caldera was probably nearly filled with the lavas of the upper member. Gradually, the fires of the East Molokai Volcano died, and streams began to erode the steep slopes vigorously.

Middle and late Pleistocene time. During a long period of erosion that followed, the deep canyons were formed on East Molokai and smaller ones on West Molokai. The sea removed a large segment of the windward coast. Gradually, the island began to submerge an unknown but large amount, culminating in a shoreline at least 560 feet above present sea level (Fig. 8-4, Stage 4), and probably as much as 1,200 feet. East and West Molokai again became two islands, and the Hoolehua plain was flooded by the sea. The large canyons were filled with alluvium as the streams aggraded their beds in adjustment to higher sea level. When the sea retreated again, it halted briefly at the 250-foot level. Small patches of coralliferous limestone formed at the mouths of gulches on the leeward side of East Molokai. As the seas receded, East and West Molokai joined to form one island again.

The waxing of ice caps on the poles caused the ocean to fall at least 300 feet and possibly as much as 450 feet below present sea level. Rainfall increased, and the streams cut deeply into alluvial fills and the sea pounded back the windward shore. As the ice caps melted, the sea rose slowly to about 100 feet above present sea level, and a narrow fringing reef was formed along part of the south shore of East Molokai.

Late Pleistocene and Holocene time. The ice sheets on the poles expanded once more, and the island re-emerged about 450 feet, exposing broad marine flats covered with "coral" sand. The wind drifted great quantities of the sand up and over the 600-foot sea cliff on the northeast coast of West Molokai. Volcanic activity was renewed on East Molokai, and huge volumes of lava erupted at the foot of the great sea cliff to form Kalaupapa Peninsula (Fig. 8-4, Stage 5). About the same time, lava rising under the ocean off the east tip of the island hit cold sea water and exploded to form Mokuhooniki tuff cone. Next, the island was resubmerged and a narrow fringing reef formed 25 feet above present sea level. Most of the dunes became lithified; others were cliffed or drowned by the sea. With further growth of the ice caps, the sea receded to about 350 feet below present sea level until the ice caps melted and the ocean rose to the present shore (Fig. 8-4, Stage 6).

Historic time. The introduction of livestock and agricultural development caused great quantities of red soil to be eroded from the uplands, partially filling 53 fishponds along the south coast, now being invaded by mangrove trees. Demand for construction materials has led to the export to Honolulu of sand and building stone from Papohaku Beach, cinders from Waiele Cone, and large blocks for riprap from West Molokai.

9

ISLANDS OF LANAI

AND KAHOOLAWE

Lanai, in the county of Maui, lies 59 miles southeast of Honolulu and 9 miles west of Lahaina, Maui. The channel between is commonly called the Lahaina Roads. Lanai is 13¼ miles long, 13 miles wide, and has an area of 141 square miles.[238] Of the eight principal islands, Lanai is the third smallest; only Kahoolawe and Niihau are smaller. Lanaihale, altitude 3,370 feet, is the highest point, and Lanai City is the only town. This island is owned by the Dole Pineapple Company, and pineapples are shipped to Honolulu for canning.

GEOMORPHOLOGY AND GEOLOGY

Lanai consists of a single basaltic dome 3,370 feet high and about 13 miles across, with its summit collapsed and its sides greatly disturbed by faulting (Fig. 9-1), but comparatively little modified by erosion since the volcano became extinct. Five fairly distinct geomorphic units are recognized: (1) the central basin; (2) the canyon country; (3) the northwest rift zone; (4) the southwest rift zone; and (5) the faulted south rift zone (Fig. 9-2). The island is elongated to the northwest and southwest because of copious outpourings of lava from fissures having these trends. Near the summit is Palawai Basin, a former caldera, which is 4 miles long and 3 miles wide. It is now partly filled with alluvium, and its formerly steep walls are smoothed by weathering and erosion. Soils 50 feet deep or more cover the summit area.[6] The lavas have a K-Ar age of 1,250,000 years.[20]

The volcano was built of thin-bedded aa and pahoehoe tholeiitic basaltic flows which, where not disturbed by faulting, dip 6° to 15°. All the volcanic rocks are grouped in the Lanai volcanic series. The sedimentary rocks consist of sand, alluvium, lithified dunes, and marine conglomerate. Their distribution is shown in Figure 9-3. Most of the lava welled out quietly from fissures. The two summit craters are known as Palawai and Miki basins. Forty-seven cones and craters exist on the slopes. The largest pit crater is 4,000 feet across, and many dissected pit craters full of throat breccia are exposed in canyon walls. Four unconformities were found, two of them indicated by talus accumulated at the base of fault scarps, and two by unsorted, unstratified debris or hillwash (Fig. 9-4).

Altogether about 375 feeding dikes are exposed, one of which contains ropy pahoehoe and two, clinkery aa (Fig. 9-5). One dike was displaced and brecciated by a fault (Fig. 9-6). Another dike contains fragments of platy rock in a matrix of black glass, indicating

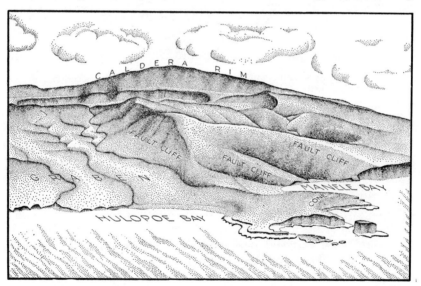

Figure 9-1—The summit caldera of Lanai, showing the high fault escarpments extending from the caldera to Manele Bay, bounding the east side of a graben or fault trough through which the last flows of lava from the caldera found their way seaward. An emerged wave-cut platform borders the cone in the foreground. (Drawn from an airplane photograph.)

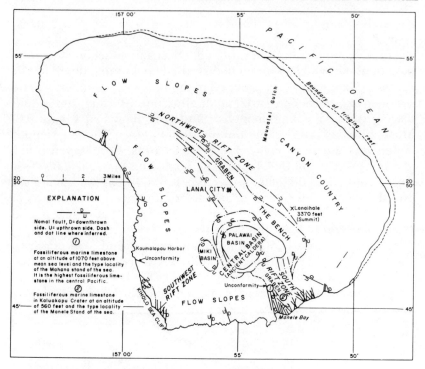

Figure 9-2—Map of Lanai showing the major geomorphic units, faults, and type localities of the Mahana and Manele stands of the sea.

a breaking up of the chilled border before the magma had ceased rising (Fig. 9-7).

The volcano was built over a northwest rift zone, a southwest rift zone, and a south rift zone, which intersect at the summit (Fig. 1-1). After a long, uninterrupted period of extrusion, the northwest and south rifts collapsed to produce the grabens that radiate from the caldera. At the same time, fault scarps more than 1,000 feet high were formed, and much rock was shattered. More than 100 fault traces are now exposed on Lanai. One of the high fault scarps shielded the whole northeast segment of the cone from later lava flows, and deep canyons were eroded on this slope.

High marine cliffs were not cut above sea level during submergence, but when the sea stood below the present ocean level, most of the south and west coasts were cliffed, in some places to heights of 1,000 feet, a process that may have been accelerated by

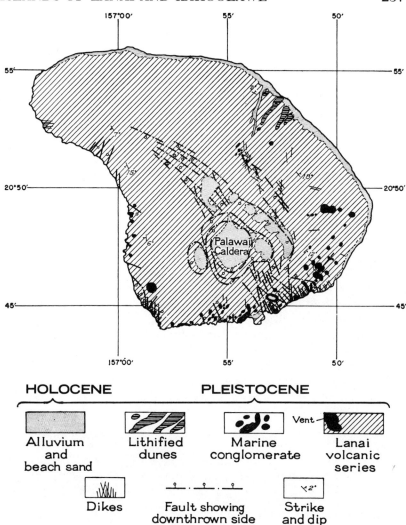

Figure 9-3—Geologic map of the island of Lanai.

submarine landslides (Fig. 9-8). The highest fossiliferous marine conglomerate ever found on any island in the central Pacific to date crops out at 1,070 feet altitude on Lanai.[196]

Lanai has been extinct longer than any of the other main islands. The islands of Niihau, Kauai, Oahu, Molokai, Maui, Kahoolawe, and Hawaii have had secondary eruptions in late Pleistocene or Holocene time.

GEOLOGIC HISTORY OF LANAI

1. Building of dome-shaped island at least 4,500 feet above present sea level by the outpouring of basalt flows from northwest, southwest, and south rift zones, with the center of activity at their intersection a little southwest of the present summit.
2. Collapse along the south and northwest rift zones, and subsidence at their intersection, forming a caldera now known as Palawai Basin.
3. Diminished volcanic activity, with most of the lava filling the sunken areas along the south and northwest rift zones. Scattered eruptions on the southeast flank near Kamaiki Point. Establishment of streams on the northeast side, as this area was protected from lava flows by the high cliffs of the caldera. Maui and Molokai were probably joined to Lanai at this time.
4. Cessation of volcanism.
5. Establishment of stream pattern over the entire island and formation of canyons on the northeast slope.

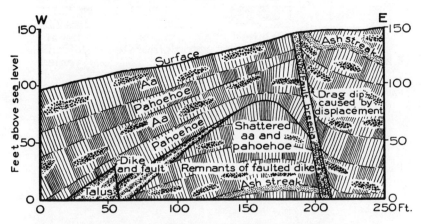

Figure 9-4—Unconformity and fault on the south coast of Lanai.

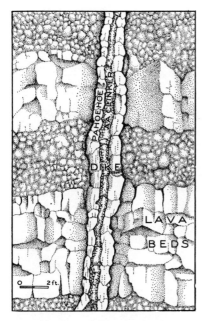

Figure 9-5—Dike of pahoehoe enclosing later aa in the sea cliff cutting the south rift, Lanai.

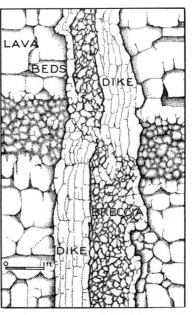

Figure 9-6—Platy dike displaced and brecciated by a fault in the west fork of Kapoho Gulch, Lanai.

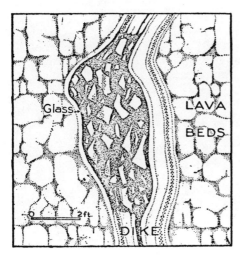

Figure 9-7—Fragments of a platy dike in a matrix of glass, indicating breaking of the border before the lava had ceased rising through the dike, Lanai.

Figure 9-8—High sea cliff crossed by faults on the southwest coast of Lanai. (Photo by H. T. Stearns.)

Figure 9-9—Emerged fossiliferous marine conglomerate on Lanai. (Photo by H. T. Stearns.)

6. Long period during which high marine cliffs were formed on the west and southwest coasts and stream erosion.

7. Gradual submergence of at least 1,500 feet and probably considerably more, resulting in the drowning and sedimentation of the valleys. Submergence culminated with the formation of a shoreline about 1,200 feet above present sea level. Continued marine abrasion along the west and south coasts and growth of coral, but no reefs.

8. Gradual emergence with possibly a very short halt 1,070 feet above present sea level.

9. Continued emergence with a short halt 560 feet above the level of the present sea, forming the Manele shoreline. Possibly the emergence was somewhat more, and then the island was resubmerged to an altitude of 560 feet.

10. Emergence of about 850 feet more and the development of a bench about 300 feet below present sea level, corresponding to

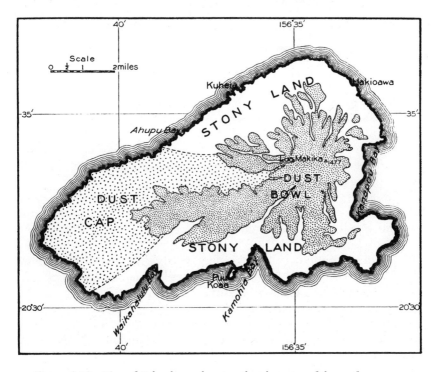

Figure 9-10—Map of Kahoolawe showing the character of the surface.

Figure 9-11—Cliff bordering Kanapou Bay, Kahoolawe Island, showing massive caldera-filling basalts and one of the major faults. (Photo by H. T. Stearns.)

the Kahipa shoreline on Oahu. Soundings indicate that narrow necks of land probably again connected West Maui and East Molokai to Lanai.

11. Resubmergence of about 400 feet and the deposition of marine sediments about 100 feet above present sea level, corresponding to the Kaena shoreline on Oahu.

12. Re-emergence of about 450 feet, corresponding to the Waipio shoreline on Oahu, and the formation of calcareous dunes on the windward slope. Vigorous marine erosion on the west and south coasts.

13. Resubmergence of about 375 feet, partly drowning the dunes at Lae Hi Point, and forming of a shoreline correlative with the Waimanalo shoreline on Oahu (Fig. 9-9).

14. Re-emergence of about 375 ± feet, followed by rapid submergence to present sea level with several halts. Continued stream and marine erosion and nearly complete filling of ancient caldera with alluvium. Introduction of livestock. Overgrazing greatly accelerated wind and stream erosion, causing

great areas of barren land and nearly annihilating the fringing reef organisms. Formation of narrow coastal plain along the northeast coast.

KAHOOLAWE ISLAND

Kahoolawe lies 7 miles off the south coast of Maui and 17 miles southeast of Lanai. It is 10.9 miles long, 6.4 miles wide, 1,472 feet high, and has an area of 45 square miles. Only a few families have lived on the island at one time, even in ancient days.[124] Now it is used as a bombing range. The geomorphic provinces are shown in Figure 9-10.

Kahoolawe is a single volcanic dome composed of thin-bedded pahoehoe and aa basalt, with a few thin local beds of fire-fountain debris and several cinder cones, the largest located on the summit. These rocks, including the associated intrusives, are named the Kanapou volcanic series after Kanapou Bay, where the type section is located (Fig. 9-11). The higher parts of the island were once covered with deep soil. Overgrazing and strong winds have caused vast quantities of soil to blow away.

The large, angular bay on the northeast coast is a high cliff exposing a great fault bounding the east side of a caldera 3 miles across and more than 800 feet deep. The caldera was filled with massive

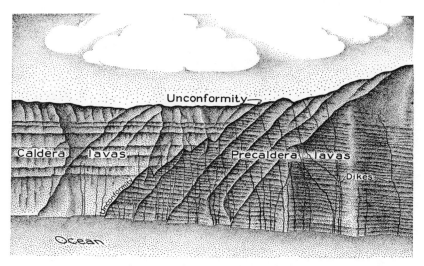

Figure 9-12—Unconformity and fault on the north side of Kanapou Bay, Kahoolawe.

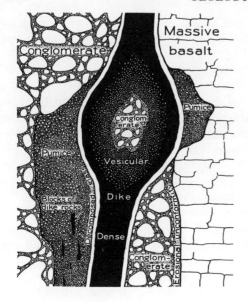

Figure 9-13—Intrusive pumice cut by a dike that encloses alluvium, both intruded into recent alluvium, Kanapou Bay, Kahoolawe. Scale: 1 inch = 2 feet.

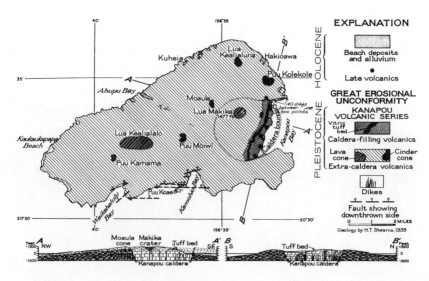

Figure 9-14—Geologic map and sections of the island of Kahoolawe. The extra-caldera volcanics also include the post-caldera volcanics.

lava typical of ponded basalts. Many of the dikes do not cut across the fault bounding the caldera (Fig. 9-12). One dike cuts contemporaneous pumice and encloses conglomerate (Fig. 9-13). A swarm of dikes running due east is also exposed in the cliff, and resting unconformably on the cliff are five Holocene cinder cones and flows. In the sea cliff forming the high south shore of the island, several faults are exposed. They apparently bound the south side of a graben that extended southwest from the caldera. The fault scarps were overflowed by lavas near the close of the dome-building epoch.

The island was built over three rifts (Fig. 1-1), and two groups of lavas are distinguished in the Kanapou volcanic series: (1) the pre-caldera lavas; and (2) the caldera-filling lavas, some of the upper members of which are slightly differentiated. Five post-erosional lavas and pyroclastics of Holocene age lie unconformably on the cliff at Kanapou Bay. Their distribution is shown in Figure 9-14.

The valleys are partly drowned, indicating submergence, and the soil has been washed away by marine erosion to at least 800 feet above sea level. Stages in the geologic development are shown in Plates 9 to 12. While this book was in press, an explanation as to why the soil has been washed away up to about 800 feet was found. The Moores[a] have described a giant wave that hit Lanai from a subsea landslide south of Lanai. The author believes, instead, that the wave was caused by a huge slice of the southwest coast of Lanai sliding into the sea and forming the cliff shown in Figure 9-8. The wave reached about 1,200 feet on Lanai, which is the height of the Mahana shoreline listed in Table 2 as having been due to a still stand of the sea, as are the Kaluakapo shorelines at 625 feet, the Manele at 560 feet, and the two unnamed at $375\pm$ and $325\pm$ feet. These shorelines were caused by the landslide as the great wave continued to surge. The Olowalu shoreline at $250\pm$ feet on Maui probably represents the height the wave reached on Maui, and the marine deposit on Kohala Mountain on Hawaii at 175 feet probably represents the height of the wave on that island.

The Moores and their colleague[b] have dated coral from the Lanai deposit by the uranium-series method as ranging from 100,000 to 134,000 years. The wave predates the Waimanalo shoreline, which is definitely dated at 120,000 years.

[a]Moore, J. G. and Moore, G. W. 1984. Deposit from a giant wave on the island of Lanai, Hawaii. Science, in press.

[b]_____ and Szabo, B. J. 1984. Age of debris from a huge Pleistocene wave on Lanai, Hawaii. EOS, Amer. Geophys. Union Trans. (abst.) 65: 1082.

10

ISLAND
OF KAUAI

Geomorphology

Kauai, 5,170 feet high and 32 miles in its longest diameter, is a dissected basaltic dome.[13] It has an area of 555 square miles and is separated from Oahu by the Kauai Channel, about 72 miles wide and 10,000 feet deep. Its form is shown in Figure 10-1. The summit plateau is what is left of the floor of a huge caldera 13 miles across. It is covered partly with Alakai Swamp, where, in some years, the rainfall is more than 50 feet (600 inches). The rim of the caldera is eroded away, but it appears to have been 400 feet higher than the present summit at some places. Marine and stream erosion and faulting have wrought havoc with the original nearly circular dome, which contained about 1,000 cubic miles of lava. The form of the dome above and below sea level and typical profiles are shown in Figure 10-2. Mana plain, on the west side of the island, is underlain by coral reefs at minus 60 feet and minus 120 feet, and the sediments bottom at minus 390 feet. The minus 60-foot reef may have been formed during the Waipio low, and the minus 390 bench was cut probably during one or more of the low stands of the sea in the Pleistocene.

Olokele caldera. In 1939 the writer started the systematic mapping of the island and discovered two calderas (Fig. 10-3). The ancient summit caldera greatly exceeds in size any in the Hawaiian Islands, and ranks among the large calderas of the world. Because

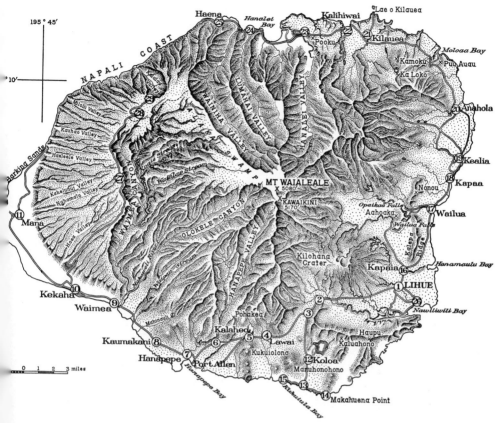

Figure 10-1—Relief map of the island of Kauai. Numbers refer to descriptions of points of geologic interest in separate guide book. (After Macdonald, Davis, and Cox, 1960.)

of the resistance to erosion of the massive, nearly horizontal bedded lavas ponded on the floor of the caldera, in contrast to the thin-bedded scoriaceous lavas outside the caldera, the topography is now inverted, and what was formerly the low ground on the summit, when the volcano ceased erupting, is now the highest ground on the island. Figure 10-4 shows how talus from the former faults is now exposed adjacent to the ponded caldera lavas; the fault cliffs that shed the talus have been eroded away.

The faults bounding the caldera have great displacements. Running south from the caldera is a graben known as the Makaweli depression. The Kalalau fault, with more than a 2,700-foot throw, runs northeast from the caldera. It is readily seen in the north wall of Kalalau Valley, from the view point at the end of the auto road on

its rim. The fault was mapped by the writer in 1939, but its relation
to the caldera-bounding faults is still not understood, although it
appears to be of the same age. It may be an extension of the proba-

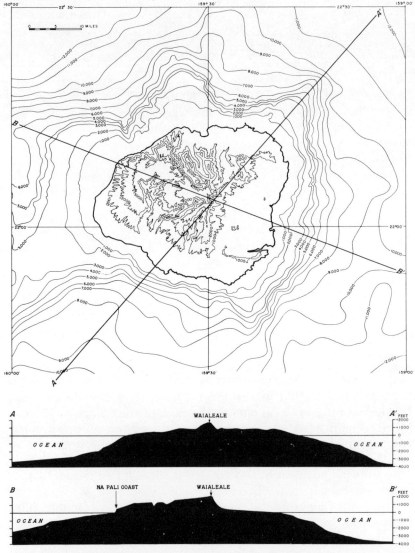

Figure 10-2—Map of Kauai showing subaerial and submarine contours, and
profiles of the volcanic dome along lines A-A' and B-B'. (After Macdonald,
Davis, and Cox, 1960.)

ble Waimea Canyon fault projected over the island and down the
north side (Fig. 10-5).

Haupu caldera. Haupu caldera formerly indented the southeast
slope of the Kauai volcanic dome, much as Kilauea caldera lies on
the side of Mauna Loa Volcano on Hawaii (Fig. 10-3). Erosion has
left the dense caldera-filling lavas in relief, resulting in an inver-
sion of topography. The rocks, formerly in a depression, now form
the top of Haupu Ridge, also called Hoary Head. The caldera is 2.6
miles long and 1 mile wide.

Lihue depression. The Lihue depression (Fig. 10-3), 11 miles
across, is thought by some geologists to be a caldera filled with
younger lavas. Reconnaissance gravimetric surveys have indicated
a dense intrusive body under it,[94] which may be a stock of Koloa
lava under the young Kilohana cone or an offset such as occurs in
the gravimetric high near the summit of the volcanoes on the island
of Hawaii. The gravimetric data are inadequate to settle this point.

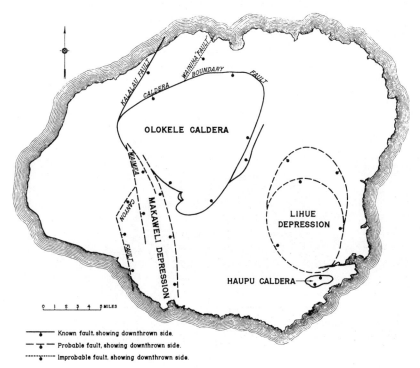

Figure 10-3—Map of the island of Kauai showing the approximate position of
the principal faults. (After Macdonald, Davis, and Cox, 1960.)

The writer proposed the theory that the depression is primarily the result of stream erosion.[8] The great amphitheater-headed valleys that must have once existed on the southeast side of the island have become filled partly with secondary eruptives, including the bulky cone of Kilohana. These volcanics have displaced the streams repeatedly and caused them to cut across former interstream divides, thus giving rise to the two anomalous ridges, Kalepa and Nonou, and to the kipukas of older rock called Puu Pilo and Aahoaka Hill. Only the inland-facing slopes of Kalepa-Nonou ridge give the Lihue depression its roughly circular form, and they may be the result of an ancient fault, because their lava beds have steep dips. Two huge calderas side by side on a single volcano would require unusual volcanic conditions.

Waimea Canyon. Waimea Canyon is a favorite scenic attraction because of its steep and colorful walls (Plate 8). The canyon is 14½ miles long and 2,750 feet deep. Cox has projected a probable fault of large throw along it (Fig. 10-3), although no fault trace has been found. The writer has expressed the opinion that Waimea Canyon does not lie at present along a fault, but has been crowded westward by lava flows erupted subsequent to its original cutting.[8] Cox has shown that these flows belong to the Makaweli formation, and that the original position of Waimea Stream was probably along a

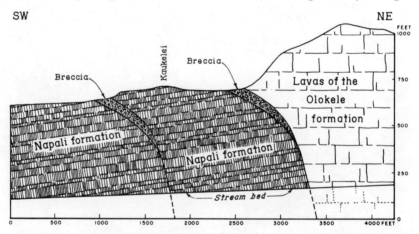

Figure 10-4—Section of the northwest wall of Olokele Canyon, Kauai, showing breccia masses along the buried fault scarps at and near the margin of the caldera, filled with lavas of the Olokele formation. (After Macdonald, Davis, and Cox, 1960.)

fault a little farther east, bounding a graben. Figure 10-6 shows how
a fault of even small displacement crossing a volcanic dome
diagonally can concentrate the direction of major drainage lines,
thus beheading smaller valleys farther downslope and giving rise to
a disproportionately large canyon.

The Wainiha and Lumahai gorges on the north slope are just as
impressive as Waimea Canyon, but they are inaccessible. The
Wainiha Gorge is 11 miles long, 3 miles wide at its widest part, and
2,000 to 3,000 feet deep. No evidence of faulting was found in these
gorges; hence, they are mute evidence of the effectiveness of
stream erosion on a steep, wet, basaltic island.

Napali Cliff.   The 2,700-foot sea cliff forming the scenic Napali
Coast on the northwest side of the island is one of the most spectacular sea cliffs in the world (Fig. 10-7). Helicopters now fly many
tourists to Kalalau Valley daily. Transients have invaded the area to
grow marijuana. Geologists are not in agreement as to the origin of
the towering cliff. Some believe it to be a high fault scarp, but the
writer believes, from a study of the undersea profile off the coast
and the great cliffs cut elsewhere in the islands by the sea, that
waves battering against the weak lavas forming the interstream divides were responsible for the cliff. Perhaps future soundings will

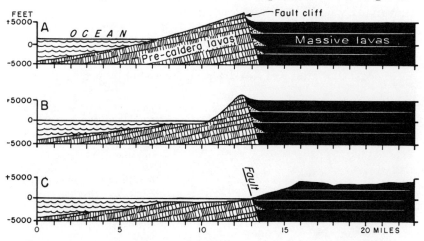

Figure 10-5—Sections showing the development of the eastern part of the
Napali Cliff, Kauai. *A*. At close of volcanism. *B*. After stream erosion had
carved valleys in the weak pre-caldera lavas. *C*. Present stage, an obsequent
fault-line scarp caused by the resistance of massive pooled lavas to wave
erosion. All lavas are part of the Napali volcanic series.

show it to be the site of a gigantic submarine landslide. Between Haena and Kalalau Valley, where the highest part of the cliff lies, the Napali formation was cut away and erosion was arrested by massive ponded lavas behind a fault scarp, possibly bounding a graben. Thus, this part of the cliff is an obsequent fault-line scarp and is due to the difference in the rate of erosion of the weak pre-caldera Napali lavas and the later dense pooled lavas. The ancient fault dips away from the coast, not toward it (Fig. 10-5).

Barking sands. The barking sands north of the little village of Mana are large sand dunes of calcareous beach sand blown inland from the beach. The "barking" is a peculiar creaking noise produced by the sand when pressed under foot. The sands will "bark" only if they have the right degree of dampness.

Wailua Falls. Wailua Falls result from the Wailua River tumbling over a very thick lava flow of the Koloa volcanic series where the river has undercut the weak underlying tuff, mudflow, and pillow lavas (Fig. 10-8).

Chutes. Waipeehee Falls are located along a road leading inland from Kealia on the east shore. The falls are a smooth lava chute cut by the stream into Koloa lavas, ending in a plunge pool. Several smooth chutes of this type exist and are the delight of the Hawaiians, who like to slide down them into the pools below. They are fairly numerous on Kauai because the dense Koloa lavas are favorable for the formation of chutes.

Haena Caves. Most tourists are taken to the Haena Caves on the north coast. Both the wet and dry caves were cut by waves during a

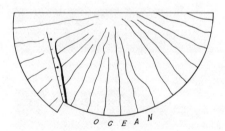

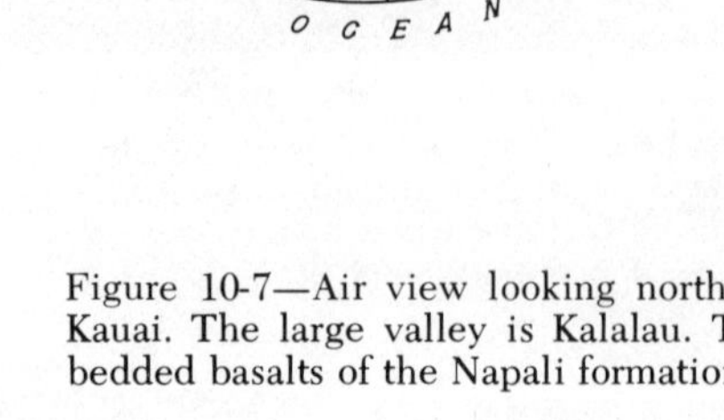

Figure 10-6—Diagram illustrating the manner in which a fault diagonally crossing the slope of a volcanic shield may concentrate and change the direction of the major drainage lines, beheading small valleys farther downslope. (After Macdonald, Davis, and Cox, 1960.)

Figure 10-7—Air view looking northeast along the great Napali sea cliff, Kauai. The large valley is Kalalau. The rocks in the foreground are thin-bedded basalts of the Napali formation. (Photo by U.S. Army.)

former higher sea level. Several prominent dikes are exposed in the cliff near the dry cave. The water in the wet caves is fresh ground water impounded by dams of relatively impermeable talus and alluvium.

Fern Grotto. Most tours now include a boat trip to Fern Grotto, a large cave on the bank of the Wailua River. The cave was caused by the removal by erosion of an ancient talus deposit, belonging to the Palikea formation, lying against the Waimea Canyon basalt series and overlain by a later Koloa lava flow. The Koloa lava forms the roof.

GEOLOGY OF KAUAI

Waimea Canyon volcanic series. The areal distribution of the rocks is shown in the map (Fig. 10-9). The rocks of the main volcanic dome are named the Waimea Canyon volcanic series. According to radiogenic measurements, the main volcano was active for more than 1.8 million years; the oldest rocks are 5.72 million years old.[125] The Waimea Canyon volcanic series has been subdivided into the four formations described below.

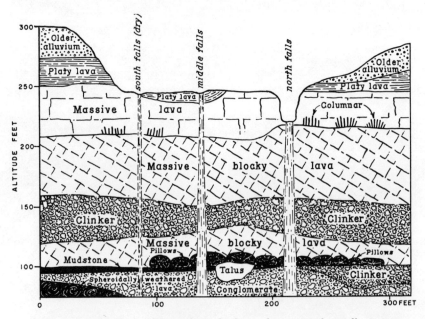

Figure 10-8—Sketch showing geological relationships at Wailua Falls, Kauai. (After Macdonald, Davis, and Cox, 1960.)

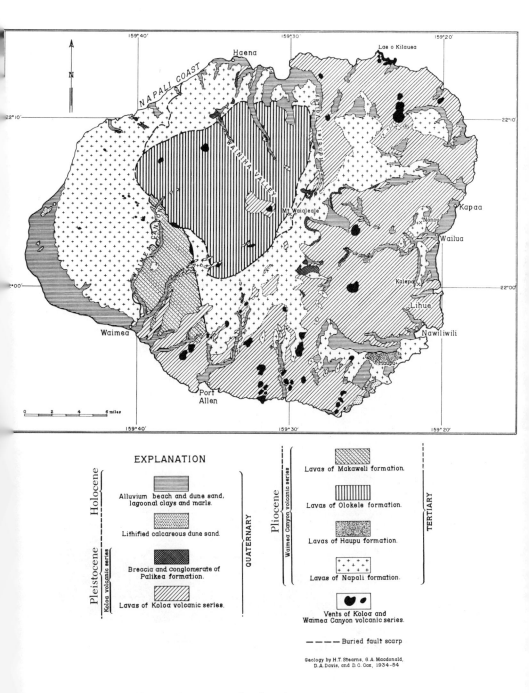

Figure 10-9—Generalized geologic map of Kauai.

Napali formation. The Napali formation comprises the thin flows of basalt that accumulated on the flanks of the volcano in all directions. They have an exposed thickness of 2,700 feet in the Napali sea cliff (Fig. 10-7). They are typical thin-bedded tholeiitic aa and pahoehoe flows, with scarce ash deposits that erupted in rapid succession from narrow fissures. Many of the feeding dikes are exposed in Waimea Canyon. Large areas of Napali lavas are veneered with later lavas. Many contain large olivine crystals, which may make up 50% of the volume of the rock. Radiogenic measurements indicate that they were erupted during a period lasting from 5.72 to 4.47 million years ago. If measured from the sea floor, this formation is 20,000 feet thick.

Olokele formation. The Olokele formation consists of massive basalt flows that accumulated in the Olokele or summit caldera. They have an exposed thickness of 2,600 feet. They do not differ in chemical composition from the scoriaceous vesicular basalts in the Napali formation, but owe their massiveness to being ponded. Masses of cemented talus breccia that fell from ancient fault cliffs are interstratified with the lavas adjacent to the former caldera wall. A single flow of alkalic basalt has been found. Lava flows usually are 40 to 100 feet thick. Ash beds are rare in this formation, as in most Hawaiian calderas. Thin soil beds are present only near the

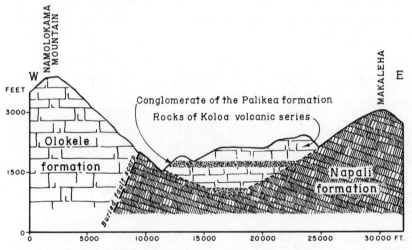

Figure 10-10—Generalized section across upper Hanalei Valley, Kauai. (After Macdonald, Davis, and Cox, 1960.)

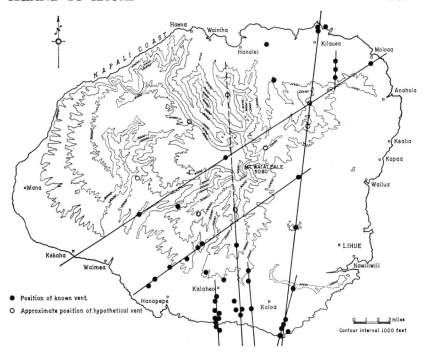

Figure 10-11—Map of Kauai showing the distribution of vents of the Koloa volcanic series. (After Macdonald, Davis, and Cox, 1960.)

top of the formation, when the time intervals between eruptions were becoming longer.

Haupu formation. The Haupu formation consists of massive basalt flows ponded in the Haupu caldera, and resembles the rocks of the Olokele formation. The flows are nearly horizontal and are predominantly olivine basalts. Firmly consolidated talus breccia is associated with the contact walls of the faults bounding the caldera. The formation covers an area of 1 by 2½ miles on Haupu Ridge (Fig. 10-9). The rocks surrounding the caldera belong to the Napali formation.

Makaweli formation. The basalts that accumulated in the Makaweli graben are called the Makaweli formation. They are indistinguishable from the Olokele formation because the graben is an extension southward of the Olokele caldera, just as the lavas in the graben along the southwest rift zone of Kilauea Volcano on Hawaii Island are indistinguishable from those in the summit caldera there. Radiogenic measurements indicate that the Makaweli basalts were erupted during the period between 4.05 and 3.80 million years ago, or after the Napali lavas were laid down. Considerable talus breccia interfingers with the Makaweli lavas where they are in contact with the older rocks. The breccia has been named the Mokuone member. In the spur below Puu Ka Pele, the breccia is 1,000 feet thick. A few conglomerate beds 2 to 25 feet thick are also found intercalated with the lava beds, and are included in the Mokuone member. Many carry abundant large olivine crystals.

Intrusive rocks in the Waimea series. Numerous dikes are exposed in the rocks of the Waimea volcanic series, but dike complexes indicating definite rift zones, such as are exposed in the Koolau Range on Oahu, do not occur. Instead, in keeping with the nearly circular shape of the ancient volcano, they are nearly radial and are comparable to the dike pattern in the ancient West Maui Volcano. However, rift zones appear to extend northeastward and west-southwestward from the eruptive center. An unusual number of dikes lie at low angles of about 45°, in contrast to dips of 70° or greater found in the other islands. Sills range from 1 to 6 feet in thickness. Some sills can be seen to be dikes locally following bedding planes.

Koloa volcanic series. The Koloa volcanic series comprise all volcanics and the interbedded sediments (Palikea formation) that are separated by a long erosion interval from the Waimea volcanic series. Canyons more than 2,500 feet deep were cut during the time interval. The volcanics are similar in occurrence and petrology to the post-erosional Honolulu volcanic series on Oahu. These volcanics were erupted after a long period of repose; hence, they generally fill valleys or lie on deep soil or ancient gravel (Fig. 10-10). The youngest ones are fresh and barren and erupted in the late Pleistocene, but the old ones are deeply weathered. Radiogenic measurements indicate 1.42 million years as their age, which places the older ones in the early Pleistocene. Thus, the post-erosional lavas on Kauai have a longer time spread than do those elsewhere in the islands.

The lavas are nepheline basalt, melilite-basalt, melilite-nepheline basalt, picrite basalt, olivine basalt, and basanite. The nepheline- and melilite-bearing lavas are not found in the older lavas, which were poured out in rapid succession during the building of the main dome; hence, the nepheline and melilite types are differentiates extruded from pods of lava that have existed at depth for a long time. Xenoliths of dunite are abundant in many of the flows (Fig. 3-18).

A thickness of 2,100 feet is exposed in the east wall of Hanalei Valley near Hanalei Peak. Some of the vents are still-uneroded cinder cones. Kilohana lava dome, near Lihue, is 6 miles across and has a well-preserved crater 250 feet deep. The vents, 40 in number, are bunched chiefly on the south and northeast side of the island (Fig. 10-11). Other vents have been eroded away. Kilauea cone on the west side of Kilauea Bay, Kauai, is a tuff cone resulting from a phreatomagmatic explosion.

Palikea formation. Because the time interval was so great between many of the eruptions of the Koloa lavas, and because of active erosion and numerous streams, many of the lava flows of the Koloa series were covered with fans, talus, and mudflows. These sediments, which in places are 700 feet thick, are named the Palikea formation (Fig. 10-9). In other places, the sea cut cliffs into early Koloa lavas that were buried by later flows (Fig. 10-12). Many of the unconformities between the flows are steep and complex, as a result of the accumulation of volcanics on a deeply dissected island still being eroded by powerful streams (Fig. 10-13). Strong earthquakes may have triggered some of the mudflows.[13] Pillow lavas are present where the lavas spread over wet ground or impounded streams (Fig. 10-8).

Intrusive rocks in the Koloa series. Dikes of olivine basalt and nepheline basalt and small plugs of gabbro occur on Kauai, but are scarce because erosion has not progressed far enough to expose many of the intrusives associated with the Koloa rocks. The so-called "lightning stones" that occur as boulders in Waimea River and the lower portions of Waialae and Koaie streams are coarse-grained gabbro.

Stratigraphy. The stratigraphic rock units on the island are summarized in Table 16.

GEOLOGIC HISTORY OF KAUAI

Tertiary time. At some time in the Tertiary, a crack opened on the floor of the Pacific, and the building of Kauai began. The depth of the water is now nearly 20,000 feet, with a pressure of roughly 8,700 pounds per square inch. Such a pressure would doubtless prevent explosive eruptions, and the lavas would pour out quietly undersea. However, isostatic adjustment of the load on the crust by the building of the Kauai dome apparently has caused the island to sink about 8,000 feet, if submerged valleys are used as an index of subsidence. Lavas erupted through radial fissures and along an east-northeast–west-southwest rift zone. The lavas welled out quietly, building a shield-shaped dome with dips of 6° (the Napali formation). As the volcano approached Stage 3 (Fig. 4-3), the summit began to collapse to form the Olokele caldera, 12 miles across. Lavas erupted in the caldera were ponded and cooled slowly, in contrast to rapid cooling of the flank lavas. Collapse southward from the summit simultaneously formed the Makaweli graben, and lava flows accumulated in it. The Haupu caldera collapsed about this time and was filled with massive basalts. A long period of repose that followed has been dated about 3.8 million years ago in the Pliocene.

As soon as soils formed and heavy rains no longer sank into the permeable lavas, streams cut canyons 3,000 feet deep, which ate into the heart of the dome through the weak Napali lavas, but cutting was slowed when the streams reached the massive Olokele lavas in the caldera. The sea battered the coast to form broad shelves backed by black cliffs of bare rock 3,000 feet high. Slowly

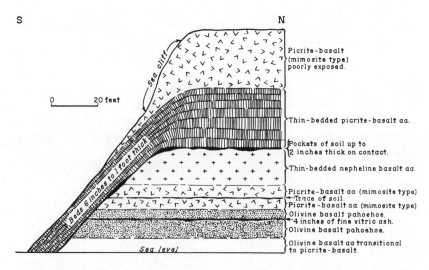

Figure 10-12—Section at the lava-mantled sea cliff 0.25 mile east of Koheo Point, Kauai.

TABLE 16

STRATIGRAPHIC ROCK UNITS ON THE ISLAND OF KAUAI

Age	Rock Assemblage	
	Sedimentary rocks	Volcanic rocks
Holocene	Beach and dune sand and alluvium.	
	～～～～～～～～～～～Local erosional unconformity～～～～～～～～	
Pleistocene	Lagoonal deposits of Mana plain, older alluvium, lithified dunes and the Palikea formation comprising mudflow breccias, and conglomerates interstratified with and at the base of the Koloa volcanic series.	Koloa volcanic series, comprising a tuff cone at Kilauea Bay, ash and tuffaceous soil beds, cinder cones, and lava flows, many of them filling valleys.
	～～～～～～MAJOR EROSIONAL UNCONFORMITY～～～～～～	
Pliocene	Makuone member of the Makaweli formation, comprising masses of breccia along the contacts of the Makaweli formation with older rocks and beds of well sorted conglomerates interbedded with the Makaweli formation.	Waimea Canyon volcanic series, comprising the Napali formation of cones, flows, and intrusives forming the major shield-shaped dome outside the caldera; the Olokele formation, thick flows that accumulated in the broad caldera on the summit; the Makaweli formation, flows that accumulated in a graben on the southwest slope; the Haupu formation, massive flows that accumulated in a small caldera on the southeast slope.

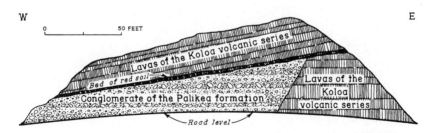

Figure 10-13—Sketch showing unconformity in highway cut 0.3 mile west of Lawai Stream, Kauai. Vertical scale is the same as horizontal. (After Macdonald, Davis, and Cox, 1960.)

the island submerged owing to isostatic and eustatic causes, and the streams in the deep valleys alluviated their floors.

Pleistocene time. About 1.42 million years ago, eruptions from the Koloa vents began to pour lava down canyon walls, displace streams, and veneer sea cliffs. Numerous smaller canyons were cut between Koloa eruptions, only to be filled again by later lavas. Sea level changes occurred because of diastrophic eustasy, and gravels were deposited as terraces to levels at least 200 feet above present sea level and for unknown depths below sea level.

Spasmodic Koloa eruptions continued up to the end of the Pleistocene, while the waxing and waning of the polar caps caused sea level to rise and fall on the island. When the sea rose, the streams aggraded their floors to form fills, and when it fell, the streams removed part or all of the fills. Thus, there are superimposed complex valley-in-valley deposits of gravel, boulders, and mud. Along some shores, when the sea was lower, sand drifted inland to form dunes, which eventually lithified after the sea rose and cut off their supply of sand. Changes of climate concurrent with the glacial and interglacial epochs affected the rainfall and vegetation in critical areas. Lagoonal sediments were deposited in the Mana plain along the southwestern side of the island, forming broad flats and leaving former sea cliffs abandoned inland by the sea. A geologic section across the island showing its present form, after the long epoch of erosion, is shown in Figure 10-14.

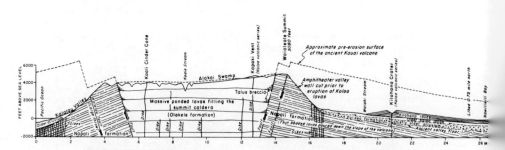

Figure 10-14—Northwest-southeast geologic section from the mouth of Kalalau Valley across the summit of Kauai to Nawiliwili Bay, near Lihue. Many more dikes exist than are shown. Thickness of bedding in caldera is exaggerated. Vertical exaggeration about 2½ × horizontal scale.

11

ISLANDS OF

NIIHAU AND LEHUA

GEOMORPHOLOGY

Niihau lies 17½ miles southwest of Kauai. Its area is 72 square miles, and its highest point has an altitude of 1,281 feet. The privately owned island has a population of 226, chiefly Hawaiians. The present form of the island is shown in Figure 11-6.

Niihau has two major geomorphic provinces—the uplands, a remnant of a shield- or dome-shaped basaltic volcano; and the lowlands, a coastal plain averaging about 75 feet above sea level, but containing numerous playa lakes only slightly above sea level (Fig. 11-1).[76] Some of the ashes from Lehua Island, a tuff cone that lies a mile off the northern tip of Niihau, are found on the coastal plain of Niihau. Kaula Island, 22 miles southwest of Niihau, is a tuff cone crowning an independent submarine volcanic dome (Fig. 11-2).[160] Its ashes were not found on Niihau.

The uplands are the dissected remnant of an ancient volcano and are covered with about 5 feet of red soil, which is underlain by 20 to 50 feet of partly decomposed basalt. Dikes exposed in the interstream divides indicate that the original dome surfaces have been worn down about 100 feet. Niihau extended about 6 miles farther east than it does now, in relation to present sea level. Like the other volcanoes, it probably had a caldera (Fig. 11-3), and at some time it may have been connected to Kauai, as the channel

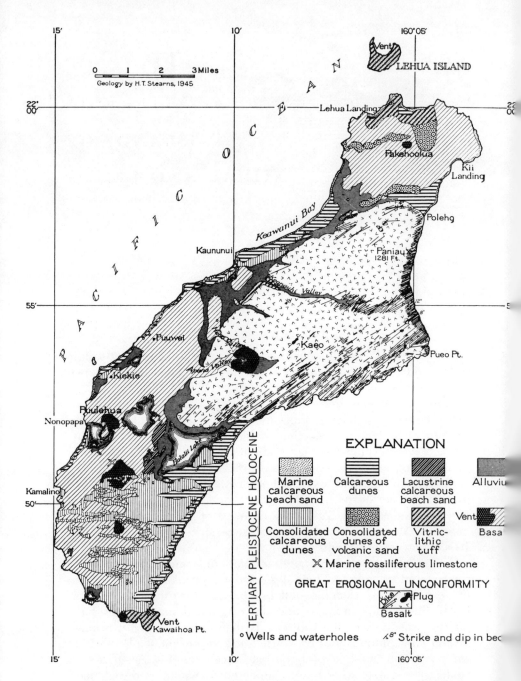

Figure 11-1—Geologic map of the island of Niihau. The Pleistocene basalts are the Kiekie volcanic series and the Tertiary basalts are the Paniau volcanic series.

between them is only 2,550 feet deep. Niihau rises 13,000 feet above the ocean floor to the north and south.

The lowlands have a complex origin. Surrounding Niihau are a submarine shelf 300 feet below sea level and 1 to 2 miles wide and a narrower shelf 60 feet below sea level. Several tuff and lava cones erupted through the broad shelf and have built it above sea level to form the coastal plain (Fig. 11-5). During the minus 350-foot stand of the sea, much sand was blown inland, especially on the southeastern coast, to form dunes 150 feet high. These dunes became cemented with the subsequent rise in sea level. Marine limestones were found up to 100 feet above sea level.

GEOLOGY OF NIIHAU

General character and age of the rocks. The highlands of Niihau, and presumably also the basement of the dome, are built chiefly of thin lava flows poured out rapidly from a dome-shaped shield volcano. The flows are tholeiitic basalt, and include both aa and pahoehoe types. No soils, and only a few thin vitric and vitric-lithic tuff beds, are interstratified with the flows in the part of the cone above sea level. Numerous dikes, half a foot to 17 feet thick, cut the dome remnant. Most of them trend northeast-southwest. Cinder cones are absent. Faulting has disturbed the beds in the heart of the dike complex. The Paniau volcanic series are the volcanic rocks composing the remnant of the ancient shield volcano of Niihau (Fig. 11-1).

The Kiekie volcanic series, of Pleistocene age, form the coastal plain of Niihau. In contrast to the thin-bedded lavas in the ancient dome remnant, the later lavas of the plain are massive and nearly horizontal, and consist chiefly of pahoehoe. Except at Kawaewae cone, the lavas welled out quietly, forming small secondary lava domes without cinders and with only a little spatter. The Lehua Island and Kawaihoa cones erupted violently, spreading ash far and wide, because sea water entered their vents. The exposed parts of their cones are subaerially deposited consolidated ash. The cones of the Kiekie volcanic series trend slightly west of north, in contrast to the northeast-trending rifts of the Paniau volcanic series.

The sedimentary rocks are composed of older and younger alluvium, calcareous beach and dune sand, playa deposits, and dunes of cemented ash. Small outcrops of highly fossiliferous emerged reef exist in three places. Recent cemented calcareous beach deposits, commonly called beach rock, lie along some of the coast.

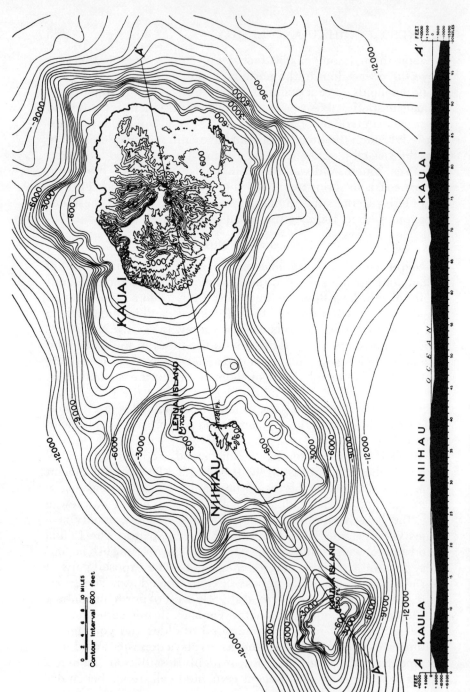

Figure 11-2—Map of Niihau and Kauai showing submarine contours and profile along the line A-A'.

The age of the Kiekie volcanic series is determined by its relation to the shorelines of probable Pleistocene age. All the lavas on the coastal plain are older than the − 350±-foot stand of the sea, which appears to be correlative with the Illinoian stage of glaciation. Most of the lithified dunes were formed during the Waipio low stand of the sea. Emerged reef of the plus 100-foot stand of the sea lies on Kawaihoa cone, and Kawaewae cone was cliffed by seas higher than the 100-foot stand. The lava forming the northern part of the coastal plain is probably of late Pleistocene age, as there is no evidence on it of the 100-foot stand of the sea, and the rocks are only slightly decomposed. In contrast, the rest of the lavas forming the plain are rotted to a depth of several feet. They are all older than the 100-foot stand of the sea, which occurred during the Yarmouth interglacial stage. The older lavas on the plain are tentatively assigned to the early (?) and middle Pleistocene.

The dome remnant was deeply eroded prior to the extrusion of the Kiekie volcanic series, and its rocks are now partly decomposed to a depth of 50 feet on the interstream ridges. The 300-foot submarine shelf, which is well developed on the dome remnant, is believed to be of Pleistocene age. The rocks of the Paniau volcanic series in the dome remnant above sea level have a radiogenic age of 3 million years.[84] It is probable that building of the dome from the ocean floor began in middle Pliocene time.

TABLE 17

STRATIGRAPHIC ROCK UNITS ON THE ISLAND OF NIIHAU

Age	Rock assemblage	
	Sedimentary rocks	Volcanic rocks
Holocene	Younger alluvium, playa deposits, and unconsolidated calcareous beach and dune sand	
Pleistocene	Lithified calcareous dunes, emerged marine limestone, dunes of volcanic sand, and older alluvium	Olivine basalts and vitric-lithic tuff of the Kiekie volcanic series
Great erosional unconformity		
Pliocene		Basalt and correlative dikes and plugs of the Paniau volcanic series

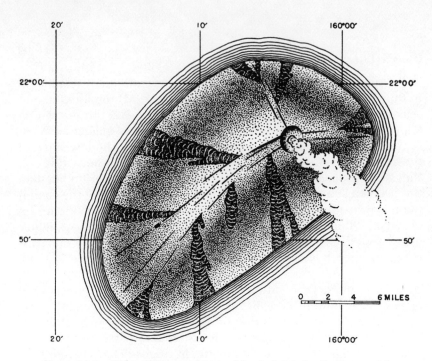

Figure 11-3—Niihau after completion of the tholeiitic basalt dome and formation of the caldera.

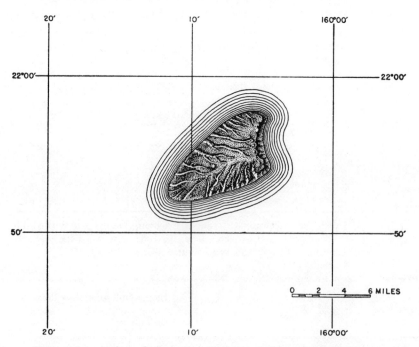

Figure 11-4—Niihau after a period of erosion and the partial submergence of the tholeiitic basalt dome.

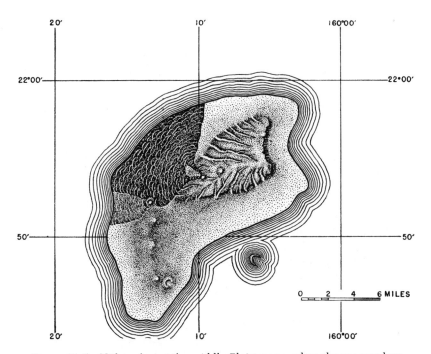

Figure 11-5—Niihau during the middle Pleistocene, when the sea was lowered by the removal of water to form the continental glaciers. Several secondary volcanic eruptions have occurred.

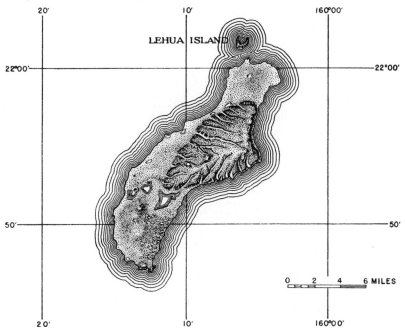

LEHUA ISLAND

Figure 11-6—Present form of Niihau, showing dunes and playa lakes in southern end of island.

The rock units are summarized in Table 17 and their distribution in Figure 11-1.

Great erosional unconformity. The rocks in the Paniau volcanic series are separated from all other rocks by a profound erosional unconformity. The Tertiary shield volcano underwent a long period of weathering, when streams cut canyons into its carapace, and the sea made cliffed headlands of the interstream divides. The Pleistocene basalts in Apana and Haao valleys rest against steep valley walls. All rocks on the coastal plain lie against cliffs or talus fans. The talus fans that extend below sea level are apparently subaerial in origin, and they indicate that the island stood relatively higher at the time they were formed. This greater altitude would have resulted in greater rainfall on the island and an accelerated rate of weathering and stream erosion.

LEHUA ISLAND

Lehua Island, about 1 mile long, nearly half a mile wide, and 702 feet high, is composed of subaerial tuff.[160] The vent lay in the sea on the north side of the islet, and a strong north wind was blowing during the eruption, as shown by the pronounced asymmetry of the cone and deposits of ash as much as 8 miles to the south. The tuff above sea level in Lehua Island is 702 feet thick, and it extends to an unknown depth below sea level. It is more than 15 feet thick on the tip of Niihau opposite Lehua Island. Much of the ash from the eruption must have fallen into the sea. The tuff is black and upon weathering turns to a tan powdery soil, which makes it easily differentiated from the red soils on the basalts. The tuff contains much glass and many fragments of vitreous basalt derived from the exploding magma. Some beds are breccias and contain many large angular fragments. There appear to be remnants of a wave-cut bench at least 30 feet above sea level on the southern shore of Lehua Island, but it was not examined on the ground.

Ash on Niihau. After the explosions on Lehua Island, ash mantled most of Niihau; remnants of Lehua tuff are found as far south as Puulehua. The ash is a foot thick on the summit ridge 1 mile northwest of Pueo Point. The few small patches shown in Figure 11-1 are by no means all of the ash-covered areas; many of the grass-covered flats in the upland country are probably covered with a foot or more of ash. Large quantities were carried down the main stream valleys to the coastal plain, as shown by 6 feet of ash from Lehua Island near the mouth of Keanauhi Valley, 7 miles southwest of Lehua Island. The whole northern part of the coastal plain now mapped as lava was covered with 5 to 15 feet of the ash. It still remains in most of the low places, but to map the area as ash-covered would obscure the Pleistocene basalt dome. Following the deposition of the ash in this area, the winds piled it into dunes, which have since become lithified. Two of these dune ridges were large enough to justify mapping.

The ash dunes extend into the sea at the western coast, where a wide marine bench has been cut into them; hence, it is concluded that the eruption occurred during the Waipio low stand of the sea in Illinoian time. The vent must, however, have opened below sea level, as the explosion was the violent hydromagmatic type.

GEOLOGIC HISTORY OF NIIHAU AND LEHUA ISLANDS

1. Building of a dome-shaped island about 2,500 feet above present sea level and about 13,000 feet above the adjacent ocean floor, by the outpouring of basalt flows from a shield volcano with its eruptive center about two miles east of Niihau, and from a strongly developed rift zone extending southwestward from the center (Fig. 11-3). By analogy with other Hawaiian domes, a caldera probably indented the summit, as shown in Figure 11-3. The eastern rim of the caldera may have been lower than the western, as the eastern side was destroyed by subsequent erosion more rapidly than the western side.

2. Cessation of volcanism and establishment of a stream pattern.

3. Long period during which high marine cliffs were formed on the eastern and southeastern coasts and lower ones on all other coasts. Streams cut canyons in the dome. Weathering formed deep red soil on the interstream divides.

4. Gradual submergence of the island by a large but unknown amount, in common with the other islands of the archipelago (Fig. 11-4). The island probably reached stability during the middle Pleistocene.

5. During the Pleistocene, many shifts in sea level occurred, from about 250 feet above to at least 300 feet below present level. A coral reef 0.5 to 1.5 miles wide, now 350 feet below present sea level, indicates long halts of the sea at that level. Reefs grew during rising seas.

6. Concurrently with the shifting seas of the Pleistocene, vol-

canism was renewed and lava and tuff built the submarine shelf above sea level. Buried cones are known to lie below sea level (Fig. 11-5).

7. During the 100-foot stand of the sea, the northern part of the coastal plain was still under water and Lehua Island had not yet erupted.

8. During the Waipio low stand of the sea, sand blowing inland built extensive calcareous dunes, and a narrow shelf was formed around the island. A lava dome built the northern part of the coastal plain above sea level, and Lehua Island was formed by a submarine explosion. Ash from Lehua Island fell over most of Niihau and soon thereafter was blown into dunes on the northern plain.

9. The sea rose to 25 feet above present sea level, drowning the seaward parts of the dunes. Vegetation spread over the rest and cementation occurred. Playa lakes formed in depressions in the lowlands.

10. The sea fell below present sea level and then rose to about 2 feet above present sea level.

11. The sea regressed to about 350 feet below present sea level during the Wisconsinan glacial epoch.

12. Rise of the sea from the glacial low stand of about 350 feet to present sea level, when modern beaches and dunes formed (Fig. 11-6).

13. Feral goats in historic time ate so much of the vegetation that much of the deep red soil on the uplands, formed during the million years or more since the cessation of volcanism there, was washed into the lowlands, filling up Hawaiian fish ponds and many of the playas. With the extinction of the goats, the introduction of kiawe, haole koa, and other desert plants is slowly reclaiming the eroded areas of the island.

12

NORTHWESTERN HAWAIIAN ISLANDS AND OFFSHORE ISLETS

NORTHWESTERN HAWAIIAN ISLANDS

Extending northwestward from Niihau are 26 islets, reefs, and shoals known as the Northwestern Hawaiian Islands or Leeward Islands. They mark the summits of submarine volcanoes (Fig. 1-2). West of Gardner Island (Fig. 1-2, no. 17), only low coral islands are found, whereas to the east are many remnants of basaltic cones. The numbers in the following classified list refer to the numbers in Figure 1-2. For further data see bibliography numbers 25, 38, 53, 68, 77, 156, 237.

Kaula is a secondary tuff cone built on a reef platform;[160] the other volcanic islands are probably eroded remnants of primary volcanic domes. The rocks are composed of andesine, picrite, olivine, and nepheline basalts.[237] Alkalic basalt is rare. The one specimen of nepheline basalt was collected on Necker Island from a dike that may have been the feeder to a secondary flow; but from the published description, this basalt appears to contain anemousite feldspar. If so, the lava probably belongs to the alkalic phase. A pilot observed a submarine eruption between Necker and Nihoa islands on August 20, 1955.[117]

Coralline algae and corals are the principal constituent of the living and emerged reefs. At Midway, and probably at some of the nearby islands, the reefs contain an appreciable number of barnacles. The emerged reef on Midway stands 5 feet above sea level and

TABLE 18

Altitudes of Northwestern Hawaiian Ilands

		Height (feet)

Volcanic Islands

17.	Gardner Pinnacles (basalt flows and dikes)	190
21.	La Pérouse Pinnacle in French Frigate Atoll (basalt flows)	122
23.	Necker (basalt flows and dikes)	277
24.	Nihoa (basalt flows and dikes)	910
26.	Kaula (tuff)	550

Emerged Coral Atolls or Near Atolls [a]

3.	Kure or Ocean (name of atoll)	—
4.	Green (sand island inside of Kure atoll)	20
6.	Midway	43
8.	Pearl and Hermes	12
9.	Lisianski	44
14.	Laysan	56

Coral Atolls or Near Atolls

1.	Unnamed	Breakers
2.	Bensaleux	Breakers
10.	Fisher	Breakers
11.	Minor	Breakers
15.	Maro (Dowsett)	Breakers
18.	Two Brothers	?
22.	French Frigate (excluding La Pérouse Pinnacle)	10

Shoals (Probably Submerged Atolls)

5.	Nero	−492
7.	Gambia	− 84
12.	Neva	− 18
13.	Springbank	−108
16.	Raita	− 54
19.	St. Rogatien	− 72
20.	Brooks	− 84
25.	Unnamed	−192

[a]The height given is measured to the top of sand dunes and does not indicate amount of emergence. The highest known emerged reef is only about 5 feet. The literature does not clearly state the evidence of emergence except for Midway and Pearl and Hermes islands.

indicates a late, apparently worldwide, emergence of this amount.[201] Test holes on Midway indicate that the reef caps a deeply eroded basaltic volcano that subsided beneath the ocean prior to the middle Miocene.[68,99] Radiogenic ages indicate Niihoa Island to be about 7 million and Necker Island to be about 10 million years old.[38] Thus, the Northwestern Hawaiian Islands considerably predate the visible part of the main Hawaiian Islands. A gravity survey for several of the Northwestern Hawaiian Islands has been completed, and no indication was found of any systematic change from southeast to northwest in Bouguer anomaly values.[95] Richard Grigg found the minus 60-foot and the minus 120-foot notch cut by the sea in the Pleistocene on most of the islands.

OFFSHORE ISLETS

Thirty-nine islets shown in Figure 1-1 lie close to the main islands. Islets numbered 1, 2, 3, 12, 16, 23, and 33 are secondary tuff cones of late Pleistocene or Holocene age. Those numbered 4, 5, 8, 20 21, 22, 24, 25, 26, 28, 29, 30, 31, 34, 35, 36, 37, 38, and 39 are remnants of lava flows isolated from the main islands by marine erosion. Islets 11 and 15 are part of the dike complex of the Koolau Volcano; 7, 9, and 10 are lithified dunes of the Waipio terrace stage; 17, 27, and 32 are remnants of cinder cones; 13 is the remnant of a secondary nepheline basalt flow or crater fill; 19 is composed of reef limestone, Salt Lake tuff, and earthy sediments; 6 and 14 are emerged reef limestone; and 18 is of unconsolidated sand and has been enlarged by dredged material.

13

PETROLOGY, CHEMISTRY, AND GEOPHYSICAL PROPERTIES OF HAWAIIAN LAVAS

The lavas of the domes are now separated into a *tholeiitic suite* and an *alkalic suite*.[110] The tholeiitic suite includes all the basalts making up the bulk of the shield, such as tholeiite, olivine tholeiite, oceanite, and the single rhyodacite flow in Kuwale Ridge, Oahu, that has been previously called trachyte. The alkalic suite includes all the types of differentiated rocks that form the cap or "frosting" on the dark basaltic shield. They are alkalic basalt, alkalic olivine basalt, ankaramite, Hawaiite, mugearite, and trachyte. Hawaiite and mugearite were previously called andesites, but they are very different physically from the andesites of the continents. Trachytes are found only on Hualalai, Kohala, West Maui, and East Molokai volcanoes. *Gabbros* are coarse-grained intrusive rocks of basaltic composition found in sills, stocks, plugs, necks, pipes, and xenoliths. Xenoliths of eclogite found in Salt Lake Crater tuff contain reddish garnet crystals.[82] They are the only known eclogite inclusions found so far in oceanic areas. The age of the eclogite has been determined by radiogenic methods to be 1.4 billion years, but it may have gained argon from host rocks.[102]

Jackson and Wright concluded that: (1) the basalts are genetically related to the xenoliths, being rock fragments of the source region from which the Koolau and Honolulu volcanic series were derived by fractional melting; (2) the compositional diversity of the Honolulu series reflects heterogeneity of the upper mantle beneath Oahu; and (3) the Honolulu series magmas were generated at greater depth than the Koolau magmas. They found that rocks of the Honolulu series are zoned, compositionally, with respect to their location on the Koolau shield. The predominant rocks nearest the former Koolau caldera are melilite-nepheline basalts; these change outward to nepheline basalts and, finally, to alkalic olivine basalts. They found, also, that the xenoliths were zoned compositionally around the Koolau caldera. Those nearest the caldera are mostly dunite with subordinate lherzolite. Lherzolite becomes abundant at greater distances, and near the outer edge of the shield garnet pyroxenite and peridotite xenoliths are prominent.[85]

The K-Ar ages of some of the lavas in the Honolulu series are given in Table 19.

The strontium isotopic data also demonstrate the heterogeneity of the mantle source regions for basalt beneath Oahu. The source

TABLE 19
K-AR AGE OF SOME BASALTS OF
THE HONOLULU VOLCANIC SERIES

Vent name	Calculated age (thousands of years)
Salt Lake	431 ± 21[a]
Kalihi	460 ± 16[a]
	580 ± 2[b]
Punchbowl	296 ± 8[a]
	530 ± 4[b]
Luakaha in Nuuanu Valley	419 ± 12[a]
	360 ± 6[b]
Sugar Loaf	67 ± 3[a]
Kaau	647 ± 16[a]
Kaimuki	283 ± 12[a]
Mauumae	430 ± 4[b]
Black Point	297 ± 9[a]
	480 ± 8[b]
Black Point Dike	410 ± 4[b]
Koko	39.5 ± 1.6[a]
Kalama	34.2 ± 4.5[a]
Kaupo	32 ± 4[a]

[a]Average of Gramlich, et al.[65] The Castle basalt is omitted from the table because its age indicates contamination.

[b]Average of Lanphere and Dalrymple.[100]

regions from which the Koolau and Honolulu basalts were derived must have had different Rb/Sr ratios for a long period of time in order to develop the differences in $^{87}Sr/^{86}Sr$ observed in the derivative basalts.[100] Lanphere and Dalrymple concluded also that the age of the source region of the Honolulu basalts is about 1,250 m.y. They found the $^{87}Sr/^{86}Sr$ to vary from 0.70298 ± 36 to 0.70340 ± 14 in the Honolulu basalts, whereas the Koolau tholeiites varied from 0.70329 ± 16 to 0.70406 ± 12. Sun and Hanson interpret the $^{87}Sr/^{86}Sr$ versus Rb/Sr correlation for alkalic basalts (including nephelinites)

TABLE 20

CHEMICAL COMPOSITION OF TYPICAL HAWAIIAN ROCKS

[From Eaton and Murata (1960)]

Compound formula	Tholeiitic basalt series *				Alkalic basalt series †		
	A	B	C	D	E	F	G
SiO_2	50.94	50.08	46.59	62.23	50.09	62.19	43.28
Al_2O_3	12.97	13.73	6.69	12.03	19.49	17.43	14.43
Fe_2O_3	1.95	1.32	2.20	5.55	0.73	1.65	0.70
FeO	8.96	9.79	10.46	4.76	8.47	2.64	10.92
MgO	10.68	7.89	21.79	2.05	4.33	0.40	11.68
CaO	9.88	11.50	7.41	4.25	6.92	0.86	11.22
Na_2O	1.99	2.18	1.33	3.20	4.82	8.28	2.49
K_2O	0.37	0.56	0.28	1.36	1.93	5.03	0.83
H_2O+	0.12	0.02	0.37	0.33	.32	0.39	0.05
H_2O-	0.04	0.00	0.04	0.52	.08	0.14	0.03
TiO_2	1.78	2.60	1.83	2.18	2.47	0.37	4.12
P_2O_5	0.21	0.26	0.11	0.01	0.78	0.14	0.31
MnO	0.17	0.17	0.18	0.43	0.15	0.32	0.13
CO_2	0.04	0.01				0.02	
Cr_2O_3			0.13			tr.	0.10
NiO			0.12				
SO_3			0.00			0.00	0.20
Total	100.10	100.11	100.53	99.21‡	100.58	99.93§	100.54‖

* (A) Tholeiitic olivine basalt. Mauna Loa, at highway at south boundary of Waiakea Forest Reserve, 2.65 km northwest of the Olaa sugar mill, island of Hawaii. Analyst, L. N. Tarrant (31). (B) Tholeiitic basalt, Kilauea, splash from lava lake, 1917, island of Hawaii. Analyst, L. N. Tarrant. Reanalysis of a previously described sample. New analyses published with permission of H. A. Powers (19). (C) Mafitic gabbro porphyry, Kilauea, Uwekahuna laccolith in the wall of the caldera, island of Hawaii. Analyst, G. Steiger (32). (D) Granophyre, Koolau Volcano, quartz dolerite dike at Palolo quarry in the southeastern part of Honolulu, island of Oahu. Analyst, K. Nagashima (33). † (E) Hawaiite (andesine andesite), Mauna Kea, elevation 2700 feet, on northwest flank near Nohonaohae, island of Hawaii, Analyst, H. S. Washington (16). (F) Trachyte obsidian, Hualalai, Puu Waawaa, island of Hawaii. Analyst, W. F. Hillebrand (15). (G) Picritic alkalic basalt, Haleakala Volcano, lava flow of 1750(?) on the southwest slope near Makena, island of Maui. Analyst, M. G. Keyes (34). ‡ Includes 0.31 SrO. § Includes 0.03 BaO and 0.04 ZrO₂. ‖ Includes 0.05 BaO.

from oceanic islands as indicating about 2 billion years for the age of the heterogeneities in the mantle source regions.[226]
The uranium content of the tholeiitic basalts varies from 0.21 to 1.8 ppm and increases in quantity in the late differentiated lavas.[101] The chemical composition of some typical Hawaiian rocks is given in Table 20.
The proportions of the alkali rocks and rock types in the caps are shown in Tables 21 and 22.

TABLE 21
PROPORTION OF ALKALI ROCKS IN HAWAIIAN VOLCANOES[113]

	Per cent of volume of volcano
Kohala Mountain (Hawaii) ..	0.1
West Maui	3.0
East Maui (Haleakala)	0.8
Mauna Kea (Hawaii)	0.7
Waianae Range, Oahu	0.3

TABLE 22
PROPORTION OF ROCK TYPES IN CAPS OF HAWAIIAN VOLCANOES[113]

	Per cent
Alkalic basalt	41.0
Hawaiite and mugearites	56.5
Ankaramite	1.7
Trachyte	0.8

The data above indicate that the alkalic suite of rocks is derived by crystal settling, gas transfer, and filter pressing, from the parent tholeiitic magma in compartments within the upper crust. The volume of the tholeiites is 1,000 times greater in oceanic areas than the alkali lavas.[55] Trace elements differentiate the several rock types.
A very detailed study by Benson of the petrology, mineralogy, and geochemistry of the East Molokai volcanic series along the Kalaupapa trail has been made recently.[19] The study revealed that the fractionation trend is discontinuous during the growth of a basaltic shield volcano. It proceeds in several steps toward more fractionated compositions and then reverts abruptly to a less frac-

tionated composition. Petrologically, the lavas in the lower part of the section are alkalic, but chemically they are tholeiitic and are best classified as transitional between tholeiitic and alkalic basalt. The lavas in the upper part of the section are alkalic.

The Kalaupapa section can be divided into 8 subsections on the basis of the discontinuous fractionation trend. The subsections are believed to have resulted from distinct magmatic batches that are generated in the mantle on a periodic rather than on a continuous basis.

The nepheline and nepheline-melilite basalts and associated rocks are always separated from the tholeiitic and alkalic suites by a great erosional unconformity representing about 1,000,000 years of time. These unusual rocks occur only on Kauai, Niihau, West Maui, and Oahu. Some of them contain pegmatoid veinlets and cavities filled with deuteric and hydrothermal minerals.[48] Evidence has been presented that the nepheline-bearing rocks are not formed by absorption of limestone from buried reefs.[205] Analyses of typical rocks from the Honolulu volcanic series are shown in Table 23.

A few of the significant points of the geophysical structure of the Hawaiian Ridge, as summarized by Woollard,[254] follow:

1. The mantle, in general, appears to be similar to dunite, with a seismic velocity of 8.15 km/sec and a density of 3.33 gm/cc.

2. The mean density contrast of the mantle and crust is 0.475 gm/cc, giving a free board to root ratio of 1 to 6.0 for conditions of hydrostatic equilibrium.

3. The changes in crustal root for changes in surface elevation based on the preceding ratio can be reconciled closely with gravity data for changes in surface elevation, assuming isostatic conditions.

4. Mantle-like material is trapped at shallow depth in all primary pipes or necks along the Hawaiian Ridge, but presumably the mineralogy of this trapped mantle-like material is not the same as that existing in the mantle, because of loss of certain constituents by eruption and gaseous disseminations and dissimilar conditions of crystallization.

The *mantle* is the material lying between the earth's core at a depth of 2,900 km and that depth at which the velocity of seismic compressional waves increases from values of about 6.5–7.0 km/sec to 8.15 ± 0.5 km/sec. Its average depth beneath the Ridge is about 49,000 feet (15 km).[225] The average mantle velocity found in the Pacific is greater than that found in the Atlantic and under the continents. The mantle is probably heterogeneous. The density of

TABLE 23

ANALYSES OF BASALTS OF THE HONOLULU VOLCANIC SERIES[252]

	(12) 9962	(13) 9982	(14) 10402	(15) 9961	(16) 10399	(17) 10400	(18) 9960	(19)	(20) 10401	(A)	(B)
				ANALYSES—WEIGHT PER CENT							
SiO_2	45.13	42.86	43.94	38.57	36.72	37.10	36.75	36.34	37.22	43.98	37.12
TiO_2	2.94	2.94	2.32	2.79	2.82	2.90	2.41	2.87	2.02	2.73	2.64
Al_2O_3	16.40	11.46	12.60	11.71	11.56	11.12	11.98	10.14	12.08	13.49	11.43
Fe_2O_3	3.42	3.34	3.84	5.21	4.94	6.53	6.05	6.53	5.18	3.53	5.74
FeO	8.17	9.03	9.18	7.78	8.17	7.31	7.45	10.66	7.88	8.79	8.19
MnO	.07	.13	.09	.11	.13	.09	.08	.20	.11	.10	.12
MgO	5.52	13.61	11.43	13.08	13.27	12.81	12.08	10.68	12.71	10.19	12.44
CaO	11.30	11.24	10.78	12.84	14.34	13.56	13.81	13.10	13.34	11.11	13.50
Na_2O	3.62	3.02	3.84	4.22	3.93	4.56	4.75	4.54	5.12	3.49	4.52
K_2O	1.02	.93	1.02	1.20	.62	1.20	.91	1.78	.71	.99	1.07
H_2O-	.42	.12	.02	.19	.41	.04	.36	1.00	.23	.19	.37
H_2O+	1.16	.44	.36	.59	1.63	1.11	1.61	1.00	1.73	.65	1.28
CO_2	.05	none	none	.27	none	none	none	.15	none	.02	.07
P_2O_5	.66	.52	.43	1.11	.82	1.19	1.41	1.02	1.40	.54	1.16
SO_3	.17	.22	.21	.17	.31	.34	.17	.10	.17	.20	.21
BaO	.06	.04	.08	.08	.11	.13	.13	n.d.	.12	.06	.11
SrO	none	none	none	none	none	none	none	n.d.	none	none	none
Cr_2O_3	none	.04	none	.06	.07	.04	.03	n.d.	.03	.01	.05
Sum	100.11	99.94	100.14	99.98	99.85	100.03	99.98	100.11	100.05	100.07	100.02

(12) Honolulu linosaite from southwest edge of flow in gulch north of Hanauma Bay, Koko Head. Gonyer, analyst.

(13) Honolulu nepheline basanite from south tip of Black Point (Kupikipikio). Gonyer, analyst.

(14) Honolulu nepheline basanite from Kalama Crater flow at road cut on east side of Kamehameha highway between Koko Crater and Makapuu Head. Gonyer, analyst.

(15) Honolulu nepheline basalt from lower Nuuanu (Luakaha) flow, northwest bank of Nuuanu Stream above Kapena Pool. Gonyer, analyst.

(16) Honolulu nepheline-melilite basalt from Kaau lava flow on east side of Waiomao Road. Gonyer, analyst.

(17) Honolulu nepheline basalt from prominent outcrop of Training School flow. Gonyer, analyst.

(18) Honolulu nepheline-melilite basalt from Kalihi flow in Kalihi stream channel at Water Reserve boundary. Elevation 600 feet. Gonyer, analyst.

(19) Honolulu "nephelite-melilite basalt, Moiliili quarry, Oahu" (Cross, 1915, p. 22). Known as Sugar Loaf flow (Stearns and Vaksvik, 1935). Steiger, analyst.

(20) Honolulu nepheline-melilite basalt from flow north of Puu Hawaiiloa, Mokapu Peninsula. Gonyer, analyst.

(A) Average of columns (12)–(14), inclusive.

(B) Average of columns (15)–(20), inclusive.

the crust of the Pacific is also greater than that in the Atlantic. Woollard believes that the only rock that fits the conditions of the mantle is one composed predominantly of olivine, having a density of 3.33 gm/cc, as eclogites have too high a density and too low a seismic velocity.[254] Some other scientists are not in accord with this conclusion.

Normal basalts have a velocity of 4.5 km/sec and a density of about 2.35 gm/cc. Manghnani gives the relation of velocity to density in Hawaiian lavas. [254] According to Strange, low density flows

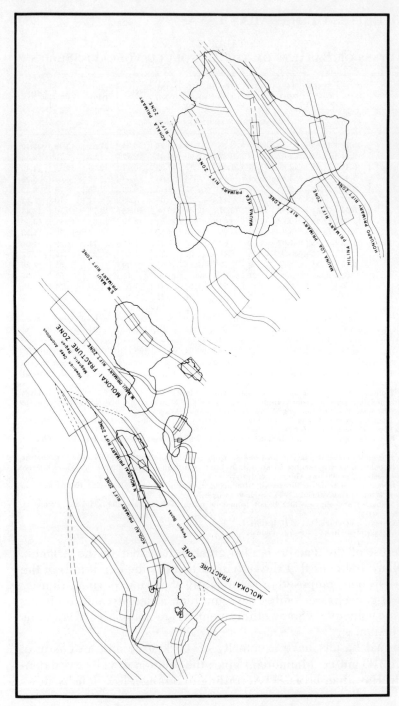

Figure 13-1—Map of islands from Oahu to Hawaii showing primary rift zones parallel to the Molokai Fracture zone and subsurface dense volcanic pipes (rectangles), as determined by aeromagnetic surveys. (After Malahoff and Woollard, 1965.)

extend down to 6,500 to 10,000 feet under the Hawaiian Ridge, indicating a submergence of this amount after the ridge had been built.[254] However, some of the low density material at the bottom of the column may be shallow, porous submarine volcanics. The crust of the Pacific has a mean density of 2.90 gm/cc.

The pipes under the ancient Koolau and Waianae calderas are marked by local gravity anomalies of about +110 mgals (+310 mgals absolute Bouguer), and densities of 2.9 to 3.2 gr/cc. Adams obtains a width of the Koolau plug of about 17,800 feet down to 10,000 feet.[254] The top of the plug is more than 2,600 feet below the surface but less than 6,600 feet; hence, it can be reached by a test hole.

The magnetic susceptibilities of Hawaiian basalts range generally from 1×10^{-3} cgs units to 4×10^{-3} cgs units, with the exception of the Kula formation on West Maui, according to Malahoff.[254] Part of his conclusions from a survey of the islands using an airborne proton magnetometer follow:

1. Positive and negative magnetic anomalies trend from east-northeast direction across the Hawaiian Ridge without major deflections and continue in a W-SW direction.

2. Deflections of the trends occur along an axis somewhat parallel to the axis of the Hawaiian Ridge on the islands of Molokai and Oahu that correspond, at least on Oahu, to volcanic rift intrusions [Fig. 13-1].

3. No significant change in the total force magnetic field occurs on crossing the Hawaiian Swell.

4. It appears that the magnetic anomalies originate from areas of differentiated rocks, richer in magnetic minerals than the parent basaltic magma or poorer in magnetic minerals than the surrounding basalt.

The gravity data indicate that the rift zones are of two distinctly different types. Rift zones such as those in Haleakala Crater on Maui have little gravity or magnetic effect and apparently are rather superficial features. However, rift zones with a large gravitational effect, such as the northwest rift zone of the Koolau volcanic center, are very basic structural features extending downward at least to the Mohorovičić discontinuity.[225]

THE MOHOLE

Mohole is a word derived from the Moho discontinuity and hole.[254] Moho is an abbreviation of the name of the man, Mohorovičić, who first described the discontinuity between the crust and the mantle. In early 1965 the decision was reached by the National Science Foundation to drill the test hole about 120 miles northeast of Maui (Fig. 2-10). The site selected at about 22° 21′ N and 155° 28′ W was the result of intensive studies by the Hawaii

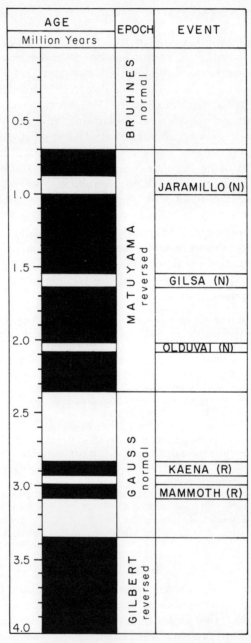

Figure 13-2—Magnetic polarity epochs during last 4 million years. (N) Normal (R) Reversed. (After McDougall and Chamberlain[128] and Aziz-ur-Rahman[127].)

Institute of Geophysics, the Western Geophysical Company, and Shor and Pollard.[190] The Mohole project was finally abandoned because of its cost.

GEOMAGNETISM

When a lava flow pours out, the ferromagnetic grains in the melt (magnetite and ilmenite) become oriented to the earth's magnetic field before the lava solidifies. Thus, they record the magnetism of the earth's field on that particular day. Instruments have been devised for measuring this remanent magnetism with great accuracy, a study that has led to the discovery that the position of the North and South poles has been reversed several times. These intervals are called normal and reversed magnetic epochs, and have been given names (Fig. 13-2). The duration of the epochs has been determined by the K-Ar method of dating the rocks in which they occur. As more measurements were made, it was found that short flips of the polarity occur within some of the magnetic epochs. These flips are called "events" and are named after places where they were discovered: for example, the Olduvai event is named after Olduvai Gorge in Africa, where the oldest fossil man was found.

A rock from the Dillingham Quarry on the north side of the Waianae Range was tested, and a new event in the Gauss epoch was found.[217] It was named the Kaena event, from Kaena Point.[128] The Kaena event now has been found to be worldwide. Paleomagnetism is the word used to describe prehistoric magnetic conditions. Rocks of the main Kauai dome have normal magnetism, but the later Koloa lavas have reversed magnetism.[229] Most of the rocks of the Waianae Range on Oahu have normal magnetism, but those of the Koolau Range have reversed magnetism. Geomagnetism of the other Hawaiian Islands has been determined.[46, 130]

14

MINERAL

RESOURCES

SEMIPRECIOUS GEMS

Pele's tears. Pele, the Hawaiian goddess of fire at Kilauea, is weeping over the deceptions carried out in her name. The jewelry stores in Hawaii have been loaded since 1962 with earrings and other ornaments made of fake Pele's tears. Pele's tears are nearly opaque black glassy droplets broken from the ends of filaments of glass drifting away from fire fountains. They are abundant around Halemaumau on Kilauea. The writer has never seen genuine tears in jewelry stores. Instead, the so-called Pele's tears sold commercially are transparent pale black obsidian tumble stones imported from the mainland, where such stones retail for about 5 cents each.

Pele's hair is abundant during eruptions on Hawaii, but is so delicate that it soon disappears. It is the glass filaments resulting from the action of the fire fountains and is similar to glass wool insulation. No attempt has yet been made to use it for jewelry.

Pele's pearls are of diverse origin. The early ones were polished gems of hemispherical calcite from cavities in the old Dillingham Quarry, located along the former railroad in Waikele Gulch behind Waipahu, Oahu. The quarry is now in a Naval Ammunition Depot area and closed to the public. Pele's pearls have been made from chalcedony from cavities in lavas found near Kailua, Oahu, and from translucent calcite found on Diamond Head and in Lualualei Valley, Oahu. Hemispherical calcite exists in cavities along with

286

stellate clusters of aragonite in a lava flow cut by the main highway 5½ miles east of Hawi, Hawaii.

Hawaiian diamonds were first cut from calcite from Diamond Head, but others have been made from quartz crystals found in the Kailua-Kaneohe area, Oahu. Perfectly terminated clear crystals of quartz 1 inch × 2 inches are found in the soil on the basalt ridges behind Kailua. Calcite crystals are abundant in the fault depression on the summit of West Molokai.

Hawaiian moonstones are banded agate and chalcedony formerly abundant in the gullies near Olomana Peak, Oahu, and in the crater of West Molokai. The Oahu material came from cavities in the basalts and dikes in the ancient Koolau caldera (Kailua volcanic series), and the ancient Waianae caldera in Lualualei Valley, Oahu. Amateur lapidaries have cut many stones.

Hawaiian sunstones are cut from clear pale yellow crystals of plagioclase feldspar, abundant on the cinder cone at Manele Bay, Lanai. They are too light-colored to be desirable. Others are abundant at Pohakea Pass, Oahu. They have been sold in the trade as Hawaiian topaz.

Hawaiian olivines (sold in the gem trade as peridots) are too small to cut, although one-sixteenth to one-eighth carat clear stones are abundant, especially in the 1840 lava flow in Puna, Hawaii. Olivines sold commercially in Hawaii are imported from the southwestern states because local specimens are too small. The green sands on the beaches of Diamond Head and Hanauma Bay, Oahu, and near South Point, Hawaii, when magnified, can be seen as perfect clear crystals of olivine. They are washed by the waves out of tuff. Excellent crystals of augite and olivine can be collected on the slopes of Puu Io, Puu Keaaliulia, Puu Paapaa, and Puu Pa on Mauna Kea, Hawaii.

Red and yellow jasper, which takes a good polish, is found in the weathered Koolau basalt ridges behind Kaneohe. None has yet appeared in the gem trade.

Petrified (silicified) coral is found on the Ewa coral plain, Oahu, but it has little character for jewelry.

Silicified wood is common on South Point and on the Saddle Road, Hawaii, but it is poor cutting material.[153]

Zeolites were formerly abundant in the abandoned Moiliili Quarry, now on the University of Hawaii campus. The cavities in the lavas carried abundant well-crystallized zeolites.[48]

Black coral is not fossil coral, but is collected from living "trees" in deep water chiefly off Lahaina, Maui, and Kauai. It makes excellent jewelry and is the only jewel material that is unique to Hawaii. Angel pink and gold coral is recovered by a submersible off Oahu at depths of about 1,200 feet. Both are more valuable than the black coral.

Gypsum crystals, both singly and in large clusters, are abundant in the black soils in the valleys at the east end of Oahu and in the valleys on the lee side of the Waianae Range. Some clusters of crystals are six inches across. They form in the mud, an emerged marine sediment carrying abundant calcium sulphate. Crystals, commonly "fish-tail" twins, are also found in other dry areas of black "taro patch" clay.

The exhibit of Hawaiian gems at the Bishop Museum should be seen by persons interested in genuine local gemstones.

METALLIC MINERALS

Alumina deposits. From 1956 to 1958, considerable excitement occurred when Kaiser Aluminum and Chemical Company and Reynolds Metals Company explored for bauxite and other minerals that might be mined for the manufacture of aluminum. Large deposits were found in the post-erosional deeply weathered basalts of the Koloa series on Kauai, and in the Kula and Honolua series on Maui. Studies were made on how to reclaim the land once it had been mined, and delegations were sent abroad to study reclamation. However, only short government leases (21 years) were available by law, and a question of ownership complicated negotiations. Metallic minerals had not been anticipated when titles were issued. Because of government restrictions, the high cost of power, lack of harbors, distance from markets, and other disadvantages making a mining program unattractive, the companies abandoned the project.

Titanium. Titanium, which occurs in Hawaiian basalts chiefly as titaniferous magnetite, is so firmly locked with the iron that no method of economical beneficiation has yet been found. It has been concentrated in the lateritic crusts and red soils of most of the older islands by rainwater removing other minerals. The metal is in demand for use in rockets and airplanes because of its ability to withstand high temperatures. It is abundant in places on Lanai.

Pyrite. Pyrite has been reported from a drilled well in the dike complex in the northeast corner of Lualualei Valley, within the ancient Waianae caldera, and at Olomana Peak in the ancient Koolau caldera, both on Oahu.[135] It is likely to be found in all eroded calderas in the islands. Pyrite has also been found in the dike complex at Puu Pahu, eastern Oahu, in association with chlorite, quartz, calcite, and zeolites. The chlorite was deposited first, pyrite and quartz next, and then calcite. The zeolites were probably deposited at the same time as the calcite.

Manganese. Concretions containing about 27 per cent manganese and about 3 per cent copper, cobalt, and nickel lie on the ocean floor. Great quantities of manganese nodules cover the Waho shelf near Kauai.[14] In 1978, Sedco 445 mining ship, belonging to Ocean Management, Inc., recovered 1,000 tons of nodules by using hydraulic pumps. They were transshipped to Canada for processing, but the price of the metals was too low in 1978 to make mining of the nodules profitable.

NONMETALLIC MINERALS

Sulfur. A large sulfur deposit occurs on the rim of Kilauea caldera, near the road around the island of Hawaii. The deposit is one of the tourist stops within the National Park. Hot sulfurous steam is still depositing sulfur at the "Sulfur Bank." Traces of sulfur are found along other steam cracks on Kilauea, and small deposits commonly form either in the vents or close by during eruptions. Sulfur has not been mined commercially in Hawaii.

Clay. Ceramic clay, suitable for decorative pottery, is found in the deeply weathered soils in the high rainfall belts of the older volcanoes, such as on Kauai[164] and in the Koolau Range, Oahu. Considerable quantities of decorative pottery have been made from it in the past, but most deposits are too inaccessible for practical recovery; hence, the pottery makers have turned to imported kaolin. However, in 1963, Hawaiian Clay Products at Ewa, Oahu, started making bricks and pipe from local clay deposits. The clay comes from the soil on the dike complex at Waimanalo.

Aggregate and Sand. Aggregate and sand manufactured from basalt are valuable nonmetallic minerals. Dense rock satisfactory for aggregate is scarce on most of the islands. Currently it is necessary to transport some rock to Oahu from Molokai. Some of the sand used in making concrete is manufactured from basalt and coral rock. Coral beach sand is preferable but is scarce on Oahu. Large quantities were transported from Molokai on barges. Cinders from Molokai and pumice from Hawaii are also shipped to Honolulu for lightweight aggregate. Sources of black basaltic lapilli on Oahu are exhausted or lie in areas where mining is prohibited.

Cement. Cement is manufactured at two plants on Oahu, using reef limestone as the main ingredient. The silica for one plant formerly came from a rhyodacite flow on Oahu, but the rock is costly to quarry. In 1976 silica was imported from Australia.

Cinders. Cinders from Hawaii are generally used instead of soil for raising orchids, because they hold moisture and afford excellent drainage. Cinders and pumice from the last Puna eruption have been used extensively in the macadamia orchards on Hawaii to facilitate the gathering of nuts.

Building stone. Building stone consists of five types: (1) Reef and beach rock, a pleasant yellowish-white limestone easily worked; (2) Dense basalt for cut stone. Its use has declined in recent years as the old oriental workmen skilled in splitting the stone have died; (3) "Moss" rock is widely used. It is weathered and pitted basaltic boulders from the arid areas of Oahu; (4) "Hilo" rock, a thin layered pahoehoe quarried on Hawaii Island, is in vogue for veneer because of its light weight, ease of cutting, and interesting texture; (5) Tuff, formerly quarried on Diamond Head and Punchbowl craters, Oahu, is easily cut and sawn, but its use has practically ceased owing to short supply.

The value of mineral production in Hawaii reached a total of $58,727,000 in 1981.

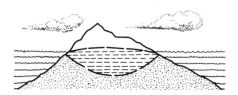

15

WATER

SURFACE WATER

Most streams in the islands are very flashy, and most are ephemeral, except those draining eroded dike complexes or areas of perched ground water. The permeability of the younger volcanoes is so great that no runoff occurs, and no well-defined stream channels exist, even though the rainfall may exceed 200 inches per year. No perennial stream enters the sea between the Wailuku River near Hilo, along the entire coast line of Kilauea, Mauna Loa, and Hualalai volcanoes, and the entire western and north side of Kohala Mountain, a distance of more than 220 miles. Except for a short stretch of the windward slope of East Maui, no streams reach the sea. No streams reach the coast on Kahoolawe Island, Lanai Island, West Molokai, the Waianae Range on Oahu, or on Niihau Island. Only on Kauai do perennial streams flow to the sea along most of the coast. There, the low flow of the streams is maintained by persistent rainfall in the mountains and by perched springs.

Surface water is so undependable that only a few small hydroelectric plants are operated on Kauai and Hawaii. However, surface water is carefully conserved for irrigation, and night flows are stored in small reservoirs. The great complex of tunnel and ditch systems ranks among the wonders of the islands. They are rarely seen by the tourist, but to ride mules along narrow ditch trails blasted out of the face of high precipitous cliffs on Kohala Mountain is one of the great adventures awaiting the intrepid visitor. It takes 160 miles of tunnels and ditches on East Maui alone to carry the surface water to the cane fields on the Isthmus.

Only a few small surface reservoirs for more than overnight storage have been built because of the lack of suitable sites, the excessive leakage, and the flashy runoff. The Wahiawa reservoir on Oahu is among the successful ones, and at times it goes dry. Extreme floods accompanying cloudbursts cause considerable property damage and loss of life. Photographs of Hawaiians riding surfboards on Kalakaua Avenue at Waikiki during floods have received widespread publicity. Runoff rates have exceeded 3,000 second-feet from one square mile in Manoa Valley, Oahu, and rates doubtless have been 6,000 second-feet or more for a square mile for some floods on Kauai. Records of the stream flows are published annually by the U.S. Geological Survey.

GROUND WATER

Ground water is Hawaii's most valuable mineral resource. Without it there would be no cities, no tourist business, and no sugar industry. The average consumption of water per person in Honolulu was 216 gallons daily in 1977. It takes approximately 1 ton of water to make 1 pound of sugar, and the islands produce more than 1,000,000 tons of sugar a year. The U.S.G.S. reports the draft from wells, springs, and tunnels on Oahu in 1979 as about 408 million gallons per day. An additional flow from the Pearl Harbor springs into the harbor is 90 million gallons per day. Honolulu alone con-

TABLE 24

TOTAL GROUND-WATER DRAFT FOR THE HAWAIIAN ISLANDS
IN MILLIONS OF GALLONS
(Data furnished by U.S. Geological Survey)

		1977	1978	1979
Hawaii	Est.	14,600	17,367	16,000[a]
Kauai		16,000	15,433	17,437
Lanai		917	778	500
Maui		97,500	88,518	68,556
Molokai		558	486	428
Oahu		149,000[a]	140,983	142,159
	Totals	278,375	263,565	245,080

[a] Estimated.

sumes about 130 million gallons per day. The occurrence and development of fresh ground water is an inseparable part of the fascinating story of modern Hawaii.

The permeability of basalts exceeds that of most other rocks on earth. The order of potential yield, in general, for basalts is: (1) interstitial spaces in clinker; (2) cavities between beds; (3) shrinkage cracks; (4) lava tubes; (5) gas vesicles; (6) cracks produced by mechanical forces after the flows have come to rest; (7) tree-mold holes.[202] Some lava tubes are 30 feet in diameter and, where they occur in the zone of saturation, are capable of transmitting vast quantities of water.

Basal Ground Water

Fortunately, the higher parts of the major islands have rainbelts because they protrude into the trade winds. But without highly permeable basalt, the water would run into the sea. Even with favorable rocks, island water supplies require another factor—the difference in the weight of fresh water and ocean water. The specific gravity of fresh water is 1.0 and sea water 1.0262 at 22° C. This difference, although small, causes fresh ground water to float on salt water as cream floats on milk. The relationship is known as the Ghyben-Herzberg principle, named for the discoverers who were investigating the occurrence of water on the island of Norderney, Germany. The principle is illustrated in Figure 15-1.[1]

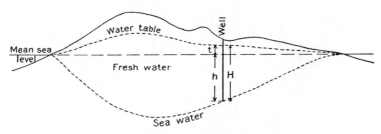

Figure 15-1—Section of the island of Norderney, Germany, showing the application of the Ghyben-Herzberg theory. (After Herzberg.)

Such factors as the change in density of the ocean with depth, temperature of the ground water, and chemistry of the salt water in the earth, make the calculation only approximate; hence $h = 40t$ is in common use. If fresh water stands 2 feet above sea level in a well (h = head), the depth of fresh water below sea level (t) will be

theoretically about 80 feet.[241] Because of diffusion and mixing, the
actual depth of fresh water is usually less than the theoretical
depth.

The principle can be applied where the rocks are not cut by
impermeable fault or dike barriers. Such barriers transect the volcanic piles and impede water movement through the island mass.
Artesian water is abundant on Oahu along much of the shore because a caprock, formed by deeply buried soils on the basalt and
mud laid down by rivers and the sea, prevents the fresh ground
water from running freely into the sea. The caprock causes the
water table to build up, thereby depressing the salt water. Originally the artesian head in the center of Honolulu was 42 feet, which
meant that fresh water extended about 1,600 feet below sea level.
Heavy pumping has lowered the static level in the city center about
14 feet, causing many of the deeply drilled wells to go salty or
brackish. Figure 15-2 shows the ground-water areas on Oahu. Fig-

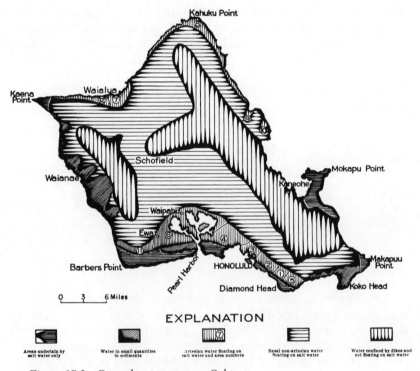

Figure 15-2—Ground-water areas on Oahu.

ure 15-3 shows a section through Oahu and the occurrence of ground water in relation to geologic structure. The cause of the different artesian basins (isopiestic areas) is the thick fills of alluvium and marine muds in the major valleys, caused by the deep submergence of Oahu.

Wells equipped with automatic water-stage recorders on Oahu indicate that the aquifer is very compressible. The water level in the wells rises and falls in response not only to general pumping in the basin and to rainfall variations, but also to changes in barometric pressure, to the tides, and to earthquakes. Between 1927 and 1931 the levels were affected by earthquakes in Central China, Alaska, Japan, New Guinea, New Caledonia, Mexico, Peru, Fiji, Chile, the Philippine Islands, the Aleutian Islands, the Kurile Islands, New Zealand, Hawaii Island, the Caroline Islands, Burma, Nicaragua, the Solomon Islands, Bonin Island, and the Mariana Islands. Formerly, when trains existed on Oahu, they would affect the water level in nearby wells by their weight compressing the aquifer. The maximum fluctuations are produced by long-period Rayleigh surface waves.[52]

Maui-type well. The Maui-type well, named by the writer in

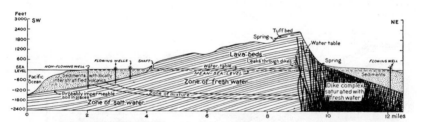

Figure 15-3—Diagrammatic section of the Koolau Range at Honolulu, showing the geologic structure of the Honolulu artesian system and the zone of fresh water separated by a zone of mixture from the underlying salt water. The diagram illustrates why wells too far seaward yield only salt water and do not flow. It also shows that when increased draft or prolonged dry weather causes the zone of mixture to rise, wells near the inland edge of the coastal plain are in less danger of going salty than those farther seaward. A Maui-type well (labeled "shaft") has a great advantage over artesian wells because it taps the water-bearing lavas above sea level, rather than several hundred feet below sea level. The sediments, with locally interstratified volcanics, are the caprock of the artesian system. The artesian water is derived from rainfall on the lava beds and from leakage through the dikes bounding the dike complex. The flowing well on the right derives its supply from the dike complex. Such wells are not in danger of going salty because the complex is saturated with fresh water to great depths, but the yield of such wells is usually small. Wells near Waimanalo are supplied from such a structure.

1932 from an installation on Maui, consists of a vertical or an in-clined shaft to the water table with one or more infiltration galleries driven with their floors generally about three feet below the water table. The writer located, designed, and supervised the construc-tion of the first Maui-type well on Oahu for the United States Navy, ¼ mile east of Aiea in 1936 (Fig. 15-4), with a tested capacity of 21,000,000 gallons per day. Later, he located the Waiawa shaft, also for the Navy, which is capable of yielding 50,000,000 gallons per day, and is among the largest yielding wells in the world. A visit to Halawa well, a Maui-type well of the Honolulu Board of Water Supply, is one of the interesting trips offered free to tourists. It has a pumping capacity of 15 million gallons per day.

During the construction of well 5 in 1933, just above the town of Lahaina, Maui, the writer descended 323 feet down the vertical shaft in a steel bucket, and rode to the heading of the dimly lighted infiltration or skimming tunnel in the flat-bottomed steel-lined boat used to transport rock to the hoist. The following was written at the time.

The boat was pushed by two Filipinos wading noiselessly in water to their chests. The boat glided along nearly half a mile to the heading in semi-darkness and in deep silence. Occasionally the boat would grate raucously against a projecting rock and break the silence. The loose clinker and

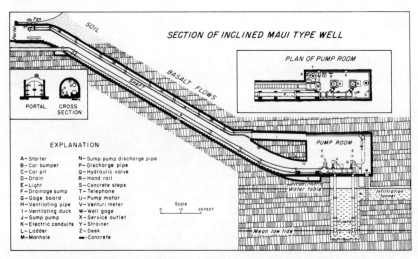

Figure 15-4—Typical Maui-type well equipped with deep-well turbines at Aiea, Oahu.

highly fractured lava rock appeared ready to tumble down with a mighty splash at any moment, but they are too rough to slide and probably will stand for centuries without support. Often a layer of red doughy lava was passed or the boat glided between ragged rock walls gleaming with tiny specks of light, reflected from thousands of olivine crystals. In other places the walls were covered with pearly drops of water. Another boat laden with broken rock came like a phantom out of the darkness. We passed at special sidings where the tunnel had been widened. Finally the boat rounded a bend, and the sound of air drills warned of our approach to the heading. There two more Filipinos were drilling holes rapidly into the rock face, to be filled later with sticks of dynamite. Blasting is done every 8 hours. We talked to these gnomes in pidgin English and found that they preferred work under ground to work in the hot cane fields above. Our guide stated, however, that the native Hawaiians would not work underground because of superstitions about caves. The air was fresh and cool in contrast with the hot humid day outside, in spite of the absence of the usual air ventilating pipe. The rock is so cavernous and jointed that the powder smoke disappears rapidly after each blast, partly as a result of circulation set up by the moving water.

Unlike water-development tunnels driven into a dike complex where water pours down from the roof and squirts from the drill holes, the heading of this tunnel was dry. The only evidence of water being encountered was the decreased drawdown on the chart at the bottom of the shaft which records the water level automatically while the pumps are operating. Water was encountered so gradually that the record showed an increased yield

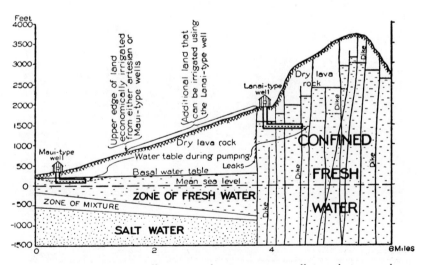

Figure 15-5—Diagram illustrating the Lanai-type well in relation to the geologic structure and water table. Fault barriers, as well as dikes, were effective on Lanai for holding the water at high levels.

only after several weeks of tunneling. In dry seasons the salt content of the water averages 50 grains per gallon, and the water surface stands only 1½ feet above sea level. Consequently only the freshest water can be skimmed from the top, just as cream is skimmed from a pan of milk.

The boat trip back to the shaft was faster because the boat moved with the current. The boys walked faster and faster as the current increased near the shaft. Finally the whir of the motors and pumps pushing 10,000,000 gallons a day through 322 feet of pipe to the surface was heard. The water is clear as a crystal in the pump sump. The comminuted rock, from blasting at the heading, settles to the bottom of the tunnel before it reaches the sump. Again in the hoist bucket, a cord was jerked to signal the operator above, and up we went to the top. Out in the brilliant tropical sunlight, surrounded by high mountains, green fields, and a wide expanse of blue ocean, one felt suddenly hoisted into reality again, and the journey under the mountain seemed a fantasy.[7]

Confined water. Water confined at high level in vertical compartments of permeable lava rock enclosed by dikes or fault gouge barriers is in interesting contrast to the basal water floating on salt

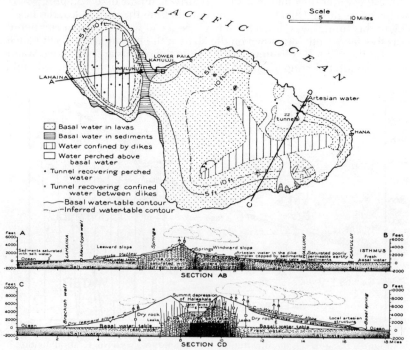

Figure 15-6—Map of Maui showing ground-water areas, 5- and 10-foot basal water-table contours, high-level tunnels, and sections shown below.

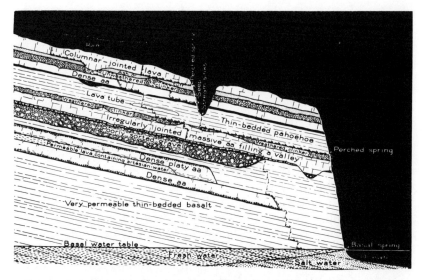

Figure 15-7—Diagram illustrating the path of percolating water in a lava terrane containing various types of interbedded perching structures, typical of the Kula volcanic series. (After Stearns and Macdonald, 1942.)

water near sea level. Several unusual tunnels have been driven to recover confined water. The Waiahole tunnel on Oahu is 14,567 feet long and cuts through the backbone of the Koolau Range, and the water then flows through a series of ditches and siphons, to irrigate extensive fields of cane above Waipahu. It is possible to ride through the tunnel in a boat. Another confined water tunnel is behind Kaunakakai, Molokai, at an elevation of 900 feet. It is the longest single tunnel driven from one portal in Hawaii. It cuts 26,824 feet through East Molokai Mountain and recovers water from wells and springs confined by dikes at high levels. It was completed in 1962 to supply irrigation and domestic water to dry West Molokai, and followed the "Stearns Plan" for developing the water resources of Molokai.[16]

Lanai-type well. The prototype for the Lanai-type well was designed by the writer to develop water to irrigate pineapple fields on the island of Lanai. The original Lanai well recovers water from behind impermeable fault barriers within the ancient caldera. When the first water was encountered, it was feared that the water was dead storage and would soon be exhausted. This problem was solved some years later by testing for tritium, the "heavy water" produced by the "Castle" atomic bomb explosion on Eniwetok Island in February 1954. Water analyses indicated the presence of tritium, which meant that the supply was not "dead," but had received percolating rain water from the slopes above it since the 1954 explosion. Figure 15-5 shows the difference between Maui-type and Lanai-type wells.

The well supplying Schofield Barracks opposite Wheeler Air Force Base gate, Oahu, is probably the deepest well of its size and yield in the world. It was located and the plan of development supervised by the writer in the extensive Schofield Plateau, where no well existed. At that time, the barracks received their supply from surface runoff, often muddy, stored in the now-abandoned Koolau reservoir. The well, a 7½- by 7½-foot shaft on a 30° incline, 1,167 feet long, was started on March 5, 1936, at an altitude of 850 feet. The original pump chamber at the bottom of the shaft was 91.7 feet long, 20 feet wide, 22.5 feet high, with its floor 287 feet above sea level. It contains 6 drilled wells in the pump chamber. Only 4 are in use, and they have depths ranging from 150 to 278 feet. Average draft is 6.0 million gallons per day. The water level stands about 280 feet above sea level. Either fault barriers or dikes must confine the water at this level. The cause of the high water level may never be known, but other wells in the area have since tapped

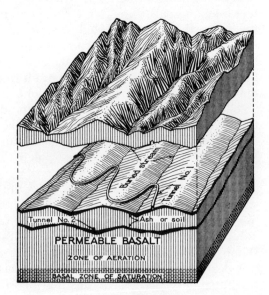

Figure 15-8—Diagram showing relation of basal water to water perched on two ash beds and tunnels driven to recover it. Most of the perched water is recovered from streams moving down the buried valleys. (After Stearns and Macdonald, 1946.)

the same underground reservoir and obtained large yields with very little drawdown. The Ghyben-Herzberg principle requires salt water to be about 40 times 280 feet, or about 11,000 feet, below sea level. It is believed that the rocks are not permeable at that depth; hence, the Schofield well obviously cannot be contaminated by sea water.

Perched water. A third type of water occurrence, known as perched water, is common in the islands, although yields from wells and tunnels driven to recover it are usually much smaller than are yields from the other types. Water is perched at high levels on impermeable beds. Miles of tunnels have been driven along ash beds in Hawaii, and 23,850 feet of tunnels at the bottom of "lava plastered" valleys and along buried soils on East Maui to recover perched water. Its chief value lies in its height above sea level, hence its flow by gravity to points of use. Figure 15-6 shows the ground-water provinces on Maui, the location of tunnels recovering perched water, and the relation of basal, confined, and perched water in sections of East and West Maui. Figure 15-7 is a diagram showing the path of percolating water in a lava terrane containing various types of perching structures. One of the tunnels in East Maui uncovered an underground waterfall with water still falling

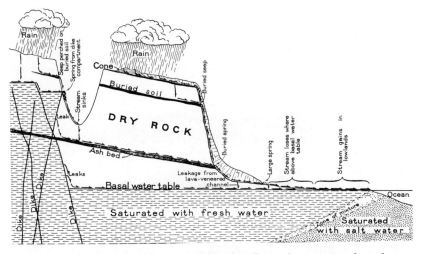

Figure 15-9—Diagram illustrating the paths of percolating water through a highly permeable basalt terrane containing a dike swarm, interbedded soil and ash beds, and a late valley-filling lava flow. (After Stearns and Macdonald, 1942.)

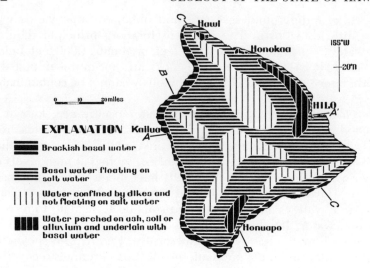

Figure 15-10—Map of Hawaii showing ground-water areas and location of sections shown in Figure 15-11 (After Stearns and Macdonald, 1946.)

over its cliff, which had been buried by a later lava flow. The fall was complete with pot holes, cobbles, and plunge pool. It is an eerie sight to stand in the dark tunnel and see the tumbling waters by flashlight. Figure 15-8 shows how it is possible to recover water from several tunnels, one above the other, without interfering with the yield of any, by driving them along different ash beds. Figure 15-9 shows the paths of percolating water through a highly perme-

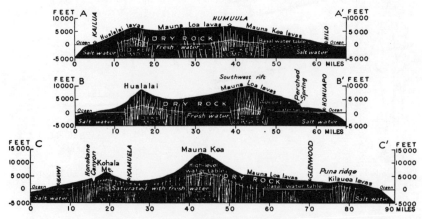

Figure 15-11—Sections showing ground-water conditions along the lines AA', BB', and CC' in Figure 15-10. (After Stearns and Macdonald, 1946.)

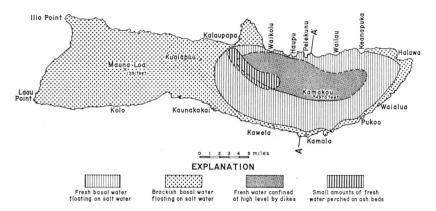

Figure 15-12—Map of Molokai showing ground-water areas. (After Stearns and Macdonald, 1947.)

able basalt terrane containing a dike swarm, interbedded soil and ash beds, and a late valley-filling lava flow.

A common question is whether Oahu will run out of fresh ground water if expansion continues at the present boom rate. The steady increase in draft from wells in the islands has caused some salt water invasion in some areas of heavy pumping, but this condition can be remedied by drilling wells farther inland at judiciously selected and properly spaced sites. Vast reserves of ground water exist yet untapped in the island; but the present tendency to export water to the dry Waianae areas and to the dry east end of the island is costly, and if these areas expand greatly, they may ultimately cause a deficiency. Excess water used to irrigate lawns and gardens in these areas does not recharge the aquifers, and is lost to the sea. Also, increased use of sewer pipes instead of cesspools reduces recharge volume. The effluent is mainly piped out to sea. These disadvantages can be offset by artificial recharge methods, since billions of gallons of water run into the sea during storms. Rain water could be sunk into permeable lavas along streams by means of shallow shafts back-filled with rock filters. Surface reservoirs to

Figure 15-13—Section across East Molokai, showing ground-water conditions. The position of the section is shown in Figure 15-12.

conserve the water, as built on the mainland, are generally infeasible in Hawaii because the gulches are mostly too steep, the banks too permeable, the sedimentation rate too fast, and the cost of filtration too high. They would be excellent, however, if planned and used for artificial recharge.

The author has recommended to the U.S. Atomic Energy Commission representative on ground water that an atomic blast be exploded at the bottom of a judiciously placed drilled hole. The huge cavity so formed would be used for increasing underground storage. Flood waters could be diverted to the underground cavity, where they would slowly percolate seaward to pumped areas.

Large quantities of water await development on Maui, Kauai, East Molokai, and in the wet slopes of Hawaii. Maps and sections showing the ground-water areas and occurrence of water are shown in Figures 15-10 and 15-11 for Hawaii, and Figures 15-12 and 15-13 for Molokai. Also, the cost of desalting ocean water is declining, so that fresh water may be made economically from ocean water within a few years. For these reasons, Hawaii is not likely to run out of water.

CLASSIFICATION OF WELLS

Wells are classified below according to the geologic structures they penetrate.

The letters in parentheses refer to the wells in Figure 15-14.

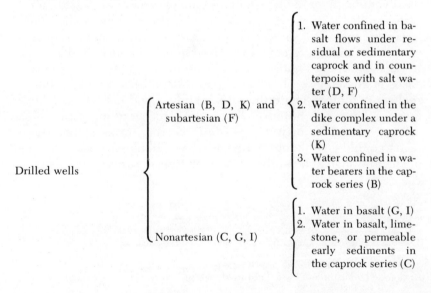

Drilled wells

Artesian (B, D, K) and subartesian (F)

1. Water confined in basalt flows under residual or sedimentary caprock and in counterpoise with salt water (D, F)
2. Water confined in the dike complex under a sedimentary caprock (K)
3. Water confined in water bearers in the caprock series (B)

Nonartesian (C, G, I)

1. Water in basalt (G, I)
2. Water in basalt, limestone, or permeable early sediments in the caprock series (C)

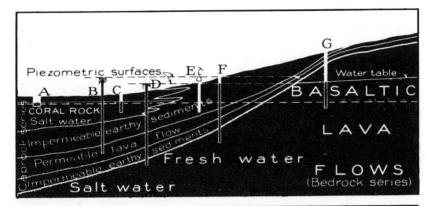

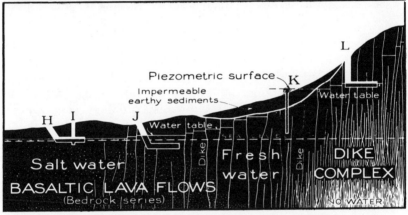

Figure 15-14—Diagrams illustrating the various types of wells and the geologic structures penetrated.

Dug wells
(nonartesian)

Supplied by the unconfined water bearers of the caprock series (A)

Supplied by basalt (H, J, L)

1. Maui-type involving the skimming principle and not in the dike complex (H)
2. Lanai-type in the dike complex and not involving the skimming principle (L)
3. Oahu-type in the dike complex but involving the skimming principle (J)

Wells supplied by the permea- ⌠ Nonartesian   ⌠ Dug well A
ble rocks of the caprock series ⎪ (unconfined) ⎨ Drilled well C
(Well E—dry because it en-   ⎨ Artesian   ⎩
tered   impermeable   sedi-   ⎩ (confined)   Drilled well B
ments)

                              ⌠ Nonartesian   ⌠ Maui-type well H, supplement-
Wells supplied by water in   ⎪ (unconfined)   ⎨ ed by drilled well I
counterpoise with salt water   ⎨   ⎩ Drilled well G
in basaltic flows of the bed- ⎪ Artesian   ⌠ Flowing drilled well D
rock series   ⎩ (confined)   ⎨ Subartesian drilled well F

                                                ⌠ Oahu-type well J in danger of
                                                ⎪   salt-water contamination by
                                                ⎪   overdraft
                                                ⎨ Lanai-type well L, not in danger
Wells supplied by the dike com- ⌠ Nonartesian   ⎩   of salt-water contamination
plex   ⎨   Drilled well K
                                ⎩ Artesian

USE OF STEAM

A small steam condenser was operated north of Kilauea caldera in 1944, and yielded about 100 gallons of water a day. Obtaining drinking water in the Kilauea Park area is a problem. The supply is obtained from roofs and rain catches, and these sources fail in droughts.

The Hawaii Thermal Power Company drilled 4 wells on the Puna rift of Kilauea in the Puna District, island of Hawaii, under the direction of Dr. Agatin Abbott in 1961. The data are summarized in Table 25.

TABLE 25

WELLS DRILLED FOR STEAM IN PUNA DISTRICT, HAWAII
BY THE HAWAII THERMAL POWER COMPANY
(Data furnished by Dr. Agatin Abbott, Dec. 31, 1964)

Hole No.	Location	Collar elev. (feet)	Depth (feet)	Bottom T.°F.	Cause of abandonment
1.	Below highway from Pahoa to Kalapana	1009	178	130	Lost tools in hole
2.	Above highway near Hole 1.	1035	556	215	Same
3.	Steaming area below Puu Honaula	563	690	200	—[a]
4.	Upper side Kapoho cone	250	290	110	—[b]

[a] The temperature was steady.
[b] Strong circulation of sea water.

A research hole was drilled to a depth of 4,137 feet on the southwest rim of Kilauea caldera at an altitude of 3,616 feet in 1973 under a National Science Foundation grant. It encountered a water table confined by dikes at an altitude of 2,016 feet.[255] The temperature at the bottom of the hole was 265° F. It was concluded that ". . . the temperatures encountered in the borehole are not high enough to comprise a commercially viable geothermal reservoir."[92]

The county, state, and federal governments combined to explore for geothermal energy in Puna on the island of Hawaii. A well was completed to a depth of 6,400 feet in April 1976, alongside Pohoiki Road, about three miles southeast of Pahoa, under the direction of the Hawaii Institute of Geophysics. The U. S. Energy Research and Development Administration committed $2,400,000 to the project. The well encountered steam with a temperature of about 600° F., and was tested several times. The pressure at the well head was 100 lbs. per square inch. According to Dr. John Shupe of the University of Hawaii, the well has a sufficient flow of steam to generate 5 to 10 megawatts of electricity, or about 10 per cent of the island's consumption of electricity.

In June 1978, the U. S. Department of Energy signed a $6,800,000 contract to build a 3-megawatt power plant in Puna. The Hawaii Electric and Light Company will operate the plant and will buy some of the power. A consortium called the Hawaii Geothermal Project-A Development Group supervised the project. It was put into operation in 1980.

In 1980, Barnwell Industries drilled a hole about 6,000 feet deep in the Opihikao area in Puna. It is reported to have hit hot rock, but was dry. The Puna Geothermal Venture, a joint venture of Thermal Power, belonging to Natomas Company, Amfac, and Dillingham Corporation, drilled a well 7,290 feet deep about 1,500 feet away from the University of Hawaii well in 1980. It was tested early in 1981 but was shut down because of excessive noise from the steam. It appears to be a success. The Campbell Estate owns 26,000 acres next to Hawaii National Park. It plans to start drilling as soon as the necessary permits are obtained.

Macdonald and Peterson have covered the prospects for developing geothermal power thoroughly in the island of Hawaii.[115,166] The author has recommended a less costly test than the Puna well by drilling near the active vent of Mauna Ulu, located within Hawaii Volcanoes National Park. He has expressed doubt that geothermal energy can be developed in the island of Oahu, although thermal water was encountered by a well in Lualualei Valley.[221]

Water with a temperature of 95° F. was encountered in a well drilled by the State Department of Land and Natural Resources between Kawaihae and Kamuela, on the island of Hawaii. Thermal water exists at Keaau also. Warm water was encountered at Olowalu, Maui,[7] and on Kauai.

A well was drilled in December 1982 at Waikii on the slopes of Mauna Kea, Island of Hawaii, at an altitude of 4,260 feet. It is 4,324 feet deep, probably the deepest water well in the world. Water stands at 1,500 feet above sea level impounded by dikes. The hole penetrated 20 feet of ash and fresh olivine basalt of the Hamakua volcanic series. The well belongs to Gerald Kremkoa, who drilled it for a subdivision supply. The submersible pump is set at 3,480 feet, is driven by a 220 HP motor and yields 160 gallons per minute with a 19-foot drawdown. The hole is cased for 3,500 feet with 500 three-quarter-inch holes in the lower 700 feet of the casing. The diameter is 17 inches at the top and 12 inches at the bottom. The temperature of the water is 87°F., or about 10° warmer than the normal geothermal gradient. The hole was drilled in 30 days by Water Resources International.

REFERENCES

1. Stearns, H. T. and Vaksvik, K. N. 1935. Geology and ground-water resources of the Island of Oahu, Hawaii: 479 pp.
2. Stearns, H. T. 1939. Geologic map and guide of the Island of Oahu, Hawaii (geologic map of Oahu enclosed): 75 pp.
3. Stearns, N. D. 1935. Annotated bibliography and index of geology and water supply of the Island of Oahu, Hawaii: 74 pp.
4. Stearns, H. T. and Vaksvik, K. N. 1938. Records of the drilled wells on the Island of Oahu, Hawaii: 213 pp.
5. Stearns, H. T. 1940. Supplement to the geology and ground-water resources of the Island of Oahu, Hawaii (includes chapters on geophysical investigations by J. H. Swartz, and petrography by G. A. Macdonald): 164 pp.
6. Stearns, H. T. 1940. Geology and ground-water resources of the Islands of Lanai and Kahoolawe, Hawaii (includes chapters on geophysical investigations by J. H. Swartz, and petrography by G. A. Macdonald; geologic map of Lanai enclosed): 177 pp.
7. Stearns, H. T. and Macdonald, G. A. 1942. Geology and ground-water resources of the Island of Maui, Hawaii (geologic map of Maui enclosed): 344 pp.
8. Stearns, H. T. 1946. Geology of the Hawaiian Islands: 106 pp.
9. Stearns, H. T. and Macdonald, G. A. 1946. Geology and ground-water resources of the Island of Hawaii (geologic map of Hawaii enclosed): 363 pp.
10. Macdonald, G. A. 1947. Bibliography of the geology and ground-water resources of the Island of Hawaii (annotated and indexed): 191 pp.
11. Stearns, H. T. and Macdonald, G. A. 1947. Geology and ground-water resources of the Island of Molokai, Hawaii (geologic map of Molokai enclosed): 113 pp.
12. Stearns, H. T. 1947. Geology and ground-water resources of the Island of Niihau, Hawaii; also Macdonald, G. A. 1947. Petrography of Niihau (geologic map of Niihau enclosed): 51 pp.
13. Macdonald, G. A., Davis, D.A., and Cox, D. C. 1960. Geology and ground-water resources of the Island of Kauai, Hawaii (geologic map of Kauai enclosed): 207 pp.

ADDITIONAL SOURCE REFERENCES

14. Andrews, J. E. 1972. Distribution of manganese nodules in the Hawaiian Archipelago, in Manganese nodule deposits in the Pacific. Hawaii Dept. Planning and Economic Development. p. 62.
15. Ault, W. U., Richter, D. H., and Stewart, D. B. 1962. A temperature probe into the melt of the Kilauea Iki lava lake in Hawaii. J. Geophys. Res. 67: 2809–2812.
16. Austin, H. A. R. and Stearns, H. T. 1954. Report to the Hawaii Irrigation Authority covering methods for development and delivery of water for irrigation of Hawaiian Homes Commission Lands at Hoolehua Island of Molokai (unpub.): 57 pp., 31 exhibits.
17. Bartrum, J. A. 1936. Honeycomb weathering of rocks near the shoreline. New Zealand J. Sci. 18: 593–600.
18. Bauer, G. R., Fodor, R. V., Husler, G. W., and Keil, K. 1973. Contribution to the mineral chemistry of Hawaiian rocks, III: Composition and mineralogy of a new rhyodacite occurrence on Oahu, Hawaii. Contr. Mineral. and Petrol. 40: 183–194.
19. Beeson, M. H. 1976. Petrology, mineralogy, and geochemistry of the East Molokai volcanic series, Hawaii. U.S. Geol. Surv. Prof. Paper 961:53.
20. Bonhommet, N., Beeson, M. H., and Dalrymple, G. B. 1976. A contribution to the geochronology and petrology of the island of Lanai, Hawaii. Geol. Soc. Amer. Bull. 88:1282–1286.
21. Brady, L. F. and Webb, R. W. 1943. Cored bombs from Arizona and California volcanic cones. J. Geol. 51: 398–410.
22. Branner, J. C. 1903. Notes on the geology of Hawaiian Islands. Amer. J. Sci. 4th ser. 16: 301–303.
23. Brigham, W. T. 1868. Notes on the volcanic phenomena of the Hawaiian Islands with a description of the modern eruptions. Boston Soc. Nat. Hist. Mem. 1: 373–374.
24. Brock, V. E. and Chamberlain, T. C. 1968. A geological and ecological reconnaissance off western Oahu, Hawaii. Pac. Sci. 22: 373–394.
25. Bryan, W. A. 1915. Natural history of Hawaii. Honolulu. 94–99.
26. Burkholder, P. R. 1963. Drugs from the sea. Armed Forces Chem. J. 17: 1–8.
27. Claque, D. A. and Jarrard, R. D. 1973. Hot spots and Pacific plate motion. Amer. Geophys. Union Trans. 54: 238.
28. _____ 1973. Tertiary Pacific plate motion deduced from the Hawaiian-Emperor Chain. Geol. Soc. Amer. Bull. 84: 1135–1154.
29. Coleman, J. M. and Smith, W. G. 1964. Late Recent rise of sea level. Geol. Soc. Amer. Bull. 75: 833–840.
30. Cotton, C. A. 1962. Low sea levels in the late Pleistocene. Trans. Royal Soc. of N.Z. 1: 249–252.
31. Coulbourn, W. T., Campbell, J. F., and Moberly, R. 1974. Hawaiian submarine terraces, canyons, and Quaternary history evaluated by seismic-reflection profiling. Mar. Geol. 17: 215–234.
32. Cross, W. 1904. An occurrence of trachyte on the island of Hawaii. J. Geol. 12: 510–523.
33. Daly, R. A. 1911. The nature of volcanic action. Amer. Acad. Arts and Sci. Proc. 47: 76–82.

34. _____ 1914. Igneous rocks and their origin. New York. Fig. 136, p. 281.

35. _____ 1916. Problems of the Pacific Islands. Amer. J. Sci. 4th ser. 41: 175.

36. _____ 1933. Igneous rocks and the depths of the earth. New York. 113, 364–372.

37. Dalrymple, G. B. 1971. Potassium-argon ages from the Pololu Volcanic Series, Kohala Volcano, Hawaii. Geol. Soc. Amer. Bull. 82: 1339–1404.

38. _____, Lamphere, M. A., and Jackson, E. D. 1974. Contributions to the petrography and geochronology of volcanic rocks from the leeward Hawaiian Islands. Geol. Soc. Amer. Bull. 85: 727–738.

39. _____, Silver, E. A., and Jackson, E. D. 1973. Origin of the Hawaiian Islands. Amer. Scientist 6: 294–308.

40. Dana, J. D. 1849. Geology, in U.S. Exploring Expedition, 1838–1842. 10: 282, 414–416.

41. _____ 1890. Characteristics of volcanoes. New York. 399 pp.

42. Day, A. L. and Shepherd, E. S. 1913. Water and volcanic activity. Geol. Soc. Amer. Bull. 24: 599–601.

43. Dibble, S. 1843. History of the Sandwich Islands: Lahainaluna, Hawaii. p. 65.

44. Dietz, R. S. and Menard, H. W. 1953. Hawaiian swell, arch, and deep, and subsidence of the Hawaiian Islands. J. Geol. 61: 99–113.

45. Doell, R. R. and Cox, A. 1961. Paleomagnetism of Hawaiian lava flows. Nature 192: 645–646.

46. _____ 1965. Paleomagnetism of Hawaiian lava flows. J. Geophys. Res. 70: 3377–3405.

47. Donn, W. L., Farrand, W. R., and Ewing, M. 1962. Pleistocene ice volumes and sea-level lowering. J. Geol. 70: 206–214.

48. Dunham, K. C. 1933. Crystal cavities in lavas from the Hawaiian Islands. Amer. Min. 18: 369–385 and 1935, 20: 880–882.

49. Dury, G. H. 1962. The face of the earth. Baltimore. 225 pp.

50. Eaton, J. P. 1962. Crustal structure and volcanism in Hawaii. In Crust of the Pacific, Geophys. Monog. No. 6: Honolulu, 13–29.

51. _____, Richter, D. H., and Ault, W. R. 1961. The tsunami of May 23, 1960, on the island of Hawaii. Seismol. Soc. of Amer. Bull. 51: 135–157.

52. _____ and Takasaki, K. J. 1959. Seismological interpretation of earthquake-induced water-level fluctuations in wells. Seis. Soc. Amer. Bull. 49: 227–245.

53. Eischer, C. 1915. The Leeward Islands of the Hawaiian group. Reprint from Sunday Advertiser. Honolulu. 1–68.

54. Ellis, W. 1917. Journal (reprint of 1827 ed.). Honolulu, Hawaiian Gazette Co.: 442 pp.

55. Engel, A. E. J. and Engel, C. G. 1964. Igneous rocks of the East Pacific Rise. Sci. 146: 477–485.

56. Emery, K. O. and Cox, D. C. 1956. Beach rock in the Hawaiian Islands. Pac. Sci. 10: 382–402.

57. Evernden, J. F., Savage, D. E., Curtis, G. H., and James, G. T. 1964. Potassium argon dates and the Cenozoic mammalian chronology of North America. Amer. J. Sci. 262: 145–198.

58. Fairbridge, R. H. 1950. Landslide patterns on oceanic volcanoes and atolls. Geogr. J. 115: 84–92.

59. Finch, R. H. 1925. The earthquakes at Kapoho, island of Hawaii, April 1924.

Seismol. Soc. Amer. Bull. 15: 122–127.

60. _____ 1933. Block lava. J. Geol. 41: 769–770.

61. _____ 1943. The seismic prelude to the 1942 eruption of Mauna Loa. Seismol. Soc. Amer. Bull. 33: 237–241.

62. _____ and Macdonald, G. A. 1949. Bombing to divert lava flows. Volcano Letter No. 506: 1–3.

63. Frazer, G. D. 1960. Pahala Ash—An unusual deposit from Kilauea Volcano, Hawaii. U.S. Geol. Surv. Prof. Paper. 400: B-354-5.

64. Funkhouser, J. G., Barnes, I. L., and Naughton, J. J. 1968. The determination of a series of ages of Hawaiian volcanoes by the potassium-argon method. Pac. Sci. 28: 369–372.

65. Gramlich, J. W., Lewis, V. A., and Naughton, J. J. 1971. Potassium-argon dating of Holocene basalts of the Honolulu volcanic series. Geol. Soc. Amer. Bull. 82: 1399–1404.

66. Green, W. L. 1887. Vestiges of the molten globe. Honolulu 2: 277.

67. Gregory, H. E. and Wentworth, C. K. 1937. General features and glacial geology of Mauna Kea, Hawaii. Geol. Soc. Amer. Bull. 48: 1719–1742.

68. Gross, M. G., Milliman, J. D., Tracey, J. I., and Ladd, H. S. 1969. Marine geology of Kure and Midway atolls, Hawaii: A preliminary report. Pac. Sci. 23: 17–25.

69. Hamilton, E. L. 1956. Sunken islands of the Mid-Pacific Mountains. Geol. Soc. Amer. Mem. 64: 97 pp.

70. _____ 1957. Marine geology of the southern Hawaiian Ridge. Geol. Soc. Amer. Bull. 68: 1011–1026.

71. Hammond, S. R. 1970. Paleomagnetic investigations of deep borings on the Ewa Plain, Oahu, Hawaii. Hawaii Inst. Geophysics Data Rep. 70–10, 60 pp.

72. Hawaiian Volcano Obs. Bull. 12. 1924: 39.

73. Hay, R. L. and Iijima, A. 1968. Nature and origin of palagonite tuff of the Honolulu group on Oahu, Hawaii. Geol. Soc. Amer. Mem. 116: 331–376.

74. Heezen, B. C. and MacGregor, I. D. 1973. The evolution of the Pacific. Sci. Amer., 29: 102–112.

75. Hess, H. H. 1946. Drowned ancient islands of the Pacific Basin. Amer. J. Sci. 244: 772–791.

76. Hinds, N. E. A. 1930. The geology of Kauai and Niihau. B. P. Bishop Mus. Bull. 71: 103 pp.

77. Hitchcock, C. H. 1909. The volcano Kilauea. Amer. Geogr. Soc. Bull. 41: 684.

78. _____ 1909. Hawaii and its volcanoes. Honolulu. 314 pp. and 1911, 271.

79. Honolulu Advertiser, Mar. 13, 1976. Report from Hawaiian Volcano Obs.

80. Inman, D. L., Gayman, W. R., and Cox, D. C. 1963. Littoral sedimentary processes on Kauai. Pac. Sci. 17: 106–130.

81. Jackson, D. B., Swanson, D. A., Koyanagi, R. Y., and Wright, T. L. 1975. The August and October 1968 east rift eruptions of Kilauea Volcano, Hawaii. U.S. Geol. Surv. Prof. Paper 890: 1–33.

82. Jackson, E. D. 1966. "Eclogite" in Hawaiian basalts. U.S. Geol. Surv. Prof. Paper 550-D: 151–157.

83. _____ 1968. The character of the lower crust and upper mantle beneath the Hawaiian Islands. XXIII Inter. Geol. Congress Rept. 1: 135–150.

84. _____, Silver, E. A., and Dalrymple, G. B. 1972. Hawaiian-Emperor Chain and its relation to Cenozoic circumpacific tectonics. Geol. Soc. Amer. Bull. 83: 601–618.

85. _____ and Wright, T. L. 1970. Xenoliths in the Honolulu volcanic series, Hawaii. J. Petrol. 11: 405–430.

86. Jaggar, T. A. 1917. Hawaiian Volcano Obs. Bull. 5: 84.

87. _____ 1920. Seismometric investigation of the Hawaiian lava column. Seismol. Soc. Amer. Bull. 10: 163, 182.

88. _____ 1938. Volcano Letter 459: 2.

89. _____ 1938. Personal communication "Miss Paris says natives told her father the Kaupulehu flow was the first (1800) and higher, and the Huehue flow was the second (1801) and lower flow."

90. _____ 1945. Protection of harbors from lava flow. Amer. J. Sci. 243A: 333–351.

91. Johnston-Lavis, H. J. 1885–86. On the fragmentary ejectamenta of volcanoes. Geologists' Assn. London Proc. 9: 421–432.

92. Keller, G. V., Murray, J. C., Skokan, J. J., and Skokan, C. K. 1974. CMS research drill hole at summit of Kilauea Volcano. Mines Mag. May: 14–18.

93. Kinoshita, W. T., Krivoy, H. L., Mabey, D. R., and McDonald, R. R. 1963. Gravity survey of the island of Hawaii. U.S. Geol. Surv. Prof. Paper. 475-C: 114–116.

94. Krivoy, H. L., Baker, M., and Moe, E. E. 1965. A reconnaissance gravity survey of the island of Kauai. Pac. Sci. 19: 354–358.

95. Kroenke, L. W. and Woollard, G. P. 1965. Gravity investigations on the Leeward Islands of the Hawaiian Ridge and Johnston Island. Pac. Sci. 19: 361–366.

96. _____ 1966. Seismic reflection investigations in the vicinity of the Hawaiian Ridge. Hawaii Inst. Geophys. Data Rep. HIG-66-14, 11.

97. Ku, T-L., Kimmel, M. A., Easton, W. H., and O'Neil, T. J. 1974. Eustatic sea level 120,000 years ago on Oahu, Hawaii. Sci. 183: 959–962.

98. Kuno, H., Yamasaki, K., Iida, C., and Nagashima, K. 1957. Differentiation in Hawaiian magmas. Jap. J. Geol. Geophys. 28: 179–218.

99. Ladd, H. S., Tracey, J. I., and Gross, M. G. 1970. Deep drilling on Midway Atoll. U.S. Geol. Surv. Prof. Paper 680-A: A1–A22.

100. Lamphere, M. A. and Dalrymple, G. B. 1979. Age and strontium isotopic composition of the Honolulu Volcanic Series, Oahu, Hawaii. Dale Jackson Memorial volume. Amer. J. Sci. 280A: 736–757.

101. Larson, E. S. and Gottfried, D. 1960. Uranium and thorium in selected suites of igneous rocks. Amer. J. Sci. 258A: 151–169.

102. Lovering, J. F. and Richards, J. R. 1964. Potassium-argon age study of possible lower-crust and upper mantle inclusions in deep seated intrusions. J. Geophys. Res. 69: 4895–4901.

103. Lum, D. and Stearns, H. T. 1970. Pleistocene stratigraphy and eustatic history based on cores at Waimanalo, Oahu, Hawaii. Geol. Soc. Amer. Bull. 81: 1–16.

104. Macdonald, G. A. 1943. The 1942 eruption of Mauna Loa, Hawaii. Amer. J. Sci. 241: 241–256.

105. _____ 1944. The 1840 eruption and crystal differentiation in the Kilauean magma column. Amer. J. Sci. 242: 177–189.

106. _____ 1953. Thomas Augustus Jaggar. Volcano Letter 519: 1–4.

107. ———— 1954. Barriers to protect Hilo from lava flow. Pac. Sci. 12: 258–277.
108. ———— 1956. The structure of Hawaiian volcanoes. Verhandel. Ned. Geol. Mihnbouwk. Genoot. 16: 1–22.
109. ———— 1961. Current problems in research—volcanology. Sci. 133: 673–679.
110. ———— 1962. Relation of petrographic suites in Hawaii. Crust of the Pacific Basin, Geophys. Mon. 6, Hawaii Inst. Geophys. 185–195.
111. ———— 1962. The 1959 and 1960 eruptions of Kilauea Volcano, Hawaii and the construction of walls to restrict the spread of the lava flow. Bull. Volcanologique 24: 249–294.
112. ———— 1963. Physical properties of erupting Hawaii magmas. Geol. Soc. Amer. Bull. 74: 1071–1077.
113. ———— 1963. Relative abundance of intermediate members of the oceanic basalt-trachyte association—A discussion. J. Geophys. Res. 68: 5100–5102.
114. ———— 1965. Hawaiian calderas. Pac. Sci. 19: 320–334.
115. ———— 1973. Geological prospects for development of geothermal energy in Hawaii. Pac. Sci. 27: 209–219.
116. ———— and Abbott, A. T. 1970. Volcanoes in the sea. Univ. Hawaii Press, 441 pp.
117. ———— and Eaton, J. P. 1964. Hawaiian volcanoes during 1955. U.S. Geol. Surv. Bull. 1171: 1–170.
118. ———— and Hubbard, D. H. 1975. Volcanoes of the National Parks in Hawaii. Hawaii National Park, Hawaii: 60 pp.
119. ———— and Katsura, T. 1962. Relationship of petrographic suites in Hawaii. Crust of the Pacific Basin, Geophys. Monograph No. 6: 187–195. 115: 58.
120. ———— 1964. Chemical composition of Hawaiian lavas. J. Petrol. 5: 82–133.
121. Malahoff, A. and Woollard, G. P. 1965. Magnetic surveys over the Hawaiian Ridge. HIC-65-11: 63 pp.
122. Mathewson, C. C. 1970. Submarine canyons and the shelf along the north coast of Molokai Island, Hawaiian Ridge. Pac. Sci. 24: 235–244.
123. ———— and Malahoff, A. 1969. Ancient shelf along the Hawaiian Ridge (abs.). San Francisco, Amer. Geophys. Union Fall Mtg., v. 50: 635.
124. McAllister, J. G. 1933. Archaeology of Kahoolawe. B. P. Bishop Mus. Bull.
125. McDougall, I. 1964. Potassium-argon ages from lavas of the Hawaiian Islands. Geol. Soc. Amer. Bull. 75: 107–128.
126. ———— 1971. Volcanic island chains and sea floor spreading. Nature, 231: 141–144.
127. ———— and Aziz-ur-Rahman. 1972. Age of the Gauss-Matuyama boundary and of the Kaena and Mammoth events. Earth and Planetary Sci. Letters 14: 367–380.
128. ———— and Chamalaun, F. H. 1966. Geomagnetic polarity time scale of time. Nature 212: 1415–1418.
129. ———— and Swanson, D. A. 1972. Potassium-argon ages of lavas from the Hawi and Pololu volcanic series, Kohala Volcano, Hawaii. Geol. Soc. Amer. Bull. 85: 3731–3738.
130. ———— and Tarling, D. H. 1963. Dating of polarity zones in the Hawaiian Islands. Nature 200: 54–56.
131. McNeil, Mary. 1964. Lateritic soils. Sci. Amer. 211: 97.
132. Menard, H. W. 1964. Marine geology of the Pacific. New York. 271 pp.

133. _____ and Hamilton, E. L. 1963. Paleogeography of the Tropical Pacific. 10th Pac. Sci. Cong. Bishop Mus. Press: 201.

134. _____, Allison, E. C., and Durham, J. W. 1962. A drowned Miocene terrace in the Hawaiian Islands. Sci. 138: 896–897.

135. Mink, J. F. and Zones, C. 1963. Pyrite mineralization in the dike complex of the Koolau volcanic series of Oahu, Hawaii. Proc. of Hawaii Acad. Sci. 37th Ann. Mtg. 1961–62: Honolulu. 26.

136. Moore, J. G. 1964. Giant landslides on the Hawaiian ridge. U.S. Geol. Surv. Prof. Paper 501–D: D–95–98.

137. _____ Jan. 5, 1965. Oral communication.

138. _____ 1965. Petrology of deep-sea basalt near Hawaii. Amer. J. Sci. 263: 40–52.

139. _____ 1965. Submarine lavas from the east rift zone of Mauna Kea, Hawaii. Geol. Soc. Amer. 61st. Ann. Mtg. (abst.) p. 38.

140. _____ 1970. Pillow lava in a historic lava flow from Hualalai Volcano, Hawaii. J. Geol. 78: 239–243.

141. _____ and Ault, W. U. 1965. Historic littoral cones in Hawaii. Pac. Sci. 19: 3–11.

142. _____, Phillips, R. L., Grigg, R. W., Peterson, D. W., and Swanson, D. A. 1973. Flow of lava into the sea, 1969–1971, Kilauea Volcano, Hawaii. Geol. Soc. Amer. Bull. 84: 537–546.

143. _____ and Krivoy, H. L. 1964. The 1962 eruption of Kilauea Volcano and structure of the east rift zone. J. Geophys. Res. 69: 2031–2045.

144. _____ and Reed, R. K. 1963. Pillow structures of submarine basalts east of Hawaii. U.S. Geol. Surv. Prof. Paper 475B: B153.

145. _____ and Richter, D. H. 1962. Lava tree molds of the September 1961 eruption, Kilauea Volcano, Hawaii. Geol. Soc. Amer. Bull. 73: 1153–1158.

145a. _____, Claque, D. A., and Normark, W. R., 1982. Diverse basalt types from Loihi seamount, Hawaii. Geology 10: 88–92.

146. Morgenstein, M. 1972. Sedimentary diagenesis and rates of manganese accretion on the Waho shelf, Kauai Channel, Hawaii: Hawaii Inst. Geophys. Data Rept. HIG–72–23, 1–40.

147. _____ 1974. Sedimentary diagenesis and manganese accretion on submarine platforms, Kauai Channel, Hawaii (Ph.D. dissert.). Honolulu, Univ. Hawaii, 172 pp.

148. Muir, I. D. and Tilley, C. E. 1957. Contributions to the petrology of Hawaiian basalts, 1. The picrite-basalts of Kilauea. Amer. J. Sci. 255: 241–253.

149. Munk, W. H. Tides of the planet earth. Lecture at Stanford Univ. Jan. 17, 1966.

150. Murata, K. J. 1960. Occurrence of CuCl emission in volcanic flames. Amer. J. Sci. 258: 769–772.

151. _____ and Richter, D. H. 1961. Magmatic differentiation in the Uwekahuna laccolith, Kilauea Caldera, Hawaii. J. Petrol. 2: 424–437.

152. Nichols, R. L. 1936. Flow-units in basalt. J. Geol. 44: 617.

153. Okamura, R. T. and Forbes, J. C. 1961. Occurrence of silicified wood in Hawaii. Amer. J. Sci. 259: 229–230.

154. Olson, S. L. and Wetmore, A. 1976. Preliminary diagnoses of two extraordinary new genera of birds from Pleistocene deposits in the Hawaiian Islands. Proc. Biol. Soc. Washington, 89: 247–258.

155. Oostdam, B. L. 1965. Age of lava flows on Haleakala, Maui, Hawaii, Geol. Soc. Amer. Bull. 76: 393–394.
156. Palmer, H. S. 1927. Geology of Kaula, Nihoa, Necker, and Gardner Islands and French Frigate Shoal. B. P. Bishop Mus. Bull. 35: 1–35.
157. _____ 1927. Lapiés, in Hawaiian Basalts. Geogr. Rev. 17: 627–631.
158. _____ 1927. The geology of the Honolulu Artesian Basin. Hon. Sewer & Water Comm. Suppl.: 26.
159. _____ 1935. Soil making processes, in Handbook of Hawaiian soils. Honolulu. 30.
160. _____ 1936. Geology of Lehua and Kaula islands. B. P. Bishop Mus. Occ. Papers 12: 1–36.
161. _____ 1947. Fern prints in lava. Amer. J. Sci. 245: 320–321.
162. Pankiwskyj, K. A. 1972. Geology of the Salt Lake Area, Oahu, Hawaii. Pac. Sci. 26: 242–253.
163. Pararas-Carayannis, G. 1969. A catalogue of tsunamis in the Hawaiian Islands. U. S. Environmental Science Services Administration: Honolulu, 95 pp.
164. Patterson, S. H. 1962. Investigation of ferruginous bauxite and plastic clay deposits on Kauai and a reconnaissance of ferruginous bauxite deposits on Maui. Open file, U.S. Geol. Surv., Wash. D.C.
165. Peck, D. L., Moore, J. G., and Kojima, G. 1964. Temperatures in the crust and melt of Alae lava lake, Hawaii, after the August 1963 eruption of Kilauea Volcano—a preliminary report. U.S. Geol. Surv. Prof. Paper 501–D: D1–D7.
166. Peterson, D. W. 1975. The behavior of Kilauea Volcano and its bearing on possible utilization of volcanic energy, in Utilization of volcano energy, Sandia Lab., Albuquerque, N. M. 229–236.
167. _____ 1976. Processes of volcanic island growth, Kilauea Volcano, Hawaii, 1969–1973. Proc. Symp. Andean and Antarctic Volcanology Probl. pp. 1–18.
168. Pirsson, L. V. 1915. The microscopical characters of volcanic tuffs. Amer. J. Sci., 4th ser. 40: 191–211.
169. Porter, S. C. 1979. Quaternary stratigraphy and chronology of Mauna Kea, Hawaii: A 380,000-year record of Mid-Pacific volcanism and ice cap glaciation: Summary. Geol. Soc. Amer. Bull. 90: pp. 609–611.
170. _____ 1972. Buried caldera of Mauna Kea Volcano, Hawaii. Sci. 175: 1458–1460.
171. _____ 1972. Distribution, morphology, and size frequency of cinder cones on Mauna Kea Volcano, Hawaii. Geol. Soc. Amer. Bull. 83: 3607–3612.
172. _____, Stuiver, M., and Yang, I. C. 1977. Chronology of Hawaiian glaciation. Sci. 195: 61–63.
173. Powers, H. A. 1935. Differentiation of Hawaiian lavas. Amer. J. Sci., 5th series, 30: 57–71.
174. _____ 1948. A chronology of the explosive eruptions of Kilauea. Pac. Sci. 2: 278–292.
175. Price, S. 1959. The unprecedented Kauai rainfall of January 1956. Proc. 9th Pac. Sci. Cong. 13: 18.
176. Resig, J. M. 1969. Paleontological investigations of deep borings on the Ewa Plain, Oahu, Hawaii. Hawaii Inst. Geophys. Data Rep. 69–2. 99 pp.
177. Richter, D. H. and Eaton, J. P. 1960. The 1959–60 eruption of Kilauea Volcano. New Scientist 7: 994–997.

178. _____ and Murata, K. J. 1961. Xenolithic nodules in the 1800–1801 Kaupulehu flow of Hualalai Volcano. U.S. Geol. Surv. Prof. Paper 424–B: 215–217.
179. Rubin, M. and Berthold, S. M. 1961. U.S. Geol. Survey radiocarbon dates VI. Radiocarbon 3: 86–98.
180. Ruhe, R. V. 1965. Relation of fluctuations of sea level to soil genesis in the Quaternary. Soil Sci. 99: 23–29.
181. _____, Williams, J. M., and Hill, E. L. 1965. Shorelines and submarine shelves, Oahu, Hawaii. J. Geol. 73: 485–497.
182. Ryall, A. and Bennett, D. L. 1968. Crustal structure of southern Hawaii related to volcanic processes in the upper mantle. J. Geophys. Res. 73: 4561–4582.
183. Saint Exupery, A. 1939. Wind, sand, and stars. Reynal and Hitchcock, New York. 100.
184. Schreiber, B. C. 1969. New evidence concerning the age of the Hawaiian ridge. Geol. Soc. Amer. Bull. 80: 2601–2604.
185. Shaw, H. R. 1973. Mantle convection and volcanic periodicity in the Pacific: Evidence from Hawaii. Geol. Soc. Amer. Bull. 84: 1505–1526.
186. _____ and Jackson, E. D. 1973. Linear island chains in the Pacific: Result of thermal plumes or gravitational anchors. J. Geophys. Res. 78: 8634–8652.
187. Shepard, F. P. 1963. Thirty-five thousand years of sea level (chapter in Essays in marine geology). Univ. So. Cal. Press, Los Angeles: 1–10.
188. _____, Macdonald, G. A. and Cox, D. C. 1950. Tsunami of April 1, 1946. Bull. Scripps Inst. Oceanog.: 391–528.
189. Shor, G. G., Jr. 1960. Crustal structure of the Hawaiian ridge near Gardner Pinnacles. Bull. Seismol. Soc. Amer. 50: 563–574.
190. _____ and Pollard, D. D. 1964. Mohole site selection studies north of Maui. J. Geophys. Res. 69: 1627–1638.
191. Stearns, H. T. 1925. Volcanoes of Hawaii and the Pacific. Mid-Pac. Mag. 29: 748–755.
192. _____ 1925. The explosive phase of Kilauea Volcano, Hawaii, in 1924. Bull. Volcanologique: 193–209.
193. _____ 1926. The Keaiwa or 1823 lava flow from Kilauea Volcano, Hawaii. J. Geol. 34: 336–351.
194. _____ 1935. Shore benches on the island of Oahu, Hawaii. Geol. Soc. Amer. Bull. 46: 1467–1482.
195. _____ 1935. Pleistocene shore lines on the islands of Oahu and Maui, Hawaii. Geol. Soc. Amer. Bull. 46: 1937–1956.
196. _____ 1938. Ancient shore lines on the island of Lanai, Hawaii. Geol. Soc. Amer. Bull. 49: 615–628.
197. _____ 1938. Large caldera on the island of Molokai, Hawaii (abst.). Geol. Soc. Amer. Proc. 1937: 116.
198. _____ 1938. Pillow lavas in Hawaii (abst.). Geol. Soc. Amer. Proc. for 1937: 252.
199. _____ 1939. Great erosional unconformity in Kohala Mountain, Hawaii (abst.). Geol. Soc. Amer. Bull. 50: 1937.
200. _____ 1940. Four-phase volcanism in Hawaii. Geol. Soc. Amer. Bull. 51: 1947–1948.
201. _____ 1941. Shore benches on North Pacific Islands. Geol. Soc. Amer. Bull. 52: 773–780.

202. _____ 1942. Hydrology of volcanic terranes. Physics of the earth—IX Hydrology. New York. 687–703.

203. _____ 1942. Origin of Haleakala Crater, island of Maui, Hawaii. Geol. Soc. Amer. Bull. 53: 1–14.

204. _____ 1945. Glaciation of Mauna Kea, Hawaii. Geol. Soc. Amer. Bull. 56: 267–274.

205. _____ 1945. Volcanism and petrogenesis as illustrated in the Hawaiian Islands: A discussion of the origin of melilite-nepheline basalts in the Pacific, Geol. Soc. Amer. Bull. 56: 873–876.

206. _____ 1945. Eustatic shore lines in the Pacific. Geol. Soc. Amer. Bull. 56: 1071–1078.

207. _____ 1945. Late Geologic History of the Pacific Basin. Amer. J. Sci. 243: 614–626.

208. _____ 1946. An integration of coral reef hypotheses. Amer. J. Sci. 244: 245–262.

209. _____ 1953. The significance of pillow lavas in Pacific Islands (abst.). 8th Pac. Sci. Cong. abst. of papers: 3–4.

210. _____ 1961. Eustatic shorelines on Pacific Islands. Zeit. Für Geomorphologie, Suppl. 3: 1–16.

211. _____ 1963. Geology of the Craters of the Moon, Idaho. Craters of the Moon National Hist. Assn., Arco, Idaho: 34 pp.

212. _____ 1970. Ages of dunes on Oahu, Hawaii. B. P. Bishop Mus. Occ. Papers. 24: 49–72.

213. _____ 1972. C14 vs uranium-series dating of late Pleistocene shore deposits, Oahu, Hawaii: Geol. Soc. Amer., Abs. with Programs (Cordilleran Sec.), 4: 242.

214. _____ 1973. Geologic setting of the fossil goose bones found on Molokai Island, Hawaii. B. P. Bishop Mus. Occ. Papers. 24: 155–163.

215. _____ 1973. Potassium-argon ages of lavas from the Hawi and Pololu volcanic series, Kohala Volcano, Hawaii: Discussion. Geol. Soc. Amer. Bull. 84: 3483–3484.

216. _____ 1974. Submerged shorelines and shelves in the Hawaiian Islands and a revision of some of the eustatic emerged shorelines. Geol. Soc. Amer. Bull. 85: 795–804.

217. _____ 1974. Geologic description of quarries on Oahu, Hawaii. Div. of Water and Land Development, Dept. of Land and Natural Resources. C67: 25 pp.

218. _____ Developing geothermal power on Hawaii difficult. April 15, 1974. Honolulu Advertiser, p. A-1.

219. _____ 1975. Hawaii chapter in Fairbridge, R. (Ed.) The encyclopedia of world regional geology, Pt.1: 581–596.

220. _____. 1976. Second Supplement to the Central Maui Water Study of March 1974. Unpublished report prepared by Norman Saito Engineering Consultants, Inc. Kahului, Maui.

221. _____. Energy drills on Oahu. Feb. 13, 1976. Honolulu Advertiser, p. A18.

222. _____. 1978. Quaternary shorelines in the Hawaiian Islands. B. P. Bishop Museum Bull. 237. 57 pp.

223. _____ and Chamberlain, T. K. 1967. Deep cores and their bearing on the geologic history of the Central Pacific basin. Pac. Sci. 21: 153–165.

224. _____ and Clark, W. O. 1930. Geology and water resources of the Kau District, Hawaii. U.S. Geol. Surv. Water-Supply Paper 616: 194 pp.

225. Strange, W. E., Woollard, G. P., and Rose, J. C. 1965. An analysis of the gravity field over the Hawaiian Islands in terms of crustal structure. Pac. Sci. 19: 381–389.

226. Sun, S. S. and Hanson, G. N. 1975. Evolution of the Mantle: Geochemical evidence from alkali basalt. Geology, 3: 297–302.

227. Takasaki, K. J. and Eaton, J. P. 1959. Seismological interpretation of earthquake-induced water-level fluctuations in wells. Seismol. Soc. Amer. Bull. 49: 227–245.

228. Tarling, D. H. 1962. Tentative correlation of Samoan and Hawaiian Islands using 'Reversals' of magnetism. Nature 196: 882–883.

229. _____. 1965. The paleomagnetism of some of the Hawaiian Islands. Geophys. J. 10: 93.

230. The Lure of Waianae, anon. Hawaiian Ann. for 1931: 111.

231. Tilley, C. E. and Scoon, J. H. 1961. Differentiation of Hawaiian basalts: Trends of Mauna Loa and Kilauea historic magma. Amer. J. Sci. 259: 60–68.

232. Tilling, R. I., Holcomb, R. T., Lockwood, J. P., and Peterson, D. W. 1975. Recent eruptions of Hawaiian volcanoes and evolution of basaltic land forms. Program, Inter. Colloquium Planetary Geology, Rome, Italy. (expanded abstract) p. 149–152.

233. _____, Kayanagi, R. Y., Lyman, P. W., Lockwood, J. P., Moore, J. G., and Swanson, D. A., 1976. Earthquake and related catastrophic events, Island of Hawaii, November 29, 1975: a preliminary report. U.S. Geol. Survey Circular 740, 33 pp.

234. _____, Peterson, D. W., Christiansen, R. L., and Holcomb, R. T. 1973. Development of new volcanic shields at Kilauea Volcano, Hawaii, 1969 to 1973. Program, 9th Cong., Inter. Union for Quaternary Res. Christchurch, N.Z., Dec. 2–10, 1973 Extended Abst., 366–367.

235. U.S. Naval Oceanographic Office. 1962. A marine magnetic survey south of the Hawaiian Islands. TR 137: 47 pp.

236. Visher, F. N. and Mink, J. F. 1964. Ground-water resources on southern Oahu, Hawaii. U.S. Geol. Surv. Water-Supply Paper 1778: 4.

237. Washington, H. S. and Keyes, M. G. 1926. Petrology of the Hawaiian Islands, V. The Leeward Islands. Amer. J. Sci., 5th ser. 12: 336–352.

238. Wentworth, C. K. 1925. The geology of Lanai. B. P. Bishop Mus. Bull. 24: 72 pp.

239. _____ 1937. The Diamond Head black ash. J. Sed. Petrology 7, Bull. 5: 91–103.

240. _____ 1938. Ash formations of the Island of Hawaii. Hawaiian Volcano Obs., 3d Spec. Rept.: 173 pp.

241. _____ 1939. The specific gravity of sea water and the Ghyben-Herzberg ratio at Honolulu. Univ. Hawaii Bull.: 12.

242. _____ 1943. Soil avalanches on Oahu, Hawaii. Geol. Soc. Amer. Bull. 54: 53–64.

243. _____ and Macdonald, G. A. 1953. Structures and forms of basaltic rocks in Hawaii. U.S. Geol. Surv. Bull. 994: 98 pp.

244. _____, Powers, H. A., and Eaton, J. P. 1961. Feasibility of a lava-diverting barrier at Hilo, Hawaii. Pac. Sci. 15: 352–357.

245. _____ and Powers, W. E. 1941. Multiple glaciation of Mauna Kea, Hawaii. Geol. Soc. Amer. Bull. 52: 1193–1218.

246. _____ and Williams, H. 1932. The classification and terminology of the pyroclastic rocks. Nat. Res. Council Bull. 89: 40–50.

247. _____ and Winchell, H. 1947. Koolau basalt series, Oahu, Hawaii Geol. Soc. Amer. Bull. 58: 56.

248. Wetmore, A. 1943. An extinct goose from the Island of Hawaii. Condor, 45: 146–148.

249. White, E. 1949. Processes of erosion on steep slopes of Oahu, Hawaii. Amer. J. Sci. 247: 168–186.

250. Williams, H. 1941. Calderas and their origin. Univ. Cal. Dept. Geol. Sci. Bull. 25: 239–246.

251. Wilson, J. T. 1963. A possible origin of the Hawaiian Islands. Can. J. Phys. 41: 863–870.

252. Winchell, H. 1947. Honolulu series, Oahu, Hawaii. Geol. Soc. Amer. Bull. 58: 1–48.

253. Woollard, G. P. 1954. Crustal structure beneath oceanic islands. Royal Soc. Proc. A. 222: 361–387.

254. _____ et al. 1964. A report relating to Hawaii as the site for a drill hole to the upper mantle (to the NSF by the staff of the Hawaii Inst. of Geophys.) Mimeographed. See also 1965, Pac. Sci. 19: 271–393.

255. Zablocki, C. J., Tilling, R. I., Peterson, D. W., Christiansen, R. L., Keller, G. V., and Murray, J. C. A deep research drill hole at the summit of an active volcano, Kilauea, Hawaii. 1974. Geophys. Res. Letters 1: 323–326.

256. Zeuner, F. E. 1959. The Pleistocene Period. London. 447 pp.

257. In July 1965, J. C. Belshé made several electromagnetic traverses across Tuscaloosa Seamount, the largest of the so-called landslide blocks, and found a single diphole. The fathometer readings indicate a depression on the summit 3½ miles across and 300 feet deep, possibly a caldera. A core sample taken from this seamount under 9,500 feet of water, was examined by the writer and found to be fresh, bedded basaltic tuff containing foraminifera and rich in lime. One fragment was coated with a thin layer of manganese. These data appear to confirm Hamilton's interpretation that the seamounts are late submarine cones, but the presence of vesicular fragments in the tuff requires great submergence.

258. T. K. Chamberlain (oral communication December 1965) explored the Waianae coast of Oahu in 1965 in a submarine with glass portholes. He saw stepped terraces on which were potholes filled with round boulders obviously left there in the geologic past when the sea was cutting into the terraces. A high steep cliff drops off the edge of the −300-foot shelf to a depth of more than 500 feet. Continuous bathymetric measurements indicate two higher shelves with their nick points at −230 to −250 feet and at −140 to −150 feet. The present day beach sand drifts slowly downward across these shelves and is lost in the deep water.

GLOSSARY

AA. A lava flow with a rough clinkery or loose blocky surface. The rock contains deflated and stretched vesicles.

AGGLOMERATE. A term sometimes used for aa lava or lumps of lava stuck together while still hot in a spatter cone.

ALKALIC BASALT. A lava poor in silica and rich in alkalies (Na & K). Pyroxene, generally augite. Alkalic basalt is synonymous with andesite only in the geologic literature of the Hawaiian Islands.

ALLUVIUM. The sediment deposited by streams on the land.

ANDESITE. A lava generally gray in color, richer in silicon and sodium and poorer in iron than basalt.

ANKARAMITE. A rock containing abundant phenocrysts of augite and olivine.

ASH. Sand- or dust-size ejecta.

AUGITE. A common dark crystal, one of the pyroxenes.

BASALT. A dark lava rich in iron and magnesium and comparatively poor in silicon.

BASANITE. A nepheline olivine basalt.

BEACH ROCK. Cemented calcareous beach debris.

BLOCKS. Volcanic ejecta, solid when thrown out, and larger than 1½ inches across.

BLOWHOLE. A crack in the roof of a cave through which water or air is forced when waves enter the cave.

BOMBS. Volcanic ejecta, molten when thrown out, and having particular forms, such as ribbon, bread-crust, spindle, etc.

BOSS. A cylindrical intrusive body.

BRECCIA. A chaotic assemblage of compact broken rock made by explosions, faulting, landslides, and other processes.

BULBOUS DOME. A dome-shaped mass over a vent formed by the outpouring of viscous lava.

321

CALCAREOUS. Limey, rich in calcite.

CALDERA. A large crater with a diameter many times its depth, formed chiefly by collapse.

CALDERA COMPLEX. The diverse rock assemblage underlying a caldera.

CALICHE. A white secondary lime deposited by percolating water.

CINDER. A highly vesicular chunk of basalt thrown out by a fire fountain.

CINDER CONE. A mound built by small ejecta around a vent, with most of the fragments larger than ½ inch across, very vesicular, and mostly loose.

CLINKER. The spiny irregular fragments associated with aa flows.

CRATER. A depression at a volcanic vent.

DIKE. Lava that has solidified in a crack. Most dikes are cross-jointed, with a long dimension much greater than the width.

DIKE COMPLEX. The dikes and country rock underlying a rift zone.

DIKELETS. Small offshoots from dikes.

DIKE SWARMS. Many parallel, closely spaced dikes.

DOME. A shield-shaped cone of basalt. Domes form the main Hawaiian volcanoes.

DUNITE. A rock composed essentially of olivine, brought up from depth.

EJECTA. Fragments of any size hurled out by a volcanic eruption.

EOLIANITE. Hardened dune sand.

EPICENTER. The point on the earth's surface above the place of origin of an earthquake.

EUSTATIC. Simultaneous worldwide changes in sea level.

EXPLOSION CRATER. A crater formed chiefly, or entirely, by explosion.

FAULT. A fracture in the earth's crust along which movement has occurred.

FAULT SCARP. A cliff formed by fault movement.

FELDSPAR. A light-colored crystal with a complex silicate composition common in basalt.

FIRE FOUNTAINS. Fountains of liquid lava, also called "lava fountains."

FRACTURE ZONE. A fault zone where the crust of the earth has broken and slipped.

FUMAROLE. A hole from which volcanic gases issue, usually lined with chemical deposits.

GABBRO. A coarse-grained rock of basaltic composition that has cooled at depth.

GEOMORPHOLOGY. The science that treats the form, nature, origin, development, and changes in the surface features of the earth.

GHYBEN-HERZBERG LENS. The lens of fresh ground water floating on sea water. Named after two Europeans who defined it.

GOUGE. The crushed material along a fault resulting from friction caused by the grinding of rock as it slips against adjacent rock.

GRABEN. A trench bordered by fault cliffs.

GUYOT. A flat-topped seamount.

HAWAIITE. A variety of alkalic basalt with the dominant feldspar andesine.

HORST BLOCKS. Blocks which lie between two faults and higher than the surrounding land.

HYDROEXPLOSION. Any explosion caused by the contact of lava with water.

IGNEOUS ROCKS. Those formed by the solidification of magma.

INCLUSIONS. Fragments of solid rock brought up in magma.

INTERCALATED. Interbedded.

INTRUSIVE ROCK. A rock that has congealed in a fissure or other opening below ground.

JOINT PLANES. Shrinkage cracks in lava.

KAOLINITE. The common aluminum-bearing mineral formed by the weathering of rocks.

KIPUKA. An island of old land surrounded but not covered by a lava flow. It can be higher or lower than the lava flow.

LAPILLI. Small fragments of lava about ¼ inch in diameter, formed by explosions. Raindrops falling through ash and forming pellets are accretionary lapilli.

LATERITE. The red, iron-rich hardpan formed under tropical weathering conditions.

LAVA. Used to refer to either the molten or solidified rock, with a complex composition of silicates and oxides.

LAVA RINGS. Spatter ramparts forming a levee around a lava lake.

LAVA TREE. A tree mold that rises above the level of a lava flow.

LAVA TUBE. The cavern formed by the draining away of lava in a pahoehoe flow.

LITHIC. Stony.

LITTORAL CONES. Cones formed by lava flows exploding where they enter the sea.

MAGMA. Liquid lava beneath the surface.

MELILITE. A complex silicate mineral.

MOHOLE. A deep bore hole to penetrate the earth's mantle below the Mohorovičić discontinuity. The site for the first mohole was off the coast of Maui.

MUDFLOW. A deposit resulting from the flowage of heterogeneous debris lubricated with large amounts of water; also the mass in motion.

MUGEARITE. A variety of alkalic basalt with the dominant feldspar oligoclase.

NEPHELINE. A sodium or potassium aluminum silicate mineral.

NEPHELINITE. A dense variety of basalt containing nepheline instead of feldspar.

OBSIDIAN. Volcanic glass formed by lava chilling too quickly to crystallize. Tachylyte is the technical name of basaltic glass.

OCEANITE.   A rock containing more than 35 per cent olivine phenocrysts.

OLIGOCLASE.   A mixture of sodium and calcium aluminum silicates, one of the many feldspars.

OLIVINE.   A green crystal with a complex silicate composition common in basalts.

PAHOEHOE.   Lava with a smooth or ropy surface spread chiefly through tubes and characterized by round vesicles.

PALAGONITE.   A waxy silicagel mineraloid; an alteration product of ash.

PALI.   The Hawaiian word for cliff.

PELAGIC DEPOSITS.   Deep ocean muds.

PELE'S HAIR.   Glassy hairs formed by lava fountains, named after Pele, the Hawaiian goddess of volcanoes.

PELE'S TEARS.   Black droplets of lava broken from the ends of Pele's hair.

PERIDOTITE.   A rock composed chiefly of olivine.

PHENOCRYSTS.   Crystals readily seen by the naked eye.

PHREATIC EXPLOSION.   An explosion caused by steam without the presence of molten lava.

PHREATOMAGMATIC EXPLOSION.   An explosion caused by lava in contact with ground water.

PICRITE-BASALT.   A rock carrying abundant augite and/or olivine phenocrysts. A general term for ankaramites and oceanites.

PILLOW LAVA.   Spheroidal masses of lava formed by hot lava flowing over wet ground or into water.

PISOLITE.   Small pellets formed by rain drops falling through an ash cloud.

PIT CRATER.   A crater formed by collapse.

PLUG.   A roughly cylindrical intrusive body filling a vent. Also called a "neck" or "pipe."

PUMICE.   Frothy or highly vesicular ejecta, chiefly glass.

PYROCLASTIC ROCKS.   Rocks formed by volcanic ejection.

PYROXENE.   A dark-colored crystal causing most of the dark color in basalt; it is a complex silicate.

RIFT.   A lengthy fissure in the earth's crust.

RIFT ZONE GRABEN.   The sunken trench over a rift zone.

SCORIA.   Slaggy vesicular ejecta.

SEAMOUNT.   A submarine volcano.

SHIELD VOLCANO.   A broad, fairly flat lava cone having the shape of a shield. Commonly called "lava cone" or "lava dome."

SILL.   Lava intruded between beds.

SOLFATARA.   A fumarole that gives vent chiefly to sulfurous gases.

SPATTER.   Flattened volcanic ejecta around a vent, commonly adhering to each other.

SPATTER CONE.   A pile of spatter around a vent.

SPHEROIDAL WEATHERING. Concentric shells formed by weathering, commonly with a hard core.

STALACTITE. A pendant hanging from the roof or walls of a cave, formed by the dripping of fluid lava.

STALAGMITE. A small mound on the floor of a cave, formed by the drip from a stalactite.

STAND OF THE SEA. A halt of the sea long enough to leave marine deposits.

TACHYLYTE. Basaltic volcanic glass. *See* Obsidian.

TALUS. Broken rock at the base of cliffs.

TEPHRA. A general term for all volcanic ejecta.

THOLEIITE. The primary or primitive basalt from which other types of lavas, such as the alkalic basalts, trachytes, nepheline basalts, etc., have differentiated. Tholeiites make up the bulk of Hawaiian mountains.

TRACHYTE. A lava containing more silica than basalt; it usually weathers to a light gray color.

TREE MOLD. A hole in a lava flow caused by lava making a cast of a tree trunk.

TSUNAMI. A sea wave caused by an earthquake or submarine landslide.

TUBE. A lava cavern through which pahoehoe lava has flowed.

TUFF. Hardened volcanic ash.

TYPE LOCALITY. An outcrop from which a geologic formation is named.

UNCONFORMITY. A former surface representing a time interval separating rocks.

VENT. A hole through which magma reaches the surface.

VESICULAR ROCK. Rock having bubble holes formed by gas.

VITRIC. Glassy.

VOLCANIC RIFT ZONE. A zone of fissures from which lava has issued.

VOLCANICS. A general term for all products laid down by a volcano.

XENOLITH. A fragment of older rock floated up from depth in lava flows.

INDEX